i

Ram Publications

Complete VLF-TR Metal Detector Handbook (The)
   Thoroughly explains VLF/TR metal/mineral detectors and
   HOW TO USE them. Compares VLF/TR's with all other types.

Detector Owner's Field Manual
   Explains total capabilities and HOW TO USE procedures of all types of
   metal detectors.

Electronic Prospecting
   Learn how to find gold and silver veins, pockets, and nuggets using easy
   electronic metal detector methods.

Gold Panning Is Easy
   This excellent field guide shows you how to FIND and PAN gold as quickly
   and easily as a professional.

Modern Metal Detectors
   This advanced handbook for home, field, and classroom study gives the
   expertise you need for success in any metal detecting situation, hobby or
   professional, and increases your understanding of all fields of metal detector use.

Professional Treasure Hunter
   Discover how to succeed with PROFESSIONAL METHODS, PERSISTENCE,
   and HARD WORK.

Robert Marx: Quest for Treasure
   The exciting, almost unbelievable true account of the discovery and salvage
   of the Spanish treasure galleon, *Nuestra Señora de la Maravilla,* lost at sea,
   January 1656.

Successful Coin Hunting
   The world's most authoritative guide to FINDING VALUABLE COINS with
   all types of metal detectors. The name speaks for itself!

Treasure Hunter's Manual #6
   Quickly guides the inexperienced beginner through the mysteries of FULL
   TIME TREASURE HUNTING.

Treasure Hunter's Manual #7
   The classic! THE book on professional methods of RESEARCH, RECOVERY,
   and DISPOSITION of treasures found.

Treasure Hunting Pays Off!
   An excellent introduction to all facets of treasure hunting.

The Advanced Handbook on
MODERN METAL DETECTORS

By
Charles L. Garrett

By CHARLES GARRETT

Modern Metal Detectors
Successful Coin Hunting
Treasure Hunting Pays Off!
Treasure Hunting Secrets
Electronic Prospecting (with Lagal)
Complete VLF-TR Metal Detector Handbook (The) (with Lagal)

To my wife, Eleanor, and our children.

ISBN 0-915920-49-2
Library of Congress Catalog Card No. 83-62839
Modern Metal Detectors
© Copyright 1985.
Charles L. Garrett.

First Edition Printing, February 1985

87 88 89 90 10 9 8 7 6 5 4 3

Cover Design: Melvin Climer

For FREE listing of related treasure hunting books write
Ram Publishing Company • P.O. Box 38649 • Dallas, Texas 75238

CONTENTS

ILLUSTRATIONS
(Electrical Diagrams)

TABLES

(General Subjects)

About the Author

Charles Garrett's first interest in outdoor adventure was kindled, at about the age of 12, when he read the articles in a "cache" of old National Geographic Magazines he found in the attic of his aunt's home. The amazing discovery of King Tut's Tomb and other stories kindled the fire that burns to this day. He made a wish that someday he might write about his own adventures in God's great outdoors.

After he graduated from Lufkin, Texas, High School in 1950, he served four years in the United States Navy. He attended an Electrician's Mate School and spent more than three years aboard a World War II Liberty Ship, the U.S.S. Bottineau APA235. The school, and duty in the ship's electrical division, locked him in a lifetime of electronics.

When he left the Navy, he married Miss Eleanor Smith of Pennington, Texas. During the next four years, his wife taught school and supported the family, while he obtained his Bachelor of Science Degree in Electrical Engineering from Lamar State College of Technology in Beaumont, Texas.

He then worked several years in the Dallas area for Texas Instruments and Teledyne Geotech. Major responsibilities included the design of a power supply and amplifier for the Mariner II space probe; electronic radar terrain scanning displays for the United States Air Force F-111 Fighter Aircraft (This design concept is also used on the F-16); an electronically stabilized earth platform used in testing seismographs; various earth seismograph components; and a seismograph amplifier which was "planted" on the moon by Neil A. Armstrong, Apollo 11 astronaut.

During these years, he used metal detectors which he designed himself to explore Texas ghost towns. Realizing that his equipment was equal or better than existing commercial equipment, he and Mrs. Garrett founded Garrett Electronics. Since this mid-1960s beginning, the company has been a leader in metal detector development and manufactures a wider range of equipment than any other company. Garrett quality is known throughout the world.

From the beginning, he vowed "to practice what I preach," or, in other words, to use his equipment in the field, to insure it will work for his customers regardless of ground conditions and environment. Consequently, he traveled extensively using his equipment in the United States, Australia, Canada, the Caribbean Islands, Colombia, England, Mexico and seven Western European countries. In Australia, he and Peter Bridge, "Father of Australia's Electronic Gold Rush," held electronic prospecting seminars in every major city and numerous communities. As a result of that tour and Peter's effort, Australia's Modern Gold Rush blossomed, resulting in many tens of million dollars in gold being discovered with Garrett equipment.

Since the mid-1960s, his travels have taken him into every metal detecting field, including treasure hunting, coin hunting, relic hunting, ghost towning, prospecting, electronic prospecting, and the Industrial field as well. He gave the gained knowledge to others in articles, books, slide presentations, films, lectures and seminars. He became known as a treasure hunter, writer, film producer and adventurer.

For several years, he spent time learning how metal detectors could be of value in law enforcement and security. He participated in and sponsored seminars and worked with police, governmental wildlife departments, search and rescue teams, the FBI and others helping them develop the metal detector as a crime scene management tool.

He organized the American Metal Detector Manufacturers Association (AMDM) and served as its first president in 1979. In 1983, he was again elected to serve as president.

In 1979, he sponsored and founded the International Treasure Hunting Society (Search International), an association of people dedicated to the use of metal detectors. This organization holds International Treasure Hunts with thousands of metal detector users attending.

He and his company were honored when they were selected to supply security metal detectors to the 1984 Los Angeles Olympic Games and to train nearly ten thousand security people in the use of Garrett equipment. His metal detection equipment was also selected for use at the 1984 Republican National Convention in Dallas, Texas. Mr. Garrett and his security team, trained and supervised hundreds of security people during this event.

Your study of this book will convince you that MODERN METAL DETECTORS is the book, truly *the* "bible" of metal detectors. You will agree Mr. Garrett succeeded in his determination to make each written page, table, and illustration, worth the cost of the book. You'll be amazed when you see the tremendous quantity of metal detector knowledge and the simplicity with which it is presented for your understanding. If there is one person qualified to write this book, that person is the author.

The Editor, Ram Publishing Company

Author's Note

I am indebted to all who gave of their time to help me build this book, and I extend my sincerest thanks and appreciation to them. MODERN METAL DETECTORS is a better book because of their assistance.

A very special "thank you" to my wife Eleanor, and my children, Charles, Jr., Deirdre Lynne, and Vaughan Lamar.

Roy Lagal, author and metal detector professional, after studying the original manuscript, suggested the name, MODERN METAL DETECTORS. He and I have been field "sidekicks" for sixteen years. Much of what we have learned, that no one else would take the time to learn, will be found in this book.

Robert Podhrasky, Garrett Electronics' Chief Engineer, and I have spent countless laboratory and field hours during the past seventeen years discussing metal detectors. My knowledge about metal detectors has been greatly strengthened because of our association.

Virgil Hutton, a trusted friend and field companion of Roy Lagal's and mine, made many valuable suggestions.

FBI Special Agent (retired) Dave Loveless, Garrett Electronics' Law Enforcement Field Agent and Representative, and I have spent much time together applying metal detection techniques to many law enforcement and security situations, including the 1984 Los Angeles Summer Olympic Games and the 1984 Republican National Convention. We have conducted numerous law enforcement and security seminars. Our work together greatly strengthened and expanded the use of the metal detector as an invaluable crime scene management tool and has led to many new metal detector applications and improved designs. Dave contributed extremely valuable information in the chapter on Law Enforcement. I consider him the catalyst that caused the metal detector to become an integral part of today's modern law enforcement and security scenes.

FBI Special Agent Richard Graham is the FBI's top metal detector applications expert and field instructor. Through his work, seminars, and actual metal detector land and underwater searches (and physical evidence recoveries), Richard has cast in concrete the value of the metal detector in law enforcement. He, Dave Loveless, and I, have worked together on many projects and seminars, and from them I have greatly expanded my knowledge about metal detectors in law enforcement. Richard selected MODERN METAL DETECTORS as his law enforcement seminar textbook. He made many suggestions to improve the book, especially in the chapter on Law Enforcement.

Jim Cross, of Cross International, leads the way in industrial and general applications in the use of metal detectors in underwater search and salvage. If there is an underwater problem, he'll find the solution. He gets the job done in an extremely professional manner. Thanks, Jim, for sharing your underwater know-how and expertise with me and our readers.

Jack Hube and his wife, Eleanor, work with metal detector users almost three hundred sixty-five days a year. They know the problems of detector operators and the questions they ask. Because of their input, MODERN METAL DETECTORS is a more valuable book.

From Ed Morris' military journalistic experience came the ability to collect, sort, and present difficult material in precise, usable form. At the beginning, Ed helped sort many of my notes into an organized form. Jobs like that take many hours. Thanks, Ed, for your great help!

If a book is three hundred pages long, you can be sure that someone typed at least five times that many, as manuscripts require countless pages typed, edited, re-typed, re-edited, etc. Kathleen Deckshot, a Garrett Metal Detectors' secretary, waded through hundreds of scarcely legible red ink edited pages and retyped them with near perfection. Thank you, Kathleen, for the many hours you devoted to my manuscript.

My thanks also to Andretta Lowry, Becky Boyer, and Mary Alice Penson for their most valuable editing assistance.

Thanks to many Garrett Electronics' personnel who were especially helpful. Melvin Climer, Staff Artist, did a tremendous job in designing the cover, preparing photographs, and producing almost all the illustrations; Beverly Trollinger, typist, spent many hours transcribing manuscript tapes; and Jack Lowry, Director of Marketing, read the manuscript and made many suggestions for improvement.

Bill Welsh, a former Graphics Designer with Walt Disney Productions, added further to the quality of the book. Among his artwork be sure to see the Chinese Emperor's walk-through weapons detector in Chapter 2. Tom Yaquinto of Christopher National Press turned the finished type, illustrations, and photographs into a quality book that I hope will serve you long and well.

I thank all those who submitted photographs which I used in MODERN METAL DETECTORS. Contributor's names are mentioned in the captions. All other photographs I took myself, sometime during the past twenty odd years.

This book has taken ten years to complete. At least, my earliest manuscript pages date that far back. A short while before I began to write this AUTHOR'S (final) NOTE, I reviewed my book SUCCESSFUL COIN HUNTING and noticed its First Edition printing date coincided with the earliest MODERN METAL DETECTORS manuscript, 1974!

NOTE: All metal detection equipment (except as noted), shown in photographs in this book, is (or was) manufactured by Garrett Electronics, Metal Detector Division, 2814 National Dr., Garland, Texas 75041 U.S.A.

Introduction

The purpose of MODERN METAL DETECTORS is to assist you in learning to be more successful when using your metal detector. I hope it will aid you in mastering your detector, rather than letting it master you. It is an all-encompassing, comprehensive reference and "how-to" guide to metal detectors. MODERN METAL DETECTORS is adaptable to your needs, whether you are just beginning, experienced, amateur, or professional.

MODERN METAL DETECTORS is not intended to replace, but to supplement, the other classic Ram Publishing Company metal detector books with their invaluable, up-to-date, "how-to" material.

MODERN METAL DETECTORS traces metal detector history and development from start to present. It presents complete information about all land and underwater metal detector types, how they work, their characteristics, capabilities, applications and field uses. This book is filled with "how-to" instructions and explains every phase of metal detecting: electronic theory, metal detector design, electromagnetic fields, search matrix, metals and minerals, detection characteristics of metals, and many more subjects.

Every person who has used a metal detector, or even thought someday he would, has questions about metal detectors. Some of the first questions usually asked are: "How deep will they go?"; "What are the differences among the various kinds of detectors?"; and "Which instrument is best for me?" People are becoming more knowledgeable about metal detectors, and they are starting to ask more intelligent questions. Other often-heard questions are: "What is Discrimination and Ground Elimination?"; "What is a target classifier meter?"; "Can I go deeper if I use a larger searchcoil?"; and "Do I need a BFO, VLF, or Pulse Induction metal detector to find coins, caches and gold?"

MODERN METAL DETECTORS answers these most frequently asked questions and goes far beyond them. I have endeavored to present basic, all-encompassing, up-to-date detector knowledge, so that regardless of the problems and questions you have, you will be able to find your own answers. You'll be able to bench-test your detector and take it into the field for testing to learn what you want to know. If you should have questions, you'll have the knowledge you need to ask the right questions and to know if you get the right answers. In short, this book contains the basic knowledge needed to know about how metal detectors work, what metals and minerals are detectable, and why metal detectors react the way they do to these metals and minerals.

A Glossary is included to help you build your vocabulary with a storehouse of metal detector terminology. Use these terms in your everyday thinking and conversation, and you'll find yourself quickly understanding, and becoming a part of, the fascinating field of metal detecting.

The metal detector electronic theory, applications information, and "how-to" instructions are written in an understandable manner. The Index is provided to help you quickly locate the information you seek. Test questions are also provided so that you can test yourself, chapter by chapter, to determine your progress.

Let this book become your companion. Wherever you take your metal detector, take this book. Soon, very soon, you will find yourself becoming more knowledgeable about metal detectors. You will begin to understand everything your metal detector tells you. You will find those things you search for and many more things you never dreamed of discovering. You will soon become more successful!

Charles Garrett

Charles and Eleanor Garrett visit a Great Salt Lake beach near Salt Lake City, Utah. They travel throughout the United States and other countries, testing and using detectors, to insure that Garrett instruments will perform perfectly wherever they are used by Garrett customers. Photo by Richard Graham.

CHAPTER 1

What Is a Metal Detector?

A metal detector is, simply, an electronic device that detects the presence of metal. While some metal detectors respond to certain minerals, the main design function is the detection of metal.

Metal detectors are not mystical Ouija boards, nor are they witching sticks; neither are they Geiger counters which detect energy emissions from radioactive materials, although they will detect conductive metal and ferrous mineral in association with uranium. Metal detectors are not magnetometers which measure magnetic field intensity. They are not magic wands nor direction finders; they will not point to metal either close at hand (laterally) or far away.

Metal detectors are simply electromagnetic devices that will detect the presence of conductive metals and certain minerals whenever these detectable substances come within the metal detector's detection area.

Metal detectors are not difficult to use and almost anyone of any age, after a few minutes instruction and practice, can operate a detector to find metal. Since they operate in a manner very similar to radio signal transmission and reception, tuning is about as easy as tuning a radio. In fact, some detectors even tune themselves automatically.

On the other hand, a person could use detectors a lifetime and still not know all there is to know about metal detecting. Becoming proficient in every phase of metal detecting requires study and field application.

Detectors come in various sizes and shapes. The most common configuration (Figure 1-1) is the portable, land-use instrument. A control housing (about the size of a shoe box) is attached to an adjustable length stem. A searchcoil, which contains the antenna, is attached to the lower end of the stem. The stem allows the overall metal detector length to be adjustable from approximately thirty inches minimum to approximately forty-five inches maximum. An electrical cable connects the searchcoil antenna windings to the electronic circuits inside the control housing. The control housing, in addition to containing the circuits, also contains a meter, switches, a speaker, the batteries and other components.

Electronic circuits generate current signals which power the transmitter antenna. The antenna transmits an electromagnetic

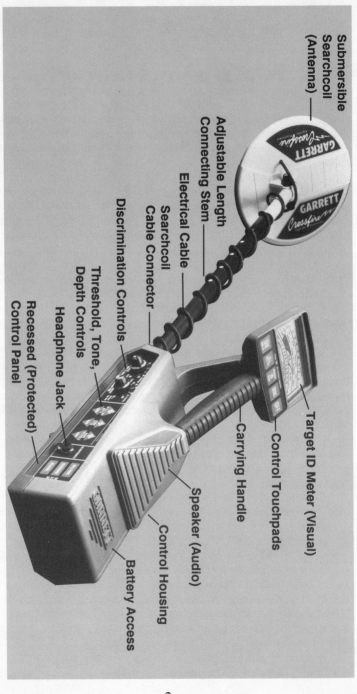

Submersible
Searchcoil
(Antenna)

Adjustable Length
Connecting Stem

Electrical Cable

Searchcoil
Cable Connector

Discrimination Controls

Threshold, Tone,
Depth Controls

Headphone Jack

Recessed (Protected)
Control Panel

Target ID Meter (Visual)

Control Touchpads

Carrying Handle

Speaker (Audio)

Control Housing

Battery Access

GARRETT

GARRETT
Crossfire

Figure 1-1: Garrett's Grand Master Hunter CX II, is a modern metal detector with microprocessor-controlled circuitry.

2

field into the medium surrounding the searchcoil. The electromagnetic field will penetrate a variety of materials, including earth soils and sand, rocks, wood, brick, stone, masonry, water, concrete, vegetable and some mineral substances and, of course, air. When metals and certain minerals interact with the electromagnetic field, metal detection occurs. Metal detectors cannot, except in certain situations, detect metal through other metal. In other words, gold coins in an iron pot with a lid cannot be detected. The iron pot and the lid can be detected, but not the coins.

Most quality constructed field type instruments are built to withstand the punishment of thousands of hours of field use and to provide the operator with unfailing operational accuracy, even though the detector may be subjected to rough, often abusive treatment. These instruments can be used in all kinds of weather and in every conceivable environmental situation, from deserts and seashores to mountains and hostile jungles. Detectors are knocked around, carried in hot and cold automobile trunks, stuffed in backpacks, and stored in home closets. They are dropped, banged around, abused, kicked, and cursed. Yet, in spite of all this, the better instruments continue to give years of unfailingly accurate, dependable service.

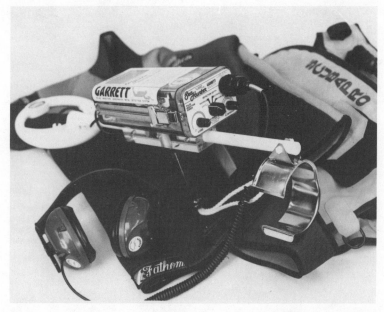

Figure 1-2: The underwater sport of treasure hunting is a popular activity. Underwater metal detectors, such as this Sea Hunter model, can be submerged to depths of 200 feet. Scuba divers use these instruments to locate sunken treasure and various other metal objects. Photo by Melvin Climer.

3

The majority of portable detectors are designed and manufactured primarily for land use. Some, however, are designed for underwater operation to depths of two hundred feet (Figure 1-2). Convertible models are designed for use on both land and underwater, also to depths of two hundred feet (Figure 1-3).

There are many other types of metal detectors including those used in law enforcement and security; construction and utility industries; medicine; traffic control; lumbering and other fields. The mechanical configurations and circuitry may differ one from the other, but, the end result, the design purpose, is the detection of metal.

A metal detector is simply a tool. It is designed to get a job done. When used correctly, for the right job, in the right location, it will help you find the metal and/or minerals for which you are searching.

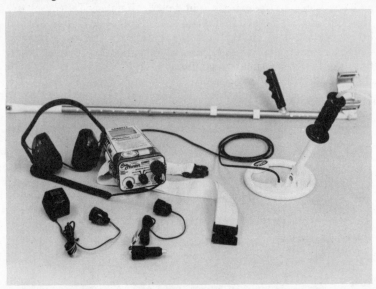

Figure 1-3: Convertible underwater detectors are manufactured for land and underwater use and are popular with beach and surf hunters. This particular model, the Sea Hunter XL500, features Pulse Induction circuitry, interchangeable searchcoils, selectable detection depth and a trash elimination mode that allows the operator to adjust the detector to ignore various unwanted types of metal. Photo by Melvin Climer.

CHAPTER 1 QUESTIONS

1. A metal detector is an _____ device that detects the presence of _____ . (Each correct answer is worth 10 points)

2. Metal detectors detect metal and certain _____ .

3. Becoming proficient in every phase of metal detecting requires _____ and _____ _____ . (Each correct answer is worth 10 points)

4. The _____ _____ contains electronic circuitry, batteries and other components while the searchcoil contains the _____ . (Each correct answer is worth 10 points)

5. Metal detectors can detect metal through almost all substances except _____ .

Each of the 5 complete questions, answered correctly, is worth 20 points. Perfect score is 100. Answers given in Appendix 2.

CHAPTER 2

The History of Metal Detectors

Ancient Chinese documents indicate that a metal detector was in use more than two hundred years before Christ. A Chinese emperor had a doorway metal detector constructed to protect himself against assassination. His craftsman constructed the doorway using a magnetic mineral called magnetite. Possibly the door frame was built something like a horseshoe magnet. Through a combination of heating and striking of the magnetite with hammers, an iron metal "attractor" came into existence. The heating and jarring caused the molecules to align themselves in the direction of the earth's magnetic field. If a person attempted to carry iron objects such as armor, swords and other weapons through the doorway, these objects would be drawn against the doorway (Figure 2-1) and held fast.

In 1881 Alexander Graham Bell, the inventor of the telephone, was working on an electrical induction device for locating metals. President James A. Garfield was shot by an assassin in July of that year, when one bullet grazed his arm and a second bullet lodged in his back. When attempts to locate the lodged bullet failed, and the President's condition worsened, his doctors turned to Bell for help, asking him to bring his detector to the White House. Seemingly conflicting reports describe what happened next. One report stated that Mr. Bell was unable to perfect his instrument in time to locate the bullet, and the president died. Another stated he attempted to locate the bullet, but failed.

In 1890, tests were made to locate sulfides through the medium of conductivity, using a telegraphic receiver connected in series with a battery and a wire brush. Electrical contacts were made in the earth, and a brush was then moved over the surface. When touching sulfides, the brush would complete the circuit causing a click in the receiver. As it could be used only on mineralized surfaces already exposed, the method was of limited value.

Further attempts were made using the Wheatstone bridge circuit for measuring resistance. Here again, conductivity was the deciding factor, but the conductivity between two points on the earth's surface was calculated indirectly by first measuring the resistance. This method also proved impractical.

Another earth conductivity method was given considerable attention. Electrical currents flowing through the ground caused electrical potential lines to be created. Equal potential points

6

CHINESE EMPEROR'S WALK-THROUGH METAL "DETECTOR"

2-1

Figure 2-1: CHINESE EMPEROR'S WALK-THROUGH METAL "DETECTOR." More than two thousand years ago, a Chinese Emperor used the first known "metal detector." Fearing attempts on his life, he instructed his craftsman to build a magnetic attractor, which he placed at the palace doorway. The device was constructed of magnetic mineral that attracted iron objects such as armor, swords, and other weapons, as these objects were carried through the doorway.

across the ground were measured by a galvanometer and then plotted. The presence of an ore body caused these lines to warp or distort. This method was fairly successful, but water layers, areas of uneven moisture, and other substances in the soil gave indications which could be misconstrued as indicating the presence of an ore body. Too, failure of this method to indicate ore would not necessarily mean barren ground. The oxidized condition existing around sulfide ore bodies forms an almost perfect insulator which prevents accurate measurement. Even so, research on earth conductivity methods occasionally takes place today as shown in Figure 2-2 where I (second person, observing control indicators) conducted an experiment in 1963. This instrument was a crevice detector, the brainchild of Dr. John C. Cook, of Teledyne Geotech.

Figure 2-2: Charles Garrett (second person in line) monitors a crevice detector which could measure variations in the earth's conductivity. Large metal objects buried in the ground or large sub-terranean cavities could be "detected" because their presence caused the earth's conductivity to vary from normal. This device was the brainchild of Dr. John C. Cook of Teledyne Geotech, located in Garland, Texas. Photo Richard Carter.

Another method, on which considerable time was spent, was one that created an intense magnetic field without the use of any electrical contact on the ore or on the earth. The presence of an electrical conductor of very low resistance (ore body) caused distortion of the magnetic field. This distortion was detected by a receiving device. This method circumvented the problems caused by moisture and like factors and was limited only by the short distance in which the intensity of the magnetic field was effective. This method was the closest that the early-day pioneers came to the modern metal detector.

Another promising method was that of Induction Balance. It could detect the presence of gold as easily as sulfides or other minerals. Difficulty was immediately apparent, however, as it was difficult to obtain the needed depth.

The idea of locating ore bodies electromagnetically was perhaps first conceived by Dr. Daniel G. Chilson in 1904 in Goldfield, Nevada. Early experiments were made to determine the conductivity of the earth, water and other earth substances, and it was found that sulfides (conductive sulfur) were the best conductors. In 1909 Chilson turned to known radio transmission/ reception techniques, experimenting with short waves.

In 1925 a new electrical gate checker was designed and employed in various factories to help cut down on rampant thefts of tools and products. Its operation was based on the use of electromagnetic waves. Two German physicists, Dr. Geffeken and Dr. Richter of Leipzig, designed the original gate checker. Their work was continued by Gebr. Wetzel of Leipzig-Plaqwitz. An electromagnetic field was caused to flow across the passageway. Metal carried by persons passing through the door caused alteration of the electromagnetic field and a signal was given. The apparatus, which was the fore runner of the modern "walk-through" detector, was adjustable to allow small objects such as watches and keys to be taken through the gate undetected, but larger objects would be detected. A small searching coil was used on those persons who produced a signal as they passed through the doorway. The coil could be adjusted to various sensitivities, allowing a few small objects, such as coins in pockets, to pass undetected.

In this same time period, Shirl Herr was recognized, according to reports, as the inventor of the magnetic balance, a device used for locating underground minerals and metals.

In 1927 a spark gap metal detector was invented and is shown in Figure 2-3.

Figure 2-3: In 1927, a Spark-Gap metal detector was invented, and one model survives to this day. Karl von Mueller and son, Okie Jake Miller, demonstrate the early-day instrument at an Oklahoma City treasure show. Photo Bob Grant.

Figure 2-4: The September, 1930 issue of POPULAR SCIENCE magazine described a "modern" metal detector. The caption reads, "Amateur treasure finder. You can buy parts to build this homemade radio prospector which will find a silver dollar buried several inches in the ground. It makes a buzzing noise when metal is near." The designer is unknown. This detector, however, was designed and built long before any present-day manufacturers came into existance. Photo by Bob Grant.

A report in POPULAR SCIENCE MONTHLY, September 1930, shows a man using a small two-coil metal detector. The man using the device was called an "amateur treasure finder." The metal detector, called a "radio prospector," was widely sold in kits. The caption said that it would find a silver dollar buried several inches underground and that it made a buzzing noise when metal was near. (See Figure 2-4.)

From the early '30s up to World War II, various companies began producing metal detector inventions based upon several of the electrical theories just presented (Figure 2-5). During World War II there was a great interest in metal detectors, with resultant rapid advances in their technology.

Figure 2-5: When Charles Garrett, Peter Bridge, and Arnold Muller (deceased) (shown in photograph) toured Australia's Victoria gold district, they visited the ranch of a gold hunter. He showed them a metal detector that pre-dates World War II. Note the two knap-sacks which contain vacuum tube electronics and batteries.

At the War's end, thousands of Army mine detectors (Figure 2-6) were placed on the market. They were eagerly bought by those ex-military persons who, having been trained in the use of such equipment, recognized the value of an Army mine detector in locating buried treasure.

Several companies sprang up in the '50s and begun producing vacuum tube and transistorized detectors for the consumer. Since transistorization resulted in smaller and lighter weight detectors, vacuum tube detector production ended in the early '60s. It was not until the late '60s and early '70s that a substantial interest in metal detectors arose and it was in the '70s that great strides in metal detector design and capability took place. Ultra-stable and very sensitive metal detectors that featured "Good/Bad" target identification and ground mineral rejection came into existence during this period. (See Figure 2-7.)

Figure 2-6: Beginning in 1945, thousands of Army mine detectors were sold by military equipment surplus stores. Ex-military persons having been trained in the use of such equipment, recognized the value of the detectors in locating buried treasure. In this photograph are shown several such detectors. Left to right: a World War II vintage, U.S. Army vacuum tube mine detector; a modern-day transistorized version; a U.S. Army instrument that detects non-metallic mines; a very early U.S. Army mine detector that was modified by famed treasure hunter Frank Fish for Johnny Kouba, who donated the detector to the Garrett museum; a Russian-built, non-metallic mine detector. Photo by Melvin Climer.

Figure 2-7: Charles Garrett tests one of the first 1970s detector models that ushered in today's high-tech designs. The equipment we have today has resulted from untold engineering man hours, and countless days using and testing instruments in the field.

12

The '80s ushered in target analyzer designs and each year these analyzers are becoming more accurate. Target identification is continually being improved. Today, modern detectors do practically everything except dig the targets: they detect it, pinpoint it, determine its size and shape, measure its depth and tell the operator whether to dig it or not. Some of this target "knowledge," however, is learned by operators who have become very efficient with their detectors, who have learned to interpret and analyze detector audio and indicator information. What tomorrow may bring, anyone can guess, but it will surely include new and improved detectors. It's exciting to think about!

During the very early years of metal detecting, the equipment was used mostly for prospecting for precious metals. The widespread use of metal detectors to locate treasure, came mostly following World War II. Since that time, metal detector operation has greatly expanded into many fields, which include searching for coins, relics, treasure, gold, silver, and other precious metals.

The application of metal detectors to law enforcement and security situations goes back many years, and a number of instances have been recorded in which metal detection equipment was used by law enforcement personnel as a crime scene management and investigative tool. (As a reference see Karl von Mueller's book, THE MASTER HUNTER MANUAL, 1973, Ram Publishing Company, now out of print). Metal detectors of both the walk-through and hand-held type, are being used in airports and many other facilities where the threat of force and violence is increasing at an alarming rate.

Metal detector applications are constantly being expanded and now extend into many fields, including, among others: medicine, archaeology, lumbering, food processing and traffic control.

New detector advances, as well as improved operating techniques and knowledge, have caused interest in the metal detector field to grow world-wide. Metal detectors are now used in perhaps every country in the world.

CHAPTER 2 QUESTIONS

1. Perhaps the first "metal detector" was built for a _____
_____ to protect his _____ . (Each correct answer
is worth 10 points)

2. According to known records one of the first metal detector
applications took place in the year _____ when attempts
were made to locate a bullet which had lodged in the body of
United States President Garfield who was shot by an assassin.

3. The first widespread use of metal detectors for treasure hunting
took place following World War II when Army _____
_____ became available.

4. Today, modern metal detectors do practically everything except
_____ _____ _____ .

5. Metal detectors are now used in perhaps every country in the
world in many hobbyist and professional fields. Name five fields
where metal detectors are used. (Each correct answer is worth 4
points)

Each of the 5 complete questions, answered correctly, is worth 20
points. Perfect score is 100. Answers given in Appendix 2.

CHAPTER 3

How Metal Detectors Work

It is not necessary to understand the scientific principles of how metal detectors work, in order to use them. You can find coins, rings, jewelry, relics, gold, silver or whatever you are searching for and not know how your detector works. However, for a better understanding of what your detector is doing, and to enhance your ability to understand why your detector just gave that peculiar sound, or why it reacts the way it does to metals and minerals, it is necessary for you to understand how a metal detector works.

Two examples will illustrate this need. First, let's say you are scanning in the field and get a detector signal. You dig down a foot and find nothing. You enlarge the hole and dig another foot and still don't find anything. You might keep on digging to five or six feet before finally giving up.

What went wrong? Was it your fault, or that of your detector? Was a target there? Well, yes, there was a target, though it may not necessarily have been a metal one. The response could have been due to some variation in mineral content. In these situations, knowing how your detector works, plus having an understanding of the various detectable minerals, will save you a great deal of effort. You will not dig at all, or perhaps no deeper than one foot, before you realize there is no metallic target in the ground.

For the second example, let's say you are searching for a small iron kettle filled with gold coins. This kettle was placed somewhere in a field, and you know that a large flat rock was placed on top of it. Unfortunately, however, there are one thousand other large, heavy flat rocks lying in the same field. The area is highly mineralized and some of the rocks contain a great amount of iron mineralization. Your chances of finding that iron kettle are many times greater if you know how to select the best detector for that particular job, how the metal detector works and how it responds to iron minerals. On the other hand, if you do not know how to select, understand, and use a detector, and you do not know anything about iron minerals, you will likely never find that iron kettle—unless you decide to dig beneath every rock in that field.

The "answers" to both the above situations are presented later in this book.

In MODERN METAL DETECTORS, theory explanations are kept simple. Only very basic detector operating characteristics are

15

described, because this book was intended not to be a theoretical work but a home, field and classroom textbook to help the metal detector user understand the basics of metal detector operation. Several comparisons of things you already know about, are given in order to show you how detectors work. To make all discussions clear, various aspects of electrical current, transmitted and received signals, and properties of metals and minerals are discussed. As you read through this book, you will realize that detectors are not difficult to understand.

When you begin studying mineralization, target identification, field applications and other subjects discussed in later chapters, you will be rewarded from your study of this background material. You will understand what your detector is telling you; why you get certain signals; and how to determine if the object you have detected is one that you want to dig. The correct and highly efficient operation of a detector is not difficult, but does require a certain amount of study, thought and field application.

RADIO TRANSMISSION AND RECEPTION

The following is a simplified explanation of how one type of instrument detects metal. You have operated one-half of a metal detector during most of your lifetime, perhaps without knowing it: the common radio. Metal detection is achieved, basically, by the transmission and "reception" of a radio wave signal. (Refer to Figure 3-1.) This block diagram illustrates the basic components of a transmitter/receiver type of metal detector. The battery is the

3-1 BLOCK DIAGRAM OF TRANSMITTER-RECEIVER METAL DETECTOR

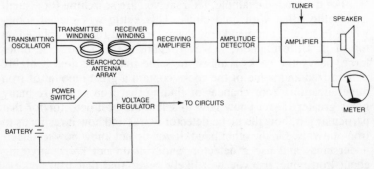

Figure 3-1: ELECTRONIC BLOCK DIAGRAM OF TRANSMITTER-RECEIVER METAL DETECTOR. This block diagram illustrates basic metal detector components. The electronic transmitter oscillator generates a signal current which travels through the searchcoil cable to the transmitter winding (antenna). As the current circulates in the antenna, an invisible electromagnetic field is generated that flows out into the air or other surrounding medium. When conductive metal and certain minerals interrupt the electromagnetic field, metal detection occurs.

power supply. The transmitter electronic oscillator generates a signal.

The transmitter signal current travels from the transmitter oscillator through a wire (searchcoil cable) to the searchcoil's transmitter winding (antenna). The transmitter antenna is a few turns of electrical wire, generally wound in a circular fashion.

ELECTROMAGNETIC FIELD GENERATION

As the current circulates in the transmitter antenna, an invisible electromagnetic field is generated that flows out into the air (or surrounding medium, i.e.: air, wood, rock, earth materials, water, etc.) in all directions. If this electromagnetic field were visible, it would appear to be in the shape of a gigantic, three dimensional doughnut, with the transmitter antenna embedded in its center.

Electromagnetic field theory states that field lines cannot cross one another. Consequently, they crowd together as they pass through the circular antenna, but they are not crowded on the outside. It is fortunate this crowding takes place, because the intensity (density) of the field lines is the very phenomenon that enables metal detection in the area adjacent to the searchcoil to take place. Note, in Figure 3-2, the area indicated as the two dimensional detection pattern. This is the site of maximum field crowding; here metal detection occurs as a result of two major

3-2   TWO DIMENSIONAL ELECTROMAGNETIC FIELD AND DETECTION PATTERNS

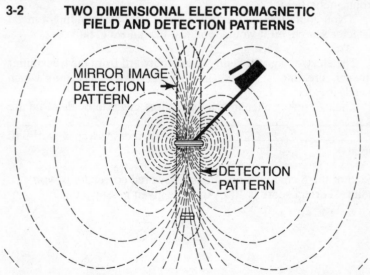

Figure 3-2: TWO DIMENSIONAL ELECTROMAGNETIC FIELD AND DETECTION PATTERN. The transmitter current flowing in the antenna generates the electromagnetic field. The detection pattern, shown by the dashed lines, is the area within which metal detection takes place. A mirror-image detection pattern is formed on the opposite side of the searchcoil, but it is not utilized.

17

phenomena: eddy current generation and electromagnetic field distortion. (Note the mirror-image detection pattern above the searchcoil.)

EDDY CURRENTS GENERATE SECONDARY ELECTROMAGNETIC FIELD

Laws of physics indicate that when electromagnetic field lines pass through metal and some minerals, the phenomena of eddy current generation and field warping take place. These phenomena are discussed, in detail, in Chapter Seven as are other characteristics of detectors and the properties of metals and certain minerals that you should know in order to understand your detector.

The searchcoil antenna array senses these disturbances that occur within the detection pattern, and the metal detector's electronic circuits produce audio and other signals that alert the operator to the presence of the detected metal and/or mineral near the searchcoil.

CHAPTER 3 QUESTIONS

1. Basically, a metal detector works about the same as a
_____ .

2. A metal detector transmitter _____ transmits an electromagnetic field.

3. If you could see the electromagnetic field surrounding a metal detector searchcoil it would look just like an ice cream cone.
    True _____ False _____

4. The electromagnetic field radiates outward from the transmitter antenna creating a _____ _____ within which metals are detected.

5. The two major phenomena that causes metal to be detected are _____ _____ _____ and _____ _____ _____ . (Each correct answer is worth 10 points)

Each of the 5 complete questions, answered correctly, is worth 20 points. Perfect score is 100. Answers given in Appendix 2.

CHAPTER 4

Modern Metal Detector Types

Detectors for individual, professional, and hobby use are of several basic circuit types: the Beat Frequency Oscillator (BFO), the Transmitter-Receiver (TR), the Very Low Frequency Ground Elimination (Canceling) (VLF), and the Pulse Induction (PI). Detectors for commercial use (industrial, military, medical, surveying, etc.) also use these same circuit types (with a few exceptions), and they may be manufactured in different configurations designed for specific applications such as public utility metal locators, airport security metal detection systems, ore sampling detectors and so on. The majority of this book is devoted to detailed discussions of the four types mentioned above and equipment used by law enforcement and security personnel, archaeologists, underwater hunters, and others. Military equipment will be discussed only briefly.

THE BASIC TYPES

The BFO, TR, VLF and Pulse Induction detectors are the most popular circuit types in use today. They will be briefly discussed in this chapter and thoroughly examined later. The order of discussion is based simply upon the order in which the equipment types became available to, and popular with, the consumer, and has no relation to their value and capabilities.

THE BFO. Transistorized BFOs, introduced in the '50s, were lighter, more compact and used smaller batteries than did the earlier vacuum tube types. Early-day models are shown in Figures 4-1 and 4-2. These BFOs would do just about every metal detecting job but were used primarily for general treasure hunting and prospecting.

Improvements in circuitry and versatility resulted in the BFO becoming very popular in the late '60s and early '70s (Figures 4-3, 4-4). The BFO earned the nickname, "The Workhorse Of The Industry," because it could do just about any job well and was extremely rugged and field worthy. Millions of dollars worth of coins, money caches (pronounced "cashes") and precious metals were found with BFOs. A '70s model is shown in Figure 4-5.

BFO production continued into the '80s, although its popularity began to wane in the mid-'70s when the more powerful and versatile VLF detectors were introduced. BFOs continue to be used, but now primarily for prospecting.

Figure 4-1: Charles Garrett holds the first metal detector he designed and built in 1963. It contains a crystal controlled Beat Frequency Oscillator circuit with vernier tuning, speaker headphones and a meter indicator. From this detector sprang many production years of Garrett Electronics' Beat Frequency Oscillator detectors.

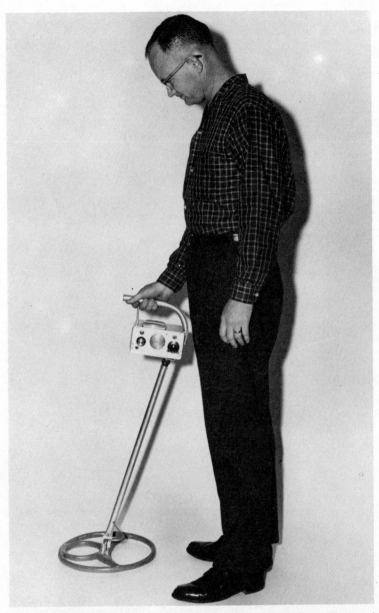

Figure 4-2: Charles Garrett demonstrates the first production model of Garrett Electronics' independently-operated dual searchcoil Hunter BFO. It was patterned after the prototype shown in Figure 4-1. The searchcoil contained two independently-operated searchcoils—a five-inch diameter searchcoil and a twelve-inch diameter searchcoil. Either could be selected simply by flipping a switch. The small searchcoil was used for coin and nugget hunting, while the large searchcoil was used for searching for larger treasures buried deeply.

Figure 4-3: Charles Garrett, in 1968, demonstrates a compact, hipmounted, Garrett Electronics' BFO metal detector. All electronics and batteries were contained in the belt mounted housing. Transistors allow construction of miniature metal detectors such as this one.

Figure 4-4: This is one of the Spartan BFO metal detectors manufactured by Garrett Electronics exclusively for Karl von Mueller of Exanimo. This miniature detector could be used with the control housing handle-mounted as shown, or on a person's belt. The control housing contained all circuitry components, a speaker, earphone jack and a battery. Note the piggyback meter.

THE TR. TRs became popular in the '60s. Transistorized versions were lighter, more compact and used smaller batteries than did the earlier vacuum tube types. TRs were primarily very good coin hunting instruments, with excellent detection depth possible. Countless millions of coins and other treasures were found with TRs.

They were not as versatile as BFO types, however. While a few cache (money) hunters used TRs, they were never popular with electronic prospectors because they were ineffective over mineralized ground and had certain non-uniform searchcoil detection characteristics. A '70s TR model is shown in Figure 4-6.

TR popularity began to wane along with that of BFOs in the mid-'70s and, while its production continues today, models are generally in the less expensive detector lines and kits.

THE VLF. VLFs became popular in the '70s. Extra depth of detection, along with ground and trash target (unwanted metal) elimination capabilities, makes these detectors the most popular type in almost every phase of metal detection activity. They can perform just about every metal detecting task in a superior fashion.

Further improvements in VLF circuitry have resulted in greater versatility, detection depth, and target identification, making the VLF position even stronger. These instruments are being used to re-scan "worked out" treasure hunting sites, and operators are

23

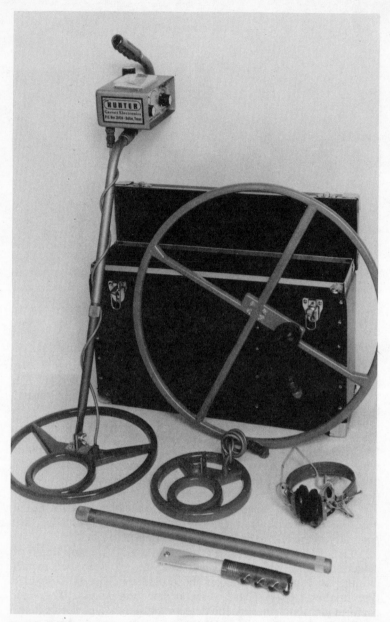

Figure 4-5: This is a 1970's model Beat Frequency Oscillator metal detector. Even though these detectors could not detect as deeply as present day detectors, millions of dollars worth of coins, money caches, and precious metals were found. Note the wide assortment of available searchcoils. The searchcoils range in size from three-quarter inch diameter (not shown) up to the large, twenty-four inch diameter, deep seeking searchcoil.

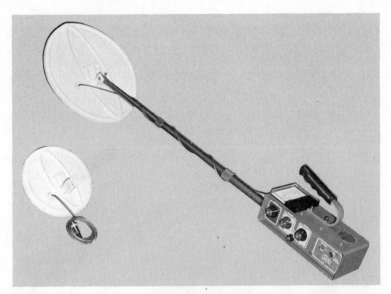

Figure 4-6: This is a 1970s model Transmitter-Receiver detector. Even though it did not feature ground canceling, it was the most popular coin hunting type detector. It was very sensitive and could detect coins to great depths. Careful manipulation of the tuner was required when these instruments were used over highly mineralized ground.

finding treasure at depths greater than was possible with BFOs and TRs. Improvements will no doubt continue to come and the VLF will remain popular. A mid-'80s VLF model is shown in Figure 4-7.

A VLF that automatically eliminates ground minerals from detection is available for the person who prefers a very easy to use, yet sophisticated, detector.

VLFs are used in practically every metal detecting situation, from coin, cache, and relic hunting, to gold hunting in mountains and streams. A wide variety of searchcoils and probes greatly expands VLF capabilities. Land and underwater instruments are available, as well as versatile instruments for law enforcement and industry.

THE PULSE INDUCTION. Pulse Induction detector popularity began to increase in the early '80s when moderately priced, high quality, versatile detectors were introduced. Pulse instruments were available in the '70s, but they were designed primarily for underwater work and their cost was considerably higher than present models.

Pulse instruments work extremely well, even in hostile salt water environments. Consequently, when convertible types that could be used both on beaches and underwater sites were introduced, the popularity of pulse instruments increased. Salt water beach

25

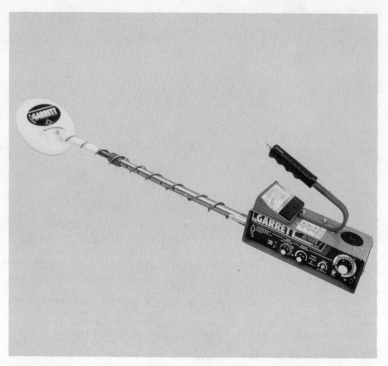

Figure 4-7: This instrument, the Master Hunter 7 A.D.S., is one of today's modern metal detectors. These models feature computerized circuitry and are so capable they will do practically everything except dig targets.

hunting had been somewhat non-productive in salt water environments that also contained iron earth minerals (magnetic black sand). Pulse detectors changed all that and opened up a new sport. Consequently, Pulse Induction metal detectors have become the most popular of all underwater types. A convertible land/sea pulse detector is shown in Figure 4-8.

INDUSTRIAL, COMMERCIAL AND LAW ENFORCEMENT EQUIPMENT

Industrial metal detection equipment is designed primarily for two applications: metal locating and pipe tracing. Metal locators are used by construction crews, utilities, plumbers and others to locate buried and concealed metal objects, such as manhole covers, meter and valve boxes and sprinkler system components. In prior years field crews used whatever metal detectors were available including BFO, TR, VLF, and a deepseeking RF (radio frequency) or two-box type.

Beginning in the early '80s, however, sophisticated VLF circuit types with a multitude of searchcoils became popular. Attach-

Figure 4-8: This young lady, Sally Blue, is searching for coins, jewelry, and other treasure on Texas' Padre Island with a convertible, land/sea, Sea Hunter XL500 Pulse Induction detector. This instrument can be used on the beach, in the surf, or carried to water depths of 200 feet. Photo by Melvin Climer.

27

ments that convert standard VLF configurations to the two-box type (Figure 4-9), are preferred because of their large object, deep seeking capability and their ability to ignore subterranean water and mineral pockets, a problem that plagued users of the older types.

Figure 4-9: Charles Garrett teaches 1984 Los Angeles Olympics' security guards in the correct use of Garrett's Deepseeking instruments. Garrett Electronics was the supplier of metal detectors to the summer games. These Deepseeker models were used in the search for hidden bombs and other explosive and injurious devices. Photo Dave Loveless.

Tracing equipment is used world-wide to locate and trace the countless millions of miles of buried and concealed metal pipe, cable, and conduit. Modern-day instruments not only can locate these metal objects, but they can trace, measure depth, and locate breaks. A great amount of time and money is saved by users of this equipment.

Modern-day industrial equipment manufacturers have combined metal locating and pipe tracing circuitry into one versatile instrument (Figure 4-10), which can be used as a deepseeking locator to find manhole covers, valve boxes, etc., and as a tracer to locate and trace pipes, cable, and conduit. These multiple-use instruments do all the jobs and functions that formerly required two or more instruments. In addition, the new instruments are more capable and deeper seeking.

Numerous metal detector systems are in use in industries such as lumbering and food processing. Detector systems locate nails, wire, spikes, and other metal objects in tree logs prior to sawing. They locate metal objects in food products in processing plants.

28

Figure 4-10: This industrial instrument, Model LT-2000, can be used to locate not only buried and concealed metal objects but also trace and measure depth of pipes, cable and conduit. These multiple-use instruments do all the jobs and functions that formally required two or more instruments.

Traffic control systems abound with metal locators that sense the presence and flow of vehicular traffic. Figure 4-11 shows where vehicular traffic signal monitor antennas are buried in grooves cut into pavement near a traffic intersection.

Airport, industrial, and other security people use both hand-held (Figure 4-12) and walk-through (Figure 4-13) metal detectors to locate weapons, tools, and other metal objects on people as they pass through gates, out of buildings, and in and out of controlled areas.

Law Enforcement and Crime Scene Investigators utilize almost all types of detectors in their search for metal evidence and in searching individuals for hidden and concealed metal weapons. Both land and underwater types have proven themselves many times in these exciting fields.

29

In the fields of Security and Law Enforcement there are few areas where metal detectors are not of decided value.

Figure 4-11: Traffic control systems abound with metal locators that sense the presence and flow of vehicle traffic. This is a street location where traffic monitor metal detector searchcoils are embedded in grooves cut into the pavement.

MILITARY EQUIPMENT

Military mine detection equipment is continually being improved. Private industry, through military grants, develops much of this equipment. Military equipment is extremely rugged and environmentally protected. Some instruments are sensitive enough to locate tiny metal pins in otherwise all plastic mines. Mine detectors are produced not only for the use of the individual soldier, but highly sensitive vehicle mounted detectors are also in widespread use.

"Detectors" have been perfected that locate all-plastic mines and voids. Underground caves, tunnels, and storage facility locators have been developed to find hidden underground storage areas and facilities that might be constructed prior to enemy withdrawal from captured battle areas. I helped develop one such type in the early '60s during the Vietnam War. Of course, military operations often include commercial, deep seeking detectors in many applications, including the locating of unexploded bombs that must be removed from practice bombing ranges and war-torn battlefield sites.

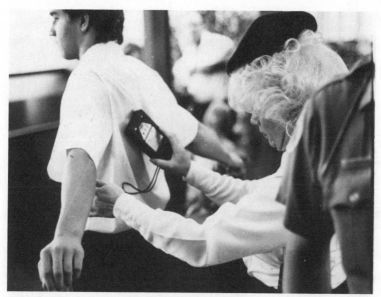

Figure 4-12: This hand-held Pocket Scanner metal detector, Model 11616 is used by a lady security guard at the Salt Lake City, Utah airport. She is searching the person for concealed metal objects which triggered a walk-through metal detector.

Figure 4-13: This walk-through metal detector is one of a thousand metal detectors that Garrett deployed at the 1984 Los Angeles Summer Olympic Games. The walk-through detector was placed in this metal wrap-around, street cross-over, cage. All persons wishing to pass into this secured area had to walk through the metal detector. The devices are so sensitive they can detect the presence of a single coin.

CHAPTER 4 QUESTIONS

1. The most popular metal detector circuit types are (give descriptive words): _____ _____ _____ (BFO); _____ _____ (TR); _____ _____ _____ (VLF); _____ _____ (PI). (Each correct answer is worth 2 1/2 points)

2. The most popular, capable and versatile of these four types (question 1) is the _____ .

3. Treasure hunters will always be able to find treasure because over the years, as detectors are improved, the new models generally detect _____ than previous models.

4. VLF metal detectors can perform just about every metal detecting _____ in a superior fashion.

5. VLF's are used in practically every metal detecting situation including _____ , _____ and _____ hunting and _____ . (Each correct answer is worth 2 1/2 points)

6. The most popular type of underwater detector is the Pulse Induction, because it "ignores" _____ earth minerals and _____ water. (Each correct answer is worth 5 points)

7. Convertible type metal detectors are available and can be used on dry land as well as in the surf.

      True _____   False _____

8. The Industrial and Utility use of metal detection equipment includes two major applications: metal _____ and pipe _____ . (Each correct answer is worth 5 points)

9. Walk-through and hand-held metal detectors are generally thought of as _____ type metal detectors.

10. In the fields of security and law enforcement, there are few areas where _____ are not of decided value.

Each of the 10 complete questions, answered correctly, is worth 10 points. Perfect score is 100. Answers given in Appendix 2.

CHAPTER 5

Metal Detector Applications

The uses to which metal detectors are put are limited only by mankind's imagination. During the past fifty or so years, they have been used to detect and locate practically every kind of metal and detectable mineral.

Approximately ninety-five percent of those who use metal detectors for treasure hunting do so to search for coins, jewelry and other small objects which might be found on beaches and playgrounds and in parks and various other places where people congregate. (See Figures 5-1 and 5-2.) Practically anyone can learn to use a metal detector and find places to search. Coins have been lost everywhere people have been, and people have been practically everywhere. This aspect of treasure hunting is relatively easy; it is not necessary to travel long distances to find good coin hunting locations.

Figure 5-1: Approximately ninety-five percent of those who use metal detectors, search for coins, jewelry and other small objects lost in beaches, playgrounds, parks and various other places where people congregate. Practically anyone can use a metal detector to find treasure, as this family is doing in this park. Photo by Melvin Climer.

Other treasure hunting activities such as prospecting (Figure 5-3), relic hunting, and cache hunting, often require some travel to

Figure 5-2: Charles Garrett, second from left, explains proper metal detector operation to two Scout leaders, Brad Taylor and Dick Walker and two young Scouters at the 1980 Boy Scout Jamboree which was held at Fort AP Hill, Virginia. These Scout leaders then trained hundreds of other Scouts who used detectors in various competition and handicapped awareness programs. Photo by Dave Loveless.

get to good locations. Too, more metal detector expertise is usually required for greatest success in these specialized fields.

Industrial users such as utility, construction, and electrical companies, save time and money by employing detectors to locate pipes, electrical conduits and land markers. Imagine, for instance, the inconvenience and repair expense involved should a bulldozer's blade rip into a buried telephone cable containing thousands of telephone lines. To avoid needless destruction, field crews scan the ground with metal detecting devices prior to digging, trenching, or disturbing the ground in any manner (see Figure 5-4).

Law enforcement personnel use detectors to locate guns, knives, weapons, stolen goods, physical evidence, and other metal objects concealed and hidden in the ground, buildings, water, and other locations. Often, detectors are used to locate metal objects hidden in clothing or body cavities of a suspect (Figure 5-5.)

Archaeologists use detectors not only for locating and retrieving of metal objects but for many other applications as well. (See Chapter 26 for a discussion of THE ARCHAEOLOGICAL USE OF METAL DETECTORS).

Numerous manufacturers need various detector types for unusual metal detecting jobs. Lumber mills use instruments to search for nails, spikes, and wire in trees and logs (Figure 5-6). A single nail or spike can damage expensive sawblades in the twinkling of an

Figure 5-3: Roy Lagal, world renown electronic prospector, treasure hunter, and author examines a piece of nearly pure silver that he located near a mine dump at Cobalt, Ontario, Canada. Millions of dollars worth of discarded ore has been located by electronic prospectors who scan the countryside and mine dumps near abandoned mines.

Figure 5-4: A field crewman operates an LT-2000 Pipe Tracer/Metal Locator equipped with a twelve-inch diameter locator searchcoil. He scans ahead of earth moving equipment to locate subterranean cables, pipes and other metal objects.

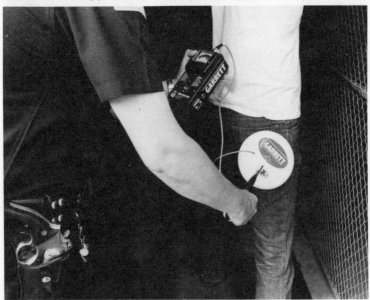

Figure 5-5: Often, detectors are used to locate metal objects hidden in a suspect's clothing or body cavities. Here, a Law Enforcement Officer is using an Inspector, Model G-100, to scan an employee who is suspected of removing tools from this plant site.

Figure 5-6: A lumber mill inspector uses a VLF metal detector to search for nails, spikes, wire and other metal objects in trees and logs that can damage sawblades. Photo by Roy Lagal.

eye. Correctly designed metal detectors can prevent this kind of destruction.

One lumber mill foreman needed a detector to take into a jungle, deep in the heart of Africa, to scan saw logs to locate embedded metal objects before they damaged sawblades. He could hardly believe the quantity of metal objects that were embedded in the trees in this isolated forest. Apparently, the spikes, nails, and other metallic trash became part of these trees during World War II.

Metal detectors are widely used in food processing plants to locate "tramp" (unwanted) pieces of metal that may have broken loose and fallen into food processing containers.

One food processing plant manager had another problem: someone dropped a meat hook into two thousand pounds of sausage. It was ground up along with the sausage and the pieces of metal had to be located, but the sausage had already been processed and packaged into links. Leasing a detector with an open searchcoil the manager hand fed the sausage links through the detector searchcoil and reported that all of the meat hook metal pieces were located.

Another manufacturer had a problem with a foam rubber reclaimer. As foam is processed, it comes out of the machine in sheets six feet wide by six inches thick. A heated wire is stretched across the opening of a machine to cut the foam into layers of

37

various thicknesses from one-half to two inches. Oftentimes metal objects, such as pins, are present in the foam. When the foam is pushed into the heated wire, the metal pins touch the wire, causing it to break. The manufacturer uses a detector to locate these tiny pieces of "tramp" metal before they reach the wire.

MODERN METAL DETECTOR APPLICATIONS

Some metal detector applications are listed below. This list is by no means complete, but it will suggest the extent to which metal detectors are used. If you know of applications other than these, please write to the Editor, Ram Publishing Company, P.O. Box 38649, Dallas, Texas 75238 U.S.A.

ELECTRONIC PROSPECTING

Hunting gold nuggets.

Hunting silver nuggets.

Locating veins (gold, silver, copper, lead, zinc and other conductive metals).

Searching for isolated natural gold and silver pockets.

Locating mineral zones by prospectors.

Identifying metal/mineral ore samples (bench testing.)

High grading mine and rock piles to detect conductive metal ore specimens.

Identifying various rock and mineral specimens by rockhounds.

Detecting high grade ore, as well as certain gems that contain iron and/or conductive metal.

Detecting minerals and metals bearing uranium.

Grading conductive metal ore by electronic prospectors.

Locating black sand concentrations by gold pan and dredge operators.

INDUSTRIAL

Tracing electrical wiring and conduit.

Tracing and locating pipe.

Detecting nails, spikes, barbed wire, staples, bullets and other metal pieces in trees and logs that are to be milled.

Detecting foreign or "tramp" bodies in food processing.

Detecting nails and other metallic devices used in building construction. (Nails indicate location of studs, etc.)

Detecting spikes, nails and other metal objects that have become embedded in non-metal radial tires prior to recapping.

Locating underground pipe, lawn sprinklers, sprinkler heads.

Locating staples, nails, and other metallic objects in paper before further processing.

Locating metallic objects in food processing plants.

Locating staples during automatic processing of paper money.

Detecting pins, staples, and other metallic objects in foam processing plants.

Locating manhole covers and other underground metal objects in the ground, under highways, and in building construction.

Detecting the presence of electrical pipes, conduits, etc., ahead of bulldozers and other earth digging and excavating equipment.

Counting quantities of items going through food processing plants, such as cans, etc.

Detecting the illegal removal of books from libraries.

Locating steel reinforcement rods in concrete slabs, highways, etc.

Detecting metal in plant vats by glassware manufacturers.

Checking bales of hops for "tramp" metal. (Hops are used to flavor beers.)

Locating pipe, cable and reinforcing rods in floors by pest control personnel to determine the correct places to drill holes for pest control chemicals.

Locating all metal objects that lie concealed (in fields) in the path of reapers and other farm machinery.

Detecting metal objects mixed in with ore or coal, etc., in processing plants.

Locating concrete rebar to determine if construction meets specifications, standards, etc.

Locating steel reinforcement in atomic reactor plants prior to drilling and installation of additional reactor strengthening devices.

Locating nails, spikes, etc., used to attach sheet rock and other wall coverings.

Finding broken or sunken lawn sprinkler heads.

LAW ENFORCEMENT

Locating (by police and other law enforcement personnel) weapons concealed on individuals and/or hidden in various parts of their anatomy.

Locating guns, knives and other metal material evidence in buildings.

Quick searching by police patrol squads for weapons on suspects.

Detecting bullets and metal arrow points in animal carcasses by wildlife officers when investigating poaching cases.

Locating all metal objects at aircraft and other crash and wreck sites.

Searching of crime scenes thoroughly to locate physical evidence.

Locating evidence at arson and bombing sites, such as gas cans, bomb parts, etc.

Detecting illegal fishing nets by fish and wildlife officers.

Detecting I.D. tags implanted in fish by fish and wildlife

officers.

Locating buried bodies through detection of rings, jewelry, fillings in teeth, etc., by crime scene investigators.

MEDICAL

Locating and tracing of metal particles swallowed by humans. Detecting foreign metal particles accidentally lodged in various parts of the human body, such as the feet and eyes. (People step on needles and pins, and metallic slivers from grinding wheels are occasionally propelled into eyeballs.)

Detecting bullets in the human body. (Bullet locating might seem easy until you consider that a bullet may enter into a person, strike a muscle or a bone, and be deflected, traveling a long distance through the body before it finally comes to rest. Detectors can locate bullets much more easily and quickly than can X-ray processes.)

Tracing the flow of metallic objects through various body cavities in experimental medicine.

MILITARY

Locating bullets, or other metal objects in cadavers by medical examiners.

Locating land mines and other military devices.

Locating unexploded bombs at military bombing practice sites.

Locating underground ammunition storage vaults.

PROFESSIONAL

Detecting metallic objects at archaeological sites.

Locating lost rings and jewelry by insurance agents.

Locating stakes, corner posts, and other markers, by surveyors.

Locating only bronze, brass and other highly conductive metals at archaeological sites. (These items are more likely to bear legible inscriptions of names, dates, etc., than corrosive metals.)

Defining site perimeters on archaeological sites.

Verifying the presence of metal objects at archaeological sites to assist in determining whether ground level of dig has been reached.

Locating metal building hinges, locks, reinforcement rods which will help define building outlines, etc., at archaeological sites.

Firemen locating fire hydrants covered with snow.

Locating, by Civil Defense personnel, automobiles, fire hydrants, emergency equipment and countless other things covered during snow and mud slides, flooding, earthquakes, etc.

SECURITY

Detecting weapons on people at airports, in business establishments, courtrooms, etc.

Detecting the presence of weapons on prison visitors and

inmates.

Detecting letter and package bombs.

Searching incoming parcels and packages for metallic weapons in institutions.

Detecting weapons on people at sports events, Olympics, etc.

TRAFFIC CONTROL

Counting vehicles on roadways.

Controlling signal lights and other traffic flow devices.

TREASURE HUNTING

Hunting coins.

Hunting rings.

Hunting jewelry.

Hunting caches (buried money usually in some type of container.)

Detecting relics, buried in the ground and concealed in buildings.

Locating bottle and trash dumps (usually by persons who want to dig for bottles and relics.)

Locating money, caches and relics in buildings.

Finding coins under clotheslines and fence rows where clothing has been hung.

Locating discarded mile marker nails along railroad tracks.

Locating buried barbed wire.

Locating fence post holes from prior years by detecting differences in soil mineral content.

Identifying targets to determine value. (Most commonly illustrated by discriminating, classifying and target elimination metal detectors where coin and treasure hunters determine whether objects are worth digging; accomplished by "measuring" the conductivity of the metal. Fortunately, gold, silver and copper are good conductors; iron, foil, bottlecaps and other junk are not.)

UNDERWATER

Locating underwater sunken shipwreck treasure.

Locating sunken boats, motors, toolboxes, etc. (One woman used a detector to locate a toolbox that was dumped from a boat in which her husband was riding. The husband had drowned and she was attempting to locate the exact spot where the boat overturned.)

Locating sunken helicopters. (A helicopter was located in Possum Kingdom Lake in Central Texas.)

Locating weapons, money, and other metal objects thrown into wells and cisterns.

Locating metal objects by underwater divers and archaeologists to define a wreck site, archaeological perimeters, etc.

Detecting whether sonar-detected sunken objects are metal

(underwater searchcoils). When only metal objects are searched for, this technique saves valuable diver time.

MISCELLANEOUS

Detecting metallic particles in cows' stomachs.

Locating buried caskets. Oftentimes, underground caskets shift beneath the ground because of water flow or earth movement. One company produces a casket with metal rings embedded in each of the four corners. Specialized metal detectors can then be used to locate the rings and prevent grave digging machines from penetrating these "misplaced" or "lost" caskets.

Analyzing and determining the purity of metals and coins. (For example, determining the relative purity of silver and silver coinage).

Detecting iron mineral placed in U.S.A. paper currency. (This mineral is placed in U.S.A. paper money to give it long wearing qualities. It can be detected with certain metal detectors).

Locating brass valves and other brass fixtures in junk yards and metallic junky areas. (This can best be accomplished by using certain of the BFO detectors).

Detecting underground earth anomalies. (Certain types of detectors can be used for detecting underground anomalies, such as voids, crevices in ice, caves, etc.)

Detecting razor blades, metallic slivers, or other metallic trash in Halloween candy.

Determining if lead sinkers have been used to increase fish weight at fishing competitions.

I wrap up this chapter with an account of how one lady envisioned a detector should NOT be used.

A dealer, demonstrating a detector to a lady, told her that very large metal objects could be found to depths of more than fifteen feet. "Oh," the lady exclaimed. "I don't want that detector. I wouldn't have it!" "Why not," the dealer questioned. "Well," replied the prospective customer, "I am buying this detector for my husband and I'm the one who will have to dig the holes. I sure don't want to dig holes fifteen feet deep, and besides, I'm not even that tall!"

CHAPTER 5 QUESTIONS

1. The uses to which metal detectors are put are limited only by mankind's _____ .

2. Practically every kind of metal and detectable mineral has been searched for by metal detector users for _____ years. (A) 25; (B) 50; (C) 75; (D) 100.

3. Approximately ninety-five percent of those who use metal detectors for treasure hunting, often search for coins.

   True _____   False _____

4. Coins have been lost everywhere people have been and people have been practically _____ .

5. Law enforcement personnel use metal detectors to locate _____ , _____ , and other metal objects concealed on individuals or hidden in the ground, in buildings, in water and at other locations. (Each correct answer is worth 10 points)

6. In your field(s) of interest list ten items you can find with a metal detector.

7. List five items that a metal detector will not detect.

Questions 1-5: Each complete question, answered correctly, is worth 20 points. Perfect score is 100. Answers given in Appendix 2.

Questions 6 and 7 are group or classroom discussion type questions. No points are given for correct answers. You should, however, be able to give complete answers.

Figure 5-A: Charles Garrett and John Quade, star of stage, screen and television, take a few moments from treasure hunting to discuss a movie they plan to film entitled GOLD AND TREASURE ADVENTURES. This movie is now available, on a loan basis from Garrett Electronics, to all clubs and other interested groups. Charles and John sit on a bridge near buildings, as seen in the background, that were constructed for use during the filming of the PLANET OF THE APES movie series. Photo by Bob Grant.

Metal Detector Development

If a complete history of metal detector development could be written, the manuscript could easily weigh a hundred pounds. Such a treatise would be a gigantic task, but of small value to the average detector user. What is needed, and what this book was written to provide, is a presentation of the characteristics of metal detectors and how these characteristics relate to the metal detector operator in the field. The better the understanding a person has about why metal detectors respond the way they do to metals and certain minerals, the greater will be that person's success.

Consequently, everything in this book was written to help metal detector users have a better understanding of the operation of their equipment. This book contains no involved theory, nor detailed, drawn-out explanations of who first produced any given feature, circuit, or detector type. There are so many claims and counter-claims as to who first developed the many improved designs that an accurate determination probably could never be made. He who was first may be last, and he who was last may be first.

Up into the late 1800s, seekers of metals had forked tree limbs and Miner's Compass Dip Needle Instruments (Figure 6-1) to use in their quest for metals. In the early 1900s, vacuum tubes found their way into metal detector design and retained a foothold until the '50s when mass-produced transistors became available. In spite of their bulkiness and weight, vacuum tube metal detectors were good; they served their users well, though sales of metal detectors prior to World War II were small.

The war all but stopped production of commercially produced metal detectors, but in the late '40s and early '50s several new companies began producing detectors of various designs.

Following World War II, the demand increased sharply; more manufacturers began to produce detectors, and competition became very spirited. At least one of the post-World War II companies used the basic design of the vacuum tube Army mine detectors, while others produced machines which were similar in design to the pre-war TR detectors.

During the '50s, Raytheon and other companies printed detector schematics in their how-to transistor circuit books. Consumer BFOs patterned after these designs began to appear on the scene. The status quo prevailed until near the end of the '50s.

New companies began producing deeper seeking, more versa-

Figure 6-1: Fred Mott, noted historical researcher demonstrates a 1920s model miner's Compass dip needle. The instrument was designed for prospectors, but was also in widespread use by treasure hunters. The instrument was held, as shown, in the plane of the magnetic meridian (north and south). Readings were taken when the needle stopped swinging. The operator then advanced forward some predetermined distance, stopped, and took another reading. At the point where the instrument showed a slight dip in needle position, an ore body was supposed to be buried beneath the ground. The stronger the dip of the needle, the stronger was the magnetic attraction. This instrument was donated to the Garrett Electronics museum by Mr. H. Champagne of Dracut, Massachusetts. Photo by Melvin Climer.

tile detectors during the '60s. Since then, competition among manufacturers has been extremely keen and has resulted in new and improved instruments. Manufacturers continually strive to update and improve their products.

BFO AND TR DEVELOPMENT

In the early days, detector tuning drift problems plagued the manufacturers, and users were frustrated as they had to continually adjust their tuning controls. However, the concentrated effort spent on this problem resulted in stable BFO and TR detectors which began to be produced during the late '60s.

The operating frequencies of BFO instruments varied widely among manufacturers. If the transmission frequency was too low, between, say, 50 and 150 kilohertz, detector sensitivity was relatively poor, yet metals classification was good. Frequencies higher than about 500 kilohertz resulted in extreme ground mineralization pick-up, but air tests showed sensitivity to be amazingly good. Mid-range BFO frequencies of about 250 to 350 kilohertz proved to be the best all-around operating frequencies (refer to Figure 6-2). Good depth was achieved with moderate ground interference. (See Chapter 12 for a detailed discussion of BFOs.)

The optimum radio frequency range for TRs was determined to be between 80 and 100 kilohertz; lower frequencies resulted in

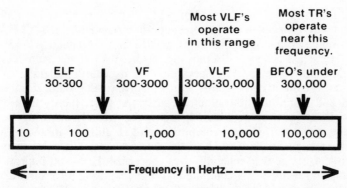

Figure 6-2: FREQUENCY RANGE VERSUS METAL DETECTOR TYPES. This table gives the operating frequency range for the most popular types of metal detectors.

less sensitivity. (See Chapter 13 for a detailed discussion of TR detectors.)

VLF DEVELOPMENT

The first Very Low Frequency ground eliminating detectors were developed in the '70s. Even today, most ground eliminating detectors continue to be designed to operate in the very low, 3 to 30 kilohertz range. These frequencies (lower than those of BFOs or TRs) allow iron mineral detector response to be isolated from metal target detector response. VLF type detectors respond only to metal, "ignoring" iron mineralization. Thus, they are not subject to troublesome responses (as are TRs) when operated over highly iron-mineralized ground, and depth of detection is improved.

It was soon learned that it was important to build VLF ground eliminating detectors with a wide tuning range, because iron mineral composition varies so greatly throughout the world; detectors needed to be built that would operate satisfactorily in all locations.

The first VLF type detectors were produced with only one mode, that being, ground elimination all-metal detection. Operators soon grew tired of digging junk targets at great depths and demanded detectors with trash elimination discriminating capabilities.

When manufacturers added TR discriminating circuits to VLFs, the VLF/TR ground elimination detector was born. A VLF/TR detector features two modes: a VLF ground eliminating (canceling) all-metal mode and a TR discrimination mode. Since the TR discrimination mode responds (unfortunately) to iron ground minerals, it has limitations, but does provide a measure of junk target elimination.

Most VLFs operated at approximately 5 kilohertz. Excellent depth was achieved at this frequency. Frequencies near 15 kilohertz produced an improvement in operation in the TR discrimina-

47

tion mode. Thus, two classes of VLF/TRs emerged. While both frequency range detectors were superb instruments, the VLF 5 kHz range produced greater depth and the higher frequency 15 kHz detectors had an edge in coin hunting because of the better TR mode characteristics while operating over iron earth minerals.

Next came VLF detectors which incorporated ground elimination and discrimination simultaneously. At first, these "motion detectors," as they were called, required extremely fast whipping of the searchcoil. Circuit complexity and an almost "insane" use of far too many integrated circuit components, left a lot to be desired as far as field reliability was concerned. However, improvements and refinements continue and today we have VLF circuitry of all types that is far superior to that of early models (Figure 6-3). Some manufacturers use the VLF designation while others use "VLF/ VLF" to identify this latest, improved breed of detectors. Some manufacturers have eliminated the term "VLF" entirely. (See Chapter 10, 14 and 15 for detailed discussions of VLF circuits and detectors.)

One type of VLF detector is called the Automatic VLF Ground Elimination type that "senses" iron earth mineral composition beneath the searchcoil and automatically adjusts its circuitry to ignore or eliminate the mineral interference. This type detector has

Figure 6-3: One model (the Master Hunter 7 A.D.S.) of today's most popular type metal detectors is shown above. The most important feature of these VLF instruments is the ability to "ignore" iron earth minerals. With mineral disturbance eliminated, many other improvements including ultra deepseeking, target classification, depth measuring, and a wide range of available searchcoils were developed.

become popular with coin hunters and those who want excellent performance without knob adjusting.

PULSE INDUCTION DEVELOPMENT

Pulse Induction circuitry had its beginning in Europe in the '50s when it was applied to the manufacture of airborne instrumentation which could efficiently make geophysical and ore body location and evaluation measurements.

In the '60s, further work was done at Oxford University to apply Pulse Induction technology to the development of conductive metal detection devices. This work resulted in improved circuitry, which was applied in commercial and consumer products.

Pulse Induction circuitry became well known throughout the metal detection field when underwater metal detectors with that type of circuitry began to be marketed during the '70s. Since instruments of Pulse Induction design are practically unaffected by salt water and earth iron mineralization (black magnetic sand-magnetite), such instruments became the most popular types for underwater exploration.

Beginning in the '80s, Pulse Induction technology was applied to metal detectors that could be used under water and on land. The popularity of these convertible instruments is increasing. Improved designs, including target elimination (Figure 6-4), quickly cata-

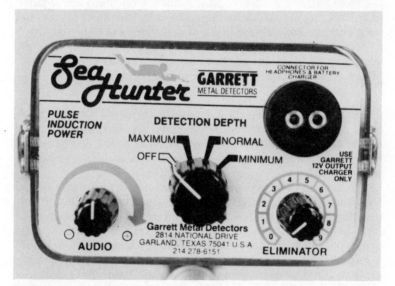

Figure 6-4: The popularity of Pulse Induction instruments is increasing. Improved designs, including target elimination, detection-depth selection, a wide range of available searchcoils, and the ability of these instruments to automatically ignore iron earth minerals and salt water, quickly catapulted Pulse Induction detectors into a permanent place in the metal detection world. This is a closeup of the Pulse Induction Sea Hunter XL500 detector.

pulted Pulse Induction instrumentation into a permanent place in the metal detection world.

TARGET CLASSIFICATION

Target classification has come a long way. Even early-day metal detectors were capable of some differentiation between small, ferrous and non-ferrous, metals. Iron targets tended to produce one type of signal, while non-ferrous metals, such as gold, silver and copper, tended to produce a slightly different signal. Thus, a knowledgeable operator could interpret the signals correctly and leave a lot of junk in the ground.

Improvements continue to be made in the capability of metal detectors. Both audio and visual indicators can classify detected targets with a good degree of accuracy resulting in greatly improved detectors. Manufacturers have achieved extremely good results and improvements continue to be made. (See Chapter 10 for a detailed discussion of target classification, trash elimination and discrimination.)

SEARCHCOIL DESIGN

Searchcoil design also continues to improve. Early-day searchcoils were nothing more than a few turns of wire wrapped around open spools. Modern searchcoil construction is highly complex. Extreme accuracy and construction reliability are required in order for today's sensitive metal detectors to achieve ground and trash elimination, extreme depth of detection, and ultra-stability.

Many different types of searchcoils have emerged over the years and some are better than others for certain kinds of work. (The various searchcoil types are discussed in Chapter 11.)

ELECTRONIC CIRCUIT DEVELOPMENT

Electronic components have vastly improved the lot of the metal detector manufacturer. In the early '50s, Germanium transistors began to be used in the construction of metal detectors, but their stability was affected by temperature, and their applications were limited.

In the mid-'50s, when the first commercially available silicon transistors were introduced by Texas Instruments in Dallas, Texas, manufacturers eagerly sought these improved devices because of their temperature stability. The result was, more stable metal detectors with more dependable operating characteristics. Figure 6-5 shows the printed circuit (PC) board and electronic components required to manufacture high quality, stable BFO detectors of the '70s era. Note the individual transistors.

As metal detectors became more complex, the PC boards grew in size. Were it not for the introduction of integrated circuits, today's detectors could not, practically speaking, be built.

Figure 6-6 shows the PC board and electronic components required to manufacture high quality, state-of-the-art detectors of the '80s. Note the various integrated circuits, each of which may have the equivalent of dozens or hundreds of transistors. Compare this figure with that of the metal detector PC board (Figure 6-5) of a decade earlier.

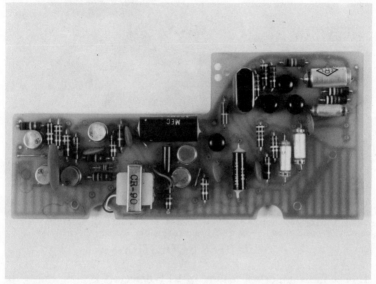

Figure 6-5: This is a printed circuit board showing the various electronic components required to manufacture high quality, stable BFO detectors of the 1970s era. Note the individual transistors and other discrete components. This complete BFO circuit has ten transistors and one diode. Compare it with the PC board shown in Figure 6-6.

Electronic circuitry improves each year, as metal detector engineers utilize new circuitry components. Integrated circuits (ICs), field-effect transistors (FETs), metal-oxide-semiconductors (MOS), and other super-high performance, super-low current consumption electronic component devices, such as biMOS, and biFETs, hybrid operation amplifiers, junction FETs, MOSFETs, and VMOS (a type of power FET), allow developments in metal detectors not possible just a few years ago.

51

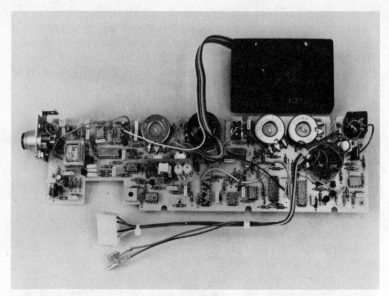

Figure 6-6: These are the printed circuit boards (one is encapsulated) and electronic components of a high quality, state-of-the-art detector of the 1980s. Note the various integrated circuits, each of which has the equivalent of dozens of transistors. Compare with the metal detector PC board, shown in Figure 6-5, of a decade earlier. Photo by Melvin Climer.

CHAPTER 6 QUESTIONS

1. The most important feature of VLF detectors is their ability to: (A) dowse for precious metals; (B) ignore all trash items; (C) ignore most iron earth minerals; (D) detect only shallow buried items.

2. The two most popular types of metal detectors in use today are the _____ and the _____ _____ . (Each correct answer is worth 10 points)

3. Which two types of detectors will "ignore" iron earth minerals and "trash" metal objects simultaneously? (Each correct answer is worth 10 points)

4. Name the two methods by which modern-day metal detectors can classify detected targets into meaningful categories. (Each correct answer is worth 10 points)

5. The metal detector manufacturer's biggest concern is the continual improvement of metal detectors so that the user: (A) will not have to dig too large a hole; (B) can win first place at all treasure hunts; (C) can find the object(s) for which he or she is searching. (D) will know which batteries give best performance.

Each of the 5 complete questions, answered correctly, is worth 20 points. Perfect score is 100. Answers given in Appendix 2.

Characteristics of Metal Detection and The Search Matrix

The purpose of this chapter is to explain how metals and certain minerals are detected, what the detectable minerals are, where they are found, why they create metal detection problems, and what the manufacturers and you can do about them.

As discussed in Chapter 3 (see Figure 3-2), metal detector searchcoils generate an electromagnetic field; one condensed portion extends downward from the bottom of the searchcoil and creates the detection pattern. Whenever detectable metals and minerals come within that pattern, the electromagnetic field is disturbed. A detector signal is produced which alerts the operator to the presence of the intrusion within the pattern.

The detection of minerals is, in most cases, undesirable. The two most troublesome minerals are the earth's natural iron, often called magnetite (black magnetic sand), and wetted salt. Not only do these minerals produce detection signals that the operator can hear (speaker or headphone audio) or see on an indicator, but they also inhibit the ability of metal detectors to detect metal.

The following two discussions, Eddy Current Secondary Electromagnetic Field Generation, and Electromagnetic Field Distortion, explain the basics of metal detection characteristics. Depending upon the metal detector type, one or more of these characteristics cause target detection to take place. An understanding of these characteristics is important to your understanding of how metal detectors work. These explanations are simplified so that you can more readily grasp an understanding of metal detectors and can, more easily, come to an understanding of why your particular metal detector reacts the way it does to metals and detectable minerals.

EDDY CURRENTS AND SECONDARY ELECTROMAGNETIC FIELD GENERATION

Whenever metal comes within the detection pattern, the electromagnetic field lines penetrate the metal's surface. Tiny circulating currents called "eddy currents" are caused to flow on the metal surface as illustrated in Figure 7-1. The power, or motivating force, that causes eddy currents to flow, comes from the electro-

EDDY CURRENT GENERATION ON METAL SURFACE

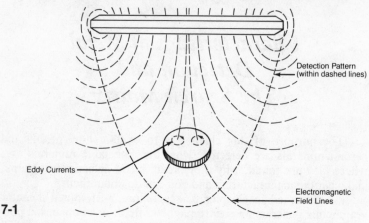

7-1

Figure 7-1: EDDY CURRENT GENERATION ON METAL SURFACE. When metal comes within the detection pattern, electromagnetic field lines penetrate the metal. Tiny circulating currents, called "eddy currents," are caused to flow on the metal's surface. The resulting power loss by the electromagnetic field (the power used up in generating the eddy currents) is sensed by the detector's circuit's. The detector alerts the operator to the presence of the metal.

magnetic field. The resulting power loss by this field (the power used up in generating the eddy currents) is sensed by the detector's circuits. Also, eddy currents generate a secondary electromagnetic field that, in some cases, flows out into the surrounding medium. The portion of the secondary field that intersects the receiver winding, causes a detection signal to occur in that winding. Thus, the detector alerts the operator that metal has been detected.

ELECTROMAGNETIC FIELD DISTORTION

The detection of non-conductive iron (ferrous) minerals takes place in a different manner. In several types of searchcoils there are, as has been explained, transmitter and receiver windings. The receiver winding is positioned with respect to the transmitter winding so that minimum transmitted power is induced into the receiver winding. In other words, the windings are "balanced." (See Figures 7-2, 13-3 and 13-4 and read Chapter 13 for a detailed discussion of this subject.)

When iron mineral comes near and within the detection pattern, the electromagnetic field lines are redistributed, as illustrated in Figure 7-3. This redistribution upsets the winding "balance," resulting in power being induced into the receiver winding. This induced power is sensed by the detector circuits and the operator is alerted to the presence of the iron mineral.

Iron mineral detection is a major problem for manufacturers and detector users. Of course, the detection of iron mineral is good

54

"BALANCED" CO-PLANAR TRANSMITTER AND RECEIVER ANTENNA WINDINGS

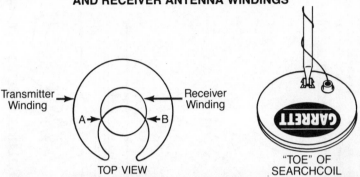

Transmitter Winding

Receiver Winding

A→

←B

TOP VIEW

"TOE" OF SEARCHCOIL

Figure 7-2: "BALANCED" CO-PLANAR TRANSMITTER AND RECEIVER ANTENNA WINDINGS. Most searchcoils contain transmitter and receiver windings. The windings are positioned in a fashion so that induced current at points A&B are of equal magnitude and of opposite polarity resulting in zero induced current in the receiver winding. When a target comes within the detection pattern, a current imbalance at points A&B results in a detection signal in the receiver winding. (See Figure 7-3.)

in some cases, as when, for example, an electronic prospector wishes to find black magnetic sand that might contain gold or silver; however, the person who is searching for metal coins, relics, gold nuggets, etc., finds iron mineral detection a nuisance.

As previously mentioned, the above explanations of eddy current and secondary electromagnetic field generation, and field distortion, are simplified. Actually, all these effects generally occur when most target detection occurs.

SEARCH MATRIX

The late E. S. "Rocky" LeGaye, a well-known and respected metal detector authority, named the ground over which a metal detector scans, the "search matrix." Any substance penetrated by the electromagnetic field is "illuminated." Many elements and minerals are within the soil, including, moisture, and iron and various other minerals, some detectable and some not. Of course, it is hoped that the targets for which we are searching are also present. (See Figures 7-4, 10-2 and 10-3.) A metal detector's response at any given moment is caused by all conductive metals and minerals and ferrous non-conductive minerals that are illuminated by the electromagnetic field.

One detector design criterion is the elimination of response from undesirable elements, permitting only that from desirable objects. This is accomplished in several ways, depending upon the type of metal detector. The various types of metal detectors and their detection characteristics are discussed in later chapters. In the remainder of this chapter, the aspects of metal detection and search

7-3
SEARCHCOIL TRANSMITTER/RECEIVER WINDINGS BALANCED (LEFT) AND IMBALANCED (RIGHT)

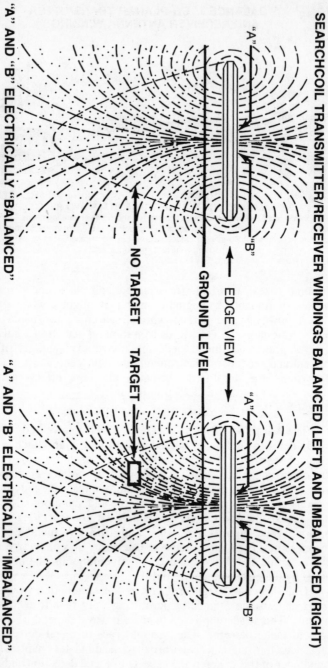

EDGE VIEW

GROUND LEVEL

NO TARGET

TARGET

"A" AND "B" ELECTRICALLY "BALANCED"

"A" AND "B" ELECTRICALLY "IMBALANCED"

Figure 7-3: SEARCHCOIL TRANSMITTER/RECEIVER WINDINGS BALANCED (LEFT) AND IMBALANCED (RIGHT). Metal detection (or searchcoil imbalance) takes place, for instance, when iron comes near and within the detection pattern. Electromagnetic field lines are redistributed as illustrated. This redistribution upsets the winding "balance" at points A&B resulting in power being induced into the receiver winding. (See Figures 7-2, 13-3, and 13-4.)

56

TYPICAL MATRIX AREA ILLUMINATED BY ELECTROMAGNETIC FIELD

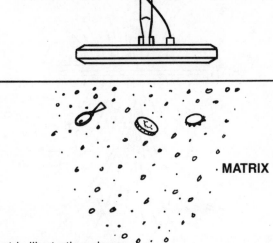

· MATRIX

This matrix illustration shows the main (detection) area illuminated by the electromagnetic field.

Figure 7-4: TYPICAL MATRIX AREA ILLUMINATED BY ELECTROMAGNETIC FIELD. This illustration shows a searchcoil hovering above the ground (called,in metal detection terminology, the search matrix). There are various elements, including soil and rocks in the matrix, that are being illuminated by the electromagnetic field. The metal detector's response, at any given moment, is caused by all conductive metals and minerals and ferrous non-conductive minerals that are illuminated by the electromagnetic field.

matrix phenomena that are common to all types of detectors are discussed.

ELECTROMAGNETIC FIELD COUPLING. "Coupling" describes the penetration of the electromagnetic field into any object near the transmitter antenna. There is perfect coupling (Figure 7-5) into some objects such as wood, fresh water, air, glass, and certain non-mineralized earth materials.

On the other hand, coupling is inhibited (Figure 7-6) when the electromagnetic field attempts to penetrate iron mineralization, wetted salt, and other substances. This inhibiting of the electromagnetic field decreases the detection capability of the metal detector. Even though some instruments, such as the VLF, can eliminate the effects of iron minerals, the electromagnetic field is still inhibited (distorted), which results in reduced detection capability and performance.

SALT WATER DETECTION. As previously explained, salt water (wetted salt) was described as having a disturbing effect upon the electromagnetic field. This is because salt water is electri-

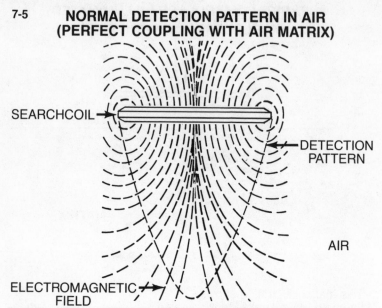

NORMAL DETECTION PATTERN IN AIR
(PERFECT COUPLING WITH AIR MATRIX)

SEARCHCOIL

DETECTION PATTERN

AIR

ELECTROMAGNETIC FIELD

Figure 7-5: NORMAL DETECTION PATTERN IN AIR (PERFECT COUPLING WITH AIR MATRIX). "Coupling" describes the penetration of the electromagnetic field into any object near the transmitter antenna. As shown in this illustration, there is perfect coupling into the air matrix. Generally, perfect coupling is achieved in objects such as wood, fresh water, air, glass and certain non-mineralized earth materials.

cally conductive. Perhaps in your high school chemistry classes you inserted two electrodes into a glass of fresh water and learned that no electrical current flowed when you attached a battery to the electrodes. You then added salt to the water and discovered that the electrodes would produce a measurable electrical current. Since salt water takes on conductive properties, eddy currents are caused to flow in illuminated saline solutions. In effect, salt ocean water "looks like" metal to some detectors! Fortunately, as you shall read in Chapter 10, manufacturers are able to design detectors capable of "ignoring" salt water.

DEPTH OF DETECTION. Numerous factors determine how deeply an object can be detected. Some of these are discussed in the following paragraphs, as well as in other chapters.

The electromagnetic field generated by the searchcoil transmitter antenna, flows out into the surrounding matrix, generating eddy currents on the surface of conductive substances. Any detectable target that sufficiently disturbs the field, is detected. Three factors determine whether the disturbance is sufficient for detection: electromagnetic field strength, target size, and surface area.

ELECTROMAGNETIC FIELD STRENGTH. The electromagnetic field that flows out into the surrounding matrix, theoreti-

7-6 DISTORTED DETECTION PATTERN IN MINERALS (COUPLING INHIBITED DUE TO MINERALS)

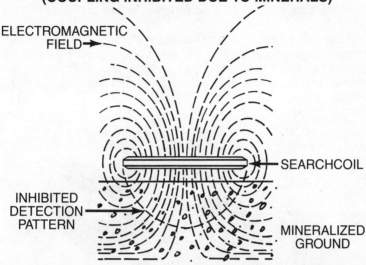

Figure 7-6: DISTORTED DETECTION PATTERN IN MINERALS (COUPLING INHIBITED DUE TO MINERALS). In some elements such as iron mineralization and wetted salt, coupling is inhibited when the electromagnetic field attempts penetration. This inhibiting of the electromagnetic field decreases detection-depth capability.

cally extends to infinity, but is extremely weak when it gets there! In fact, only a few feet away from the searchcoil, the field is greatly reduced in strength. Several factors, including attenuation (absorption by the earth, matrix materials, etc.) and distance, reduce the field strength. When all things are considered, a detector may have several thousand times less detection capability at six feet than it does at one foot, so you can understand why detectors are limited in their depth detection capability.

TARGET SIZE. The larger a metal target, the better and more deeply it can be detected. You will recall how eddy current generation causes metal detection to take place. The more eddy currents that are generated, the larger will be the detector signal produced. One object with twice the surface area of another, will produce a detection signal twice that of the smaller object but it will not necessarily be detected twice as far. By the same reasoning, a larger target will produce the same amplitude detection signal at a distance further away from the bottom of the searchcoil, as the smaller target. Size is a factor in Target Elimination (Discrimination), discussed later.

SURFACE AREA DETECTION. Metal detectors are, for the most part, SURFACE AREA detectors. They are not metallic volume (mass) detectors. The larger the surface area of a metal

59

target that is "looking at" the bottom of the searchcoil, the better that target will be detected. The actual volume or mass of the target has very little to do with most forms of detection. Prove this for yourself.

Turn your detector on and tune it to threshold. With your hand, bring a large coin in toward the searchcoil (Figure 7-7) with the *face* of the coin "looking at" the bottom of the searchcoil. Make a note of the distance at which the coin is first detected—let's say, eight inches.

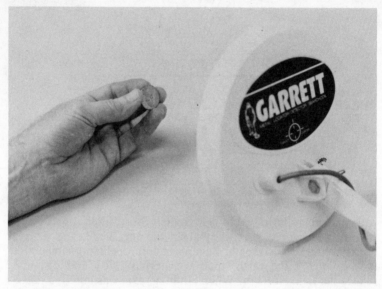

Figure 7-7: As described in the text, metal detectors are, for the most part, SURFACE AREA detectors. They are not metallic volume (mass) detectors. The larger the surface area that is "looking" at the bottom of the searchcoil, the better that target will be detected. This photograph illustrates a testing procedure, as described in the text, for proving that metal detectors are surface area detectors. Photo by Melvin Climer.

Now, move the coin back and rotate it ninety degrees so that the *edge* of the coin "looks at" the bottom of the searchcoil. Bring the coin in toward the searchcoil. You will see that the coin cannot be detected at eight inches. In fact, it probably will be detected only at a distance of four inches or less.

Another proof of surface area detection is to measure at what distance a single coin can be detected. Then stack several coins on the back side of the test coin and check to see how far the stack of coins can be detected. You'll find that the stack can be detected at only a slightly greater distance, illustrating that the greater volume of metal has very little effect on detection distance.

To repeat: Metal detectors are surface area detectors, not volume (mass) detectors. In the first test, the volume or mass of the metal did not change, only the surface area that faced the searchcoil; the signal was in proportion to the surface area facing the searchcoil. In the second test, the mass of material changed, but the illuminated *area* remained the same; the signal did not increase (significantly) when the mass increased. While these effects are not one hundred percent true for all detectors and searchcoils, for most situations the eddy current phenomenon predominates. Understanding of all these phenomena, however, may prove important to you many times as you use your detector.

FRINGE AREA DETECTION. Fringe area detection is a phenomenon of detection, the understanding of which will result in your being able to detect metal targets to the maximum depth capability of any instrument. By now, you know what is meant by the detection pattern: the area below the searchcoil where metal detection takes place. The size of this pattern depends upon the size of the target.

The detection pattern for a coin may extend, say, one foot below the searchcoil. The detection pattern for a small jar of coins may extend, perhaps, two feet below the searchcoil. (See Figure 7-8.) Within the area of the detection pattern, an unmistakable detector signal is produced.

DETERMINING SIZE & SHAPE OF SEARCHCOIL
DETECTION PATTERN

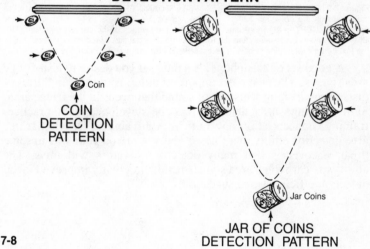

COIN
DETECTION
PATTERN

JAR OF COINS
DETECTION PATTERN

7-8

Figure 7-8: DETERMINING SIZE AND SHAPE OF SEARCHCOIL DETECTION PATTERN. As described in the text, metal objects are detected whenever they come within the detection pattern. Each object has its own detection pattern within which it will be detected. This illustration shows how to determine the detection pattern for two given targets, a coin and a jar. The detection pattern for the jar is wider at the top and extends farther away from the searchcoil bottom.

What about outside the detection pattern? Does detection take place? Yes, but the signals are too weak to be discerned by the operator EXCEPT in the fringe area around the outer edges of the detection pattern. (See Figure 7-9.)

SEARCHCOIL DETECTION PATTERN AND FRINGE AREA

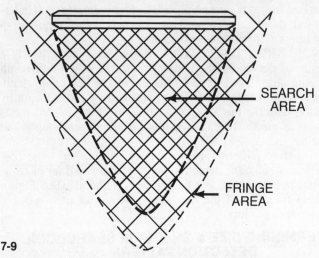

SEARCH AREA

FRINGE AREA

7-9

Figure 7-9: SEARCHCOIL DETECTION PATTERN AND FRINGE AREA. Detection takes place outside the detection pattern, but the signals are too weak to be discerned by the operator, EXCEPT in the fringe area around the outer edges of the detection pattern. This illustration shows the location and approximate proportional size of a detection pattern. See the text for an explanation of how to detect objects that come within the fringe area.

A good set of headphones is a must, if you desire to hear fringe area signals. The next most important thing, is training in the art of discerning the faint whispers of sound that occur in the fringe area. Skill in fringe area detection can be developed with practice, training, concentration and faith in your ability. Develop fringe area detection ability to a fine art and you are on your way to some great discoveries that many detector operators will miss. The ability to hear fringe area signals results in greatly improved metal detection efficiency and success.

CHAPTER 7 QUESTIONS

1. In most cases the detection of minerals is extremely desirable.
   True _____ False _____.

2. The tiny circulating currents, generated on the surface of detected metal, are called detection rings.
   True _____ False _____

3. Why is eddy current power loss and electromagnetic field distortion important?

4. The ground over which a metal detector scans is called the search area.
   True _____ False _____

5. Any substance penetrated by a metal detector's electromagnetic field is _____ .

6. A metal detector's response, at any given moment, is caused by all near by _____ metals and minerals and ferrous non-_____ minerals. (Each correct answer is worth 2 1/2 points)

7. "Coupling" describes the penetration of the _____ _____ into any object near the transmitter antenna.

8. There is perfect coupling into some objects such as wood, fresh water, air, glass and certain non-mineralized earth minerals. On the other hand, coupling is inhibited when the electromagnetic field attempts to penetrate iron _____ and wetted _____ . (Each correct answer is worth 2 1/2 points)

9. Even though VLF detectors can eliminate the detection effects of iron minerals and wetted salt, detection _____ and _____ may be reduced. (Each correct answer is worth 2 1/2 points)

10. Iron mineralization is a problem in metal detection because it causes electromagnetic field _____ .

11. Saline solutions (salt water) cause metal detector problems because the wetted salt looks like _____ to some metal detectors.

12. The depth of detection of any metal detector is determined primarily by two factors: electromagnetic field _____ and surface _____ . (Each correct answer is worth 2 1/2 points)

13. If you double the surface area of any given target it can be detected to twice the depth.
    True _____ False _____

14. The metallic volume (mass) of a target has a lot more to do with detection depth than does surface area.
    True _____ False _____

15. The reason a coin standing on edge cannot be detected as deeply as a similar coin lying flat is because the coin standing on edge "looks like" much less metallic mass than does the coin lying flat.

True _____   False _____

16. If you can detect a single coin lying flat to a depth of eight inches, two same size coins, stacked one on top of the other, both lying flat, can be detected to a depth of sixteen inches.

True _____   False _____

17. Fringe area means the area surrounding metal targets that has become saturated with electrons that have "flowed away" from the targets.

True _____   False _____

18. The most important accessory needed for fringe area detection is: (A) a good set of binoculars; (B) brand new batteries; (C) a good set of headphones; (D) an iron pot in which treasure is buried.

19. Skill in fringe area detection can be developed with practice, training, concentration and _____ in your ability.

20. Develop fringe area detection ability to a fine art and you are on your way to some great _____ that many detector operators will miss.

Each of the 20 complete questions, answered correctly, is worth 5 points. Perfect score is 100. Answers given in Appendix 2.

CHAPTER 8

Metal Detector Operational Characteristics

In this chapter, fifteen operational characteristics of metal detectors are discussed. An understanding of these characteristics is important, whether you are buying, using, or just trying to understand metal detectors. This knowledge will help you analyze manufacturers' product reports, advertisements, and dealer explanations of their products.

The characteristics are discussed in alphabetical order. (Some have abbreviated descriptions in the Glossary.)

BALANCE. Metal detector balance refers to the ease with which a detector rests in the hand when held in the normal operating position. A detector with good balance is one which requires little effort to hold the searchcoil in the air at operating height. The better the balance, the less fatigue you will notice during and after your search.

Manufacturers strive to produce well-balanced detectors. (See Figure 8-1.) It is difficult to produce perfectly balanced detectors

Figure 8-1: Manufacturers strive to produce mechanically balanced detectors so that the detector can be used for extended periods without undue tiring and muscle strain. This operator illustrates balance by showing that with one finger supporting the detector, a perfect operating angle is achieved. The searchcoil does not "pull" down necessitating the use of hand and arm muscles to keep the coil at the correct operating height. The operator simply cradles the detector in his hand as he swings the searchcoil over the ground.

because of searchcoil weight; the heavier the searchcoil, the worse the balance. Some manufacturers inject a foam substance (which has weight) into searchcoil housings to add mechanical strength and improve durability. Manufacturers are tempted to place little or no foam in their searchcoils to improve detector balance and, consequently, sales appeal. To succumb to the temptation, however, can lead to problems and expense for the user, because after a certain amount of field use, poorly constructed searchcoils may begin to deteriorate, resulting in erratic operation, drift, and other undesirable characteristics. Only the purchase of a new searchcoil can remedy the situation.

You can perform your own test to determine if a searchcoil is foam filled. Grasp the searchcoil with both hands, the bottom facing you. Press, with your thumbs, against the bottom at several places. If the searchcoil bottom does not "give" or flex, but feels solid, the searchcoil is foam filled. Another test is to "knock" on the bottom with your knuckles. Foam filled searchcoils sound solid, not hollow.

Searchcoils larger than seven-inch to eight-inch diameter (general purpose size) may imbalance a detector. In these situations, an armrest or hipmount is the answer. An armrest (Figure 8-2) dramatically improves detector balance. Hipmount configurations can solve an imbalance problem by removing the control housing from the handle and placing it on the operator's belt (Figure 8-3).

Figure 8-2: Searchcoils larger than seven-inch to eight-inch diameter may imbalance a detector. An armrest improves balance and gives an extra measure of maneuverability by reducing wrist action.

66

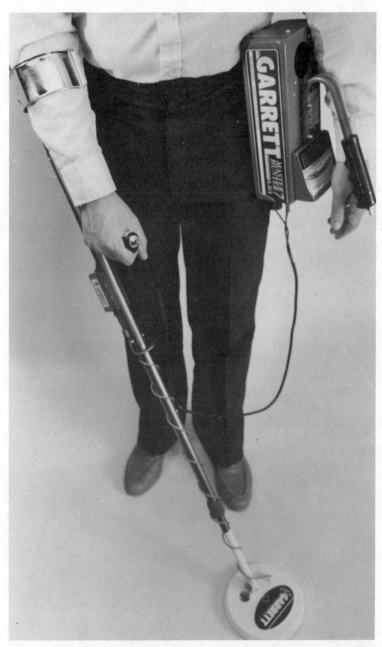

Figure 8-3: A hipmount kit also improves balance by allowing the control housing to be suspended on the operator's belt. This configuration allows the operator to scan the searchcoil for hours on end with almost no fatigue.

NOTE: Some manufacturers use the term "balance" when discussing the ability of their detectors to electronically eliminate the effects of iron earth minerals. (For a full explanation of VLF ground elimination, see Chapter 14.)

CAPABILITY. A capable detector is one that satisfactorily performs all of the functions for which it was designed. Do not confuse "versatility," discussed later, with "capability." A versatile detector is one that can perform many different metal detecting tasks; a capable one can perform specified tasks in a satisfactory manner. For example, a one hundred percent capable coin hunting detector, when the controls (Figure 8-4) are properly adjusted for a given area, and the detector is properly used, will locate all coins in that area. If that detector cannot locate all the coins, then it is only partially capable.

A detector can be capable, but not be capably used. Of the many limitations that prevent total metal detecting success, more often than not, the greatest is the lack of operator ability. The degree of success achieved with any instrument depends primarily upon how well an operator has mastered the equipment.

CONSTRUCTION. Outside of design, the construction of a metal detector is the most critical factor affecting capability, performance, dependability, versatility, overall quality, and,

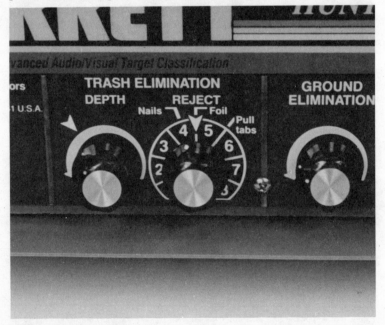

Figure 8-4: By correctly adjusting the Trash Elimination discrimination control, the greatest recovery efficiency will be achieved in each area searched. Photo by Melvin Climer.

certainly, all the other operational characteristics by which that detector can be judged.

A detector that is well-made will show it. There will be no sharp corners to rip your clothing or cut your hands. It will have a solid feel; the handle and stems will be securely attached to the control housing. The paint or finish will be uniform, without chips and scratches. The instrument will appear well-designed, with the best principles of human engineering applied to every component. It will have good, comfortable balance, not requiring a great amount of effort to hold at operating height when fitted with a general purpose searchcoil. Labels and decals will be well-designed with no peeling corners which will further peel in the field.

Look closely at the detector. Does it give the impression of quality? Does it have rough edges and unfinished parts? Do the controls turn smoothly? Does the meter function properly?

Turn it on, adjust the controls, and put it through its paces. Are there sudden squawks and squeals from the audio when the detector strikes an obstacle? Bump the control housing with your hand as illustrated in Figure 8-5. Does the instrument seem solidly built and does the audio remain at its threshold setting without having to be retuned each time it is bumped?

From the above, you may have realized that the quality of

Figure 8-5: CHECKING THRESHOLD STABILITY WITH SHOCK. This illustration shows one way of testing a detector to determine detector stability. Turn the detector on and set the audio to threshold. Bump the control housing. Does the audio remain at threshold setting without having to be retuned each time it is bumped? If not, faulty construction or a loose connection or component is indicated. This illustration is reprinted, with permission, from Ram's publication, "HOW TO TEST" BEFORE BUYING DETECTOR FIELD GUIDE. (Out of Print) Photo courtesy of Roy Lagal.

69

construction of a detector is best determined, not by looking at photographs, but by TESTING THAT DETECTOR FOR YOURSELF! As with any product, there are differences in construction quality among manufacturers. If you want to spend your money for a detector that will stand up in the field, you should DO YOUR OWN TESTING!

DEPENDABILITY. Dependability is the measure of how well a given metal detector performs in the field. How long that detector can be used without a disabling malfunction, is also a measure of dependability. If no mechanical or electrical malfunctions limit or prevent operation, that detector is dependable. No detector, of course, should be depended upon to give a lifetime of trouble-free performance. Even the most dependable, highest quality detectors may malfunction in the field. When you consider that there are perhaps two thousand components and assembly steps in the manufacture of a metal detector, and that each of those components and assembly steps are made by a human, you can understand that sooner or later something may fail. Of course, the chances of malfunction can be almost entirely eliminated in manufacture, by the use of quality components and construction techniques. Manufacturers who regularly update their products, improve quality, and field test their instruments on a continuing basis, produce the most dependable products.

It is a fact that some detectors are more dependable than others; unfortunately, there is no cut and dried method of locating the most dependable products. Your own experience is the best measure. Join a metal detector users' club; talk to other detector owners and dealers; read books and magazines. Gradually you'll learn that one or more brands and types of detectors are dependable and of consistent high quality.

DETECTION DEPTH. Usually the first question people ask when they begin thinking about metal detectors is, "How deep will that detector go?" It must be realized that that question cannot be answered with complete accuracy because many factors influence detection depth.

The major factor is how well the detector was designed and manufactured. Some other factors are: the size of the target object, its shape and composition, how it lies in the ground, how long it has been in the ground, whether detectable metals and minerals are in the search area, moisture content of the ground, the influence of near by metallic objects, what type of instrument and searchcoil the operator is using, the condition of the detector and its batteries, the extent of operator expertise, how well the operator can hear the detector responses, and how alert the operator is. There are others, but these are the primary determining factors.

DRIFT. Drift is an unwanted or undesirable change in the

70

tuning threshold of a metal detector. (See Figure 8-6.)

To understand drift, consider an example. Turn on your radio and tune it to a station. If the station continues to come in loud and clear, then the tuning does not drift. If the station fades out, the radio has drift. The same thing can sometimes happen in metal detectors. If the detector is tuned to the desired audio threshold operating point but gets louder or fades out, the detector has drift.

Drift is caused by many things, including temperature changes, component aging, battery malfunction, searchcoil expansion, contraction, and poor circuit design.

Many people do not understand drift and confuse it with ground mineral pickup. When a detector, operated over mineralized ground, is not adjusted properly to eliminate ground minerals from detection, the audio can fluctuate. This fluctuation, as the searchcoil is scanned over the ground, is often erroneously labeled as drift. Frequently, customers write to the manufacturer, claiming their detectors drift, when, in reality, the instruments are improperly adjusted and are picking up (reacting to) iron minerals.

Most detectors have some amount of drift. It is extremely difficult to build a detector that does not drift slightly, especially during warm-up time of five to ten minutes. Drift can occur as a result of temperature change, such as when you take your detector from a warm car out into the cold air, or when you plunge the searchcoil into a cold mountain stream.

Retuning, or bringing the detector audio back to threshold, can be achieved in several ways. Some detectors have an automatic audio retuning circuit that senses any change in the threshold, and automatically corrects for it. Most detectors will have a manual retuning control, a push button, or a flip switch. When the detector drifts, the retuning switch can be pressed (momentarily) to retune the circuits to threshold.

FALSE DETECTION. In the strictest sense, quality built metal detectors do not give signals when nothing has been detected. When a detector that is working correctly gives a signal, something or some condition caused that signal to be produced. Many times detector operators get a signal, dig a hole, and find nothing. Actually, of course, there was a reason for the signal, though the operator may not understand what it was. Several reasons why so called false signals are produced, are discussed in one of my other books, SUCCESSFUL COIN HUNTING, and reproduced here for your convenience.

In Chapter 3 of MODERN METAL DETECTORS the example is given in which a detector gave a signal and a hole was dug but nothing was found. The following discussions give most of the answers as to how this can occur.

On getting a signal when coin hunting, the operator may cut a

71

METAL DETECTION AUDIO DURING STABILITY, DRIFT AND ERRATIC RESPONSE.

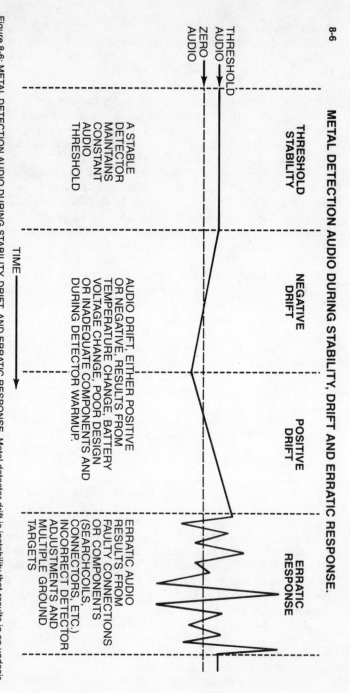

THRESHOLD AUDIO

ZERO AUDIO

TIME ➤

THRESHOLD STABILITY

A STABLE DETECTOR MAINTAINS CONSTANT AUDIO THRESHOLD

NEGATIVE DRIFT

AUDIO DRIFT, EITHER POSITIVE OR NEGATIVE, RESULTS FROM TEMPERATURE CHANGE, BATTERY VOLTAGE CHANGE, POOR DESIGN OR INADEQUATE COMPONENTS AND DURING DETECTOR WARMUP.

POSITIVE DRIFT

ERRATIC RESPONSE

ERRATIC AUDIO RESULTS FROM FAULTY CONNECTIONS OR COMPONENTS (SEARCHCOILS, CONNECTORS, ETC.) INCORRECT DETECTOR ADJUSTMENTS AND MULTIPLE GROUND TARGETS

Figure 8-6: METAL DETECTION AUDIO DURING STABILITY, DRIFT, AND ERRATIC RESPONSE. Metal detector drift is instability that results in an undesir- able change in audio threshold. To check for drift, turn a detector on and allow a few minutes warmup. If the audio threshold remains at a constant level, the detector is stable. When testing for drift, make sure the tuning selector switch (if the detector has one) is in the manual tuning position and not in the automatic tuning position.

plug, check it with the detector, and get no reading, then scan over the hole and get no reading. What is wrong? The coin may have become dislodged from its flat position, fallen further down into the hole, and came to rest in a vertical position. A deeply buried coin standing on edge is more difficult to detect because of the relatively small surface on which eddy currents can be generated. So, even though the operator sees nothing, and thinks there is nothing in the hole, he would be wise to explore a little deeper.

Again, a detector signal, but no apparent target, can sometimes be caused by tin cans or bottlecaps which have completely rusted. Carry a small, powerful magnet and rub it into the dirt. If iron rust is present, it will become attached to the magnet and the mystery of another false hole will be solved!

A detector may give a metallic response on a small bit of foil or a gum wrapper. The operator begins to dig. The piece of foil crumples or disintegrates and cannot be as readily detected.

To avoid being fooled by apparently false signals, take care in pinpointing, and learn to distinguish among responses. For example, you will learn that small bits of foil generally produce a high squeal on a detector.

Another small object which can produce a large response is a .22 caliber shell. After these shells have been buried for a year or longer they produce a very large signal. Because of their size and color, they are often overlooked after they are dug up and the operator may continue digging a deeper and deeper false hole.

In another instance, as the operator scans his detector across a hole, he gets a positive indication. He will dig a little deeper, scan with his detector again, receive another metallic response, and continue digging until soon he has a monstrous, gapping hole. You may ask, "Why does a detector give a metal indication over a hole?" The explanation for this is somewhat complex, but with study can be quite easily understood.

Most ground contains some mineralized negative-reaction iron. If the detector searchcoil is lowered to the ground, it drives the oscillator in the "negative" or "mineral" direction. In order for the operator to search correctly over such ground, the operator must adjust the detector. This manual, positive adjustment of the detector circuitry, cancels the negative reaction caused by the ground and, as the operator scans across the ground, the detector, thus, "ignores" the ground.

If, however, the searchcoil is scanned over a place in the ground where the negative-reacting iron has been removed, the detector may produce a positive indication because the negative, disturbing force was removed, allowing the positive adjustment to sound off through the speaker.

Spots of ground which have an absence or a low concentration of mineral, can be caused in several ways. A hole could be dug for a post; the post might later be removed and the hole filled with non-mineralized ground. A wash can cause this problem. A fire can create the same effect.

In ground containing conductive salts, metal detectors can react positively to the salt. The wetter the ground, the greater the positive indication. Ground that is predominantly positive, yet which contains very little moisture, will appear as neutral. However, if there is a shallow place or a sink hole that can hold moisture, the moisture will cause the salts to become conductive. As the detector is passed over this area, a positive indication is produced. Salt occurs naturally in certain areas. Also, the farmer or rancher who places a block of salt on the ground for animals to lick (a salt lick), unknowingly creates a "metal" target as rain slowly dissolves the salt, which seeps into the ground.

FRINGE AREA. "Fringe area" is the extreme outer limit of the detection pattern where detection of targets can occur. (See Figure 7-9.) Within the detection pattern, audio and meter target indications are pronounced and easily recognized. Near the outer edges of the detection pattern, targets produce weak signals. Unless the operator is wearing headphones and paying very careful attention, fringe area signals will not be recognized.

LIFE EXPECTANCY. Any well-made detector that is given reasonable care, can be expected to give many years of service. Skid plates will protect searchcoils from wear caused by constant abrasion against ground and rocks. Carrying bags are available for storage and transportation. Speaker covers allow the instrument to be operated in light rain.

Keep your detector clean by wiping it occasionally with a damp cloth. Dismantle and clean the stems to remove all traces of dirt buildup that can lock or freeze the stems. Install fresh batteries as often as needed. Do not leave batteries in a detector longer than one month without checking them. Even that long a period is risky if the batteries are in a partially run-down condition. The screws that hold the various parts of the detector together, can be occasionally tightened. When maintenance instructions are given in your instruction manual, follow them.

Do not be afraid to use your detector when and where you need it, even under poor environmental conditions. Detectors are designed to be used. They are built to be rugged and to give dependable, trouble-free operation for a long time. Land detectors are made to be scrubbed over the ground, occasionally bumped into trees and rocks, back-packed, hauled around, and stored as the need arises. Some can be submerged in water to the control housing. Any detector that cannot take normal usage is poorly designed and manufactured. So, again, don't be afraid to use your detector. Put it to work! Make it do what you want it to do and what it should do. If it's a good one, it will hold up and give many years of dependable service.

LIMITATIONS. While metal detectors are built that will do just about everything except dig the target, they do have limitations. Detectors are getting "smarter," however, and tomorrow will see improved instruments. Let's look at some of the ways in which detectors are limited.

Metal detectors cannot penetrate all earth materials. In areas where ferrous and conductive minerals are present, penetration will be restricted. The greater the amount of minerals, the greater will be the reduction in penetration. In locations where the matrix (area to be searched) is non-uniform, such as mine dumps, penetration may be seriously reduced. (See Figures 7-5 and 7-6.)

Metal detectors cannot reach out to locate targets. In order for metal to be detected, it must come into the area of the detection pattern which is located directly below the searchcoil.

Metal detectors can classify or identify metal targets with limited accuracy. Audio and meter indicators can classify metals into groups. This is called "probability" indication. Different targets can fall into the same groupings; what a detector indicates to be a coin, may turn out to be a pulltab. Probability indicator meters are getting better, however, and even with their limitations, are of value in increasing the efficiency of the operator and in helping make a decision whether to dig.

Some other limitations are also being changed. Depth of detection is a good example. A few years ago, single coins could be detected to about six inches deep; today, coins are often found at depths of two feet! A few years ago, a gallon bucket of coins could be detected at two feet; today, that same bucket can be detected to six feet-plus!

PENETRATION. "Penetration" refers to the capability of a detector to penetrate earth minerals, air, wood, rock, water, and other material to locate metal targets. The terms "penetration" and "detection depth" are often used interchangeably. Penetration ability, however, is actually one of the limiting factors in depth detection. While a detector may penetrate sand to detect an object at six feet, that same detector may only penetrate an iron mineralized matrix to detect that same object, at only two feet.

SCANNING WIDTH. Scanning width is a function of detector type and searchcoil design. All detectors can be built so that detection of shallow metal objects occurs across the full searchcoil width. The deeper the target, the more narrow the detection width at that depth. The detector pattern decreases in width as the distance from the searchcoil bottom increases. (See Figure 7-8.)

In the early days of metal detection, some searchcoils had an effective scanning width of less than one-half the diameter of the searchcoil; an eight-inch diameter searchcoil had an effective scanning detection width on shallow objects, of less than four inches. Most of today's detectors feature full searchcoil width scanning.

SENSITIVITY. Sensitivity is a measure of the ability of a metal detector to sense conductivity changes within the detection pattern, and is one of the most important operational characteristics of an electronic metal detector. The smaller the change in conductivity it takes to produce a detector signal, the more sensitive the instrument.

Detector sensitivity and depth detection are phrases often used interchangeably. Sensitivity is a measure of the ability of an instrument to detect very tiny objects, so it follows that a detector with poor sensitivity will have poor depth detection. Sensitivity is mostly dependent on, or related to, the design features of a detector: operational frequency, searchcoil design, quality or low noise characteristics of its amplifiers, and sensitive high gain receiver circuits.

As an example, gold nuggets weighing less than 0.05 grams are quite often found, with certain detectors, to depths of about three inches (7.5 cm.). Gold nuggets that tiny are only about the size of a pin head!

STABILITY. Stability is a measure of how well a given detector can hold or maintain its tuning level during a wide range of varying conditions. If the detector drifts, as described under DRIFT, this chapter, it is unstable. A perfectly stable detector is one that, once adjusted, never requires any type of retuning adjustment. Any number of things may affect stability—temperature changes, battery drift, moisture, mechanical shock (bumping a tree, for example), mechanical and electronic change due to poor detector design, change in the preset tuning due to faulty controls, loose wiring, poor connections, and so on.

VERSATILITY. The versatility of a detector refers to the number of different jobs it will perform. Some models are so versatile they will perform every treasure hunting task, others will perform only one or two tasks efficiently. Extremely versatile detectors have more than one available searchcoil. Searchcoils vary in size, with the application depending upon what they are designed to do. Capability is a factor that affects versatility. Two instruments may be equally versatile, but one of them may be far more capable, in that it can detect a given object much more deeply than the other. Some instruments are designed specifically for certain applications, such as coin hunting, weapons detection, and underwater searching.

CHAPTER 8 QUESTIONS

1. When a large searchcoil mechanically unbalances a metal detector the best solution is simply to install a smaller searchcoil.
   True _____ False _____

2. One of the major factors, that determines the detection depth capability of a metal detector, is the size of the detector's batteries.
   True _____ False _____

3. When a detector is operated over mineralized ground and is not adjusted properly to eliminate ground minerals from detection, metal detector drift will occur.
   True _____ False _____

4. When a detector gives a "false" signal, the detector has actually lied to you by producing a signal when there was no detectable target.
   True _____ False _____

5. "Negative" response means the audio volume _____ .
"Positive" response means the audio volume _____ .
(Each correct answer is worth 5 points)

6. Metal detectors have the ability to reach out laterally to detect targets.
   True _____ False _____

7. Sensitivity is a measure of the ability of a metal detector to sense conductivity changes within the detection pattern.
   True _____ False _____

8. Metal detector sensitivity and depth detection are phrases often used interchangeably (even though erroneously) when detectors are discussed.
   True _____ False _____

9. A truly stable detector is the one that can be used for hours on end without the operator experiencing any physical fatigue.
   True _____ False _____

10. A versatile metal detector is one that can perform a great many metal detecting tasks.
   True _____ False _____

Each of the 10 complete questions, answered correctly, is worth 10 points. Perfect score is 100. Answers given in Appendix 2.

CHAPTER 9

Components, Controls, and Their Functions

BATTERY SYSTEMS

Some manufacturers use 1 1/2-volt batteries and some use 9-volt transistor radio batteries in their detectors. Others use rechargeable nickel-cadmium (ni-cad) batteries of 8-volts and other voltages.

As long as detector circuits are designed properly, battery type is of little importance in determining the quality of the detector or how well it performs.

One of the most reliable battery types is the carbon-zinc. Carbon-zinc batteries are, however, more likely to leak acid when the battery is in a discharged state, than are alkaline and ni-cad units. Alkaline batteries give slightly longer life, but they cost more. If you use your detector quite often, ni-cad rechargeable batteries may save money.

Arguments continue as to which is best: non-rechargeable or rechargeable batteries. Manufacturers promote their rechargeable batteries, claiming up to one thousand dollars in savings during the life of the rechargeables. Let's study the situation.

Rechargeable batteries cost more than other battery types, and battery rechargers are expensive. It doesn't matter whether the ni-cads come standard with the detector or whether they are purchased separately. The purchaser pays the cost. The detector operator who uses a detector one hour every day will spend from forty to eighty dollars per year on disposable batteries. Rechargeable batteries can pay for themselves (if there is no catastrophic failure of the batteries), but, obviously, the length of time depends upon the battery drain of the detector, how often the detector is used, and several other operating factors.

How much can you save in battery costs if you use rechargeable batteries? The table (Figure 9-1) gives the approximate cost savings per year. This table is based upon the battery drain of the average detector and may vary, depending upon the detector used and several operating factors.

To help prevent premature failure, keep ni-cads fully charged. Recharge them as soon as possible after you use the detector.

If you use standard, off-the-shelf ni-cad rechargeables, what do you do about spare batteries? It may be wise to purchase a spare

9-1 ESTIMATED BATTERY COST SAVINGS PER YEAR WHEN RECHARGEABLE BATTERIES ARE USED

If you use your metal detector an average of this many hours per day,	your estimated yearly battery (replacement) cost savings will be:
ONE HOUR	$ 40.00 to $ 80.00
TWO HOURS	80.00 to 160.00
THREE HOURS	120.00 to 240.00
FOUR HOURS	160.00 to 320.00
FIVE HOURS	200.00 to 400.00

Based upon the above chart, from 2½ to 12½ years is the estimated time it will take you to save $1000.00 in battery replacement costs when rechargeable batteries are used.

Figure 9-1: ESTIMATED BATTERY COST SAVINGS PER YEAR WHEN RECHARGEABLE BATTERIES ARE USED. This table gives the approximate cost savings per year if you use Ni-cad rechargeables, instead of the lower cost carbon zinc batteries. The table is based upon the battery drain of the average detector and may vary, depending upon the detector used and several other operating factors.

set of carbon-zinc batteries and keep them in the refrigerator, except during the time when you take them on your detecting trips. If your detector is equipped with specially designed rechargeable battery packs, with no provision for standard off-the-shelf batteries, then you must purchase an extra rechargeable battery pack from the manufacturer.

Keep spare carbon-zinc batteries on standby for about six months, then use until they are discharged. Purchase a fresh set for spares, and repeat the process each six months. A spare set of carbon-zinc batteries may cost a few dollars, but the lost time and frustration they can avoid, make the cost seem small.

Generally, detector manufacturers provide a meter or audio indication of battery condition. To determine how accurate the meter is, continue using the set of batteries that you now have in your detector until it is obvious that the detector is no longer performing correctly. A ''motorboating,'' or other erratic signal, will tell you your detector is not performing as it should. Check the batteries and note the meter pointer position. If it occurs below the low end of the battery scale, you may be able to obtain extra battery mileage by not replacing the batteries as quickly as the meter indicates.

There is an amusing story told about one treasure hunter who was paying no attention to the condition of his detector's batteries. He began to hear a da-da-di-da sound. The speaker was producing what he thought to be Morse code signals! The treasure hunter jumped up and down, yelling to his buddy, ''Hey, I have detected a cave or something! I have located an underground radio transmitter!''

Actually, the electronic circuits were "motorboating," a condition that occurs when the battery voltage level drops too low to supply adequate power to the circuits. Internal battery resistance creates a feedback situation that causes the electronic circuits to oscillate in a da-da-di-da fashion.

Chapter 29, "MAINTENANCE AND FIELD REPAIR," gives additional information and tips on how to get more from detector batteries and how to prolong their life.

CONTROL HOUSING

The control housing in which the electronic printed circuit board, batteries, switches, etc., are generally placed, may come in all sizes, shapes, configurations, and materials. Some control boxes are quite large, while others are matchbox size. The size of the box has nothing to do with the performance of the detector, provided it's large enough for adequate housing of all the components, and the components are arranged in such a way that there is no electronic interference to create detector operating problems. Generally, the smaller the box, the lighter weight the equipment, but the weight reduction is not as great as it might appear. Where there are large boxes, keep in mind that much of what is contained in the boxes is fresh air.

Detectors manufactured today, use aluminum and plastic control boxes. Metal boxes are in themselves a Faraday-shield, whereas, plastic boxes require certain special shielding if the manufacturer wishes to prevent outside electrical interference.

Metal and plastic both can be used to advantage in the construction of metal detectors. The right type of plastic, such as ABS, is very strong and lightweight, and when properly used, lasts as long as aluminum. Plastic can be colored in the manufacturing process to produce a very attractive finish. Aluminum parts may be annodized and/or spray painted. Plastic parts may be painted. Extremely durable epoxy paints are available which can even be applied with various attractive "finish" patterns.

Many detector components are plastic, such as searchcoil housings, meter covers, knobs, semi-conductors and transistors, resistors, and others.

Some persons believe, erroneously, that housings with control panels mounted on the left, are intended for use by right handed people only. They say, these detectors cannot be held with the left hand because the controls cannot be reached with the right hand. When you think about it, most all detectors are "right-hand" designed because detectors that have top mounted controls, have main knobs that are located on the left side of the handle. Consequently, when the detector is held by the left hand, it is difficult to reach over the handle, past the arm, to adjust these controls. Anyway, since most detectors are very stable, knob twiddling is a thing of the past. Most detector controls are seldom readjusted during any one operational period. Controls that are recessed, give protection in the event the detector is dropped. Also, when using the detector in brushy country, the controls are less likely to be accidentally rotated by brush, limbs, etc.

HANDLE

The handle is used to carry the detector and to maneuver the searchcoil over the ground, up a wall, along or over any surface to be scanned. The handle should have a comfortable plastic or rubberized grip, and be located in such a way that the detector has the best possible mechanical balance.

If it is placed too far to the back, the operator must continually be "picking up" the searchcoil in order to hold it above the detecting surface. This imbalanced condition can cause a great amount of strain on the operator's arm, hand, and wrist.

The handle cannot be too far forward, or just the reverse happens. The searchcoil tends to swing upward and the operator must hold it down. Also, the greater the weight that is behind the handle, the greater the problems the operator has in stopping the searchcoil motion at the end of each sweep. An appropriately mounted and positioned armrest can lessen this problem. A well balanced metal detector is shown in Figure 8-1.

Some say the handle should not obstruct the view of meters or other indicators, but in actual practice, such obstruction is not nearly the problem competitive advertising makes it out to be. The meter could be mounted on the end of the handle, or somewhere on the connecting stem. However, to mount it on the end of the handle creates extra bulk and top heaviness; to place it there, or on the stem, increases the likelihood that it will be damaged.

CONNECTING STEM

The stem connects the control housing to the searchcoil. Some are adjustable; some have a fixed length and cannot be adjusted. The stem should be long enough for the tallest person using the detector. If it cannot be adjusted to sufficient length, a tall person will have to operate the detector in a slightly bent over position. Many detector users characteristically operate in such a stance, anyway, but sufficient length should be available in any case.

There are times when the metal detector operator will want a longer or shorter length stem. It will sometimes be necessary, when scanning a building, to lengthen the stem for ceiling scanning. When reduced to the shorter length, the detector can be stored in a suitcase, a bag, or carried in a backpack.

The locking mechanisms for telescoping stems are generally

of two kinds: a friction device, and a spring clip or "button" that locks into place in holes in the outer stem. Friction devices are good, but they do not provide automatic searchcoil alignment. Spring clip holes keep the searchcoil aligned automatically. Even the best spring clip configurations, however, allow some amount of rotational looseness of the stem parts. A combination spring clip and friction mechanism is a good design idea that is used on some instruments.

TARGET INDICATOR METERS

Meters are visual indicators and serve several functions. A meter permits the operator to observe detection functions. The indicator pointer generally operates in synchronism with speaker sounds. When the audio increases in volume, the meter pointer deflects upward; when the speaker sound decreases, the meter pointer drops downward.

Aside from noting the presence of a detected target, the meter has two other important detection functions. First, it can be used to pinpoint buried objects exactly. As you scan the searchcoil across a buried object, note where the maximum deflection of the meter pointer occurs. Maximum deflection indicates target center. If the target is large, or shallowly buried, it may be necessary to elevate the searchcoil several inches and scan over the target so that the meter pointer stays on scale. Otherwise, you will not be able to determine the point of maximum signal. Also, you can detune the metal detector to keep the meter pointer on scale.

A second important meter function is the parallel indication function. Let's say you are scanning along, listening to the speaker, and you hear a very weak sound, so weak, in fact, that you are not sure you detected a target. Scan back over the spot, paying careful attention to the meter pointer. If you see the pointer deflect, however slightly, upward over the spot where you hear the weak audio sound, then you are doubly assured that a target has been detected.

Certainly, this is not always true for all detectors under all conditions, because some detector meters are less sensitive than the speaker. Too, some people have developed what is called a "musical ear" and have the ability to hear sounds that either are extremely weak, or are composed of harmonic frequencies that occur when the detector detects metal. People with this exceptional ability can hear detection signals that do not show up on the meter.

CONTOURING

The meter can be used to indicate a fairly accurate outline of the target. When the operator has detected a target, he can approach it from various angles with the edge of the searchcoil. The meter pointer can be watched, and when it deflects upward, say, one division, a mental note can be made where on the ground this occurs, and the outline or contour of the target can be plotted. (Study Figure 9-2.)

Classifier meters and bar graphs are of great value; they give a general or probable indication of the identity of detected targets. (See Chapter 10 for a detailed discussion of classifier meters, bar graphs, and coin depth indicators.)

BURIED AND CONCEALED TARGET CONTOURING (OUTLINING) WITH VARIOUS SEARCHCOIL TYPES.

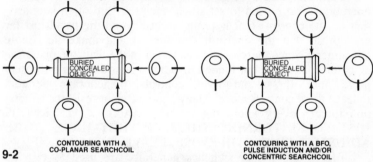

9-2

CONTOURING WITH A
CO-PLANAR SEARCHCOIL

CONTOURING WITH A BFO,
PULSE INDUCTION AND/OR
CONCENTRIC SEARCHCOIL

Figure 9-2: BURIED AND CONCEALED TARGET CONTOURING (OUTLINING) WITH VARIOUS SEARCHCOIL TYPES. This illustration shows contouring methods to follow when using various types of searchcoils. Since the windings in a co-planar searchcoil are offset from center, it is best to contour by bringing the "toe" of the searchcoil in toward the object each time a measurement is made. Other searchcoils that have windings centered about the searchcoil axis can be moved in toward the object from any point along the outer rim of the searchcoil.

CONTROLS AND SWITCHES

There are from one to a dozen control knobs and switches found on various detector models. These may be hidden within the control housing or they may be in plain sight. They permit manufacturers and operators to manipulate electronic circuitry so the detector will perform as desired.

One might think that the more controls there are, the better or more desirable the detector. In truth, it may be that THE FEWER CONTROLS THERE ARE, THE BETTER! Of course, I am not talking of low capability, single knob detectors that will do hardly more than make a sound. I am speaking of advanced, state-of-the-art, versatile, professional detectors.

The more knobs and switches there are, the more complicated the detector is to operate. Numerous knobs, all the same type and size, lined up in neat rows, add to the complexity. The design trend, and the desire of most manufacturers, is to produce instruments with as few knobs and switches as possible. People won't take the time to learn to use detectors with an excessive number of controls, and, even if they did, the manipulation procedures would be forgotten if the equipment were not used on a regular basis.

Most people would prefer a highly capable and versatile detector that they have only to turn on. Some day there may be instruments like that, but for now, and in the foreseeable future, universal, advanced circuitry detectors that can perform many functions, need certain controls for the operator to achieve desired operating characteristics. After all, on today's radios, you'll find ON/OFF, VOLUME, TONE, BALANCE, FM/AM, MUTE and other controls!

Controls should be correctly located to facilitate ease of operation. Those used to set single functions are often knobless; that is, the control shaft is brought out beyond the panel just far enough so that the operator can turn it and make the single adjustment. Since there is no knob to get in the way, the operation of other controls is not hindered. Some manufacturers purposely leave knobs off "set and forget" controls, to encourage operators to leave these controls alone. Many people cannot resist the temptation to turn every knob, but DON'T MANIPULATE KNOBS JUST TO BE TURNING THEM. IF THEY HAVE TO BE ADJUSTED, FINE; OTHERWISE, LEAVE THEM ALONE!

Toggle and rocker switches generally are used to turn on power, select modes, and check batteries. Toggle switches, as well as push button switches, are often mounted on the end of the detector handle. These provide instantaneous retuning and mode switching as explained in Chapter 10.

AUDIO INDICATORS

Sound is the most common target indication used. Speakers are the easiest audio indicators to use, as there is no fuss with headphones or dangling cords, but speakers use more power than headphones, meters, or indicator lights. As a rule of thumb, speakers use five times as much battery power as headphones.

In the BFO system, what you hear is an audio *frequency* change when a target is detected. The BFO tuning threshold is generally a frequency about fifty to sixty cycles per second. When you pass the searchcoil over a conductive metal target, the frequency increases. When you pass it over non-conductive iron minerals, the frequency decreases.

TR and VLF systems operate on fixed audio frequencies, usually of approximately 800 to 1,000 cycles. Threshold tuning is set so that you can barely hear the sound. Some detectors can be operated silent. As you pass over a metal target, there is a *loudness* change (increase); the frequency does not change as in a BFO. (See the AUDIO RESPONSE CHART Figure 10-15.)

Pulse Induction systems use a bell ringing sound. Set the threshold for faint sound; when you pass over metallic objects, the ringing sound gets louder.

MERCURY SPEAKER CUT-OUT TILT SWITCHES

Some detectors feature a mercury tilt switch that cuts out (removes) power from the speaker when the detector is laid horizontally on the ground. The sound is eliminated when targets are being dug, and battery power is conserved. Dirt clumps cannot be checked, however, if the mercury tilt switch cuts power to the speaker.

Some detectors feature a mercury tilt switch to activate a SEMI-AUTOMATIC tuning mode. When the detector is laid horizontal, an automatic mode takes over the tuning and maintains sound threshold.

Mercury tilt switches should be housed in an unbreakable capsule, because mercury coming in contact with a PC board can damage components and dissolve solder connections.

HEADPHONES

If you own a detector, you should own one or more headphone sets. Headphones are recommended for use all the time or at least when detecting in noisy areas, such as the beach or near traffic lanes (when you are looking for dropped coins around parking meters). Headphones enhance audio perception by bringing audio directly into your ears and by masking "outside" noise interference.

It can be proved that most persons can hear weaker sounds and detect deeper targets, when a good quality set of headphones is used. As proof, bury a coin at a depth that produces a faint speaker signal. Then, use headphones and scan over the spot. You'll be amazed at how much better you can hear the detector signals, with headphones, than you can with the speaker.

Headphones come in all sizes, shapes, and configurations, the most popular being stereo types that cover the ears and have adjustable earpiece controls. Many detectors do not have volume controls, but headphones equipped with volume controls allow a wide degree of loudness adjustment while not degrading detector sounds.

Manufacturers know that when detector output volume is reduced in the circuits, sensitivity can be lost. This occurs because circuit gain is reduced, thus reducing the sharp, quick audio turn-on, necessary for good operation. Even when a detector has a volume control, the manufacturer usually recommends volume be set to maximum. Most detectors are operated at full volume with the tuning (audio) control adjusted so that only a faint sound is coming from the speaker; when a target is detected, the sound can rise quickly from the faint threshold sound to maximum loudness. The user of a headphone set can adjust its volume to a lower level. Automatic VLF Ground Elimination detectors can be operated "silent" or with slight threshold sound.

A mono/stereo switch on the headphone set is desirable. If you want to use both headphone pieces, flip the switch to mono to let sound come through both earpieces. If you want to use only one headpiece, perhaps to leave the unused headpiece resting forward on your ear so that you can hear the sounds around you, flip the switch to stereo and only one headpiece will be operative. Some detectors have an internal connection, however, that sends audio into both headpieces. In that case, a mono/stereo headphone switch would be nonfunctional.

Dual, miniature telephone operator headphone types, with earplugs, are commonly used. They are good, but do not block as much sound from your ears as do the large padded kind. They are, however, lightweight and comfortable, and a pair of reasonable quality will produce a good sound. A coiled extension cord is desirable to keep the cord out of the way.

Headphones are an advantage when you want to keep others from knowing what you are doing. In most cases, a person standing within a few feet of you will not be able to hear the headphone signals unless the sound comes on very loud.

Headphone plug sizes range from one-eighth inch to one-fourth inch diameter. Make sure of the size you need before purchasing headphones. Right angle plugs may be desirable because they eliminate the possibility of the plug's being broken, as often occurs with plugs that extend straight out.

CONNECTORS

Several types of connectors are used both inside and outside the detector. Outside connectors link the searchcoil cable to a bulkhead connector, mounted usually on the lower end of the detector control housing. This cable provides the pathway for electronic signals to travel back and forth between the printed circuit board and the searchcoil windings.

Inside the detector, you may find one or more connectors, either of the printed circuit board or pin type. These are used for quick connect/disconnect of the speaker, meter, and the printed circuit board.

INDICATOR LIGHTS

Indicator lights can be installed on metal detectors to give the operator a visual, flashing-light indication, when a target is detected. Lights are not as good indicators as are speaker and meter indicators, however. Targets that produce only faint audio and meter indications may not cause indicator lights to come on. It takes more than a weak target signal to cause indicator lights to come up to sufficient brilliance to be seen, especially during daylight hours. Lights can be used in conjunction with the speaker and meter, or they can be used by themselves when silent operation is desired. Since some detectors may not have provisions whereby the speaker can be disconnected, a headphone plug can be inserted into the headphone jack to disconnect the speaker.

Indicator lights can be of several types: neon, light-emitting diodes (LEDs), and incandescent. Neon or high voltage lights take the least power, but they require voltage amplification circuitry, an added expense that offsets their advantages.

LEDs require appreciable current drains, but they can be made to blink to diminish power drain. LEDs are especially effective for night work, as sunlight reduces their brilliance.

Incandescent lighting is good, and sensitive, but requires more current than the other types and is therefore seldom used.

Remember that indicator lights are just that; they indicate the presence of a target, but with less sensitivity than a speaker or meter. They cannot be counted upon to indicate fringe area signals.

SEARCHCOILS

Searchcoils generally have some waterproofing designation. "Splashproof" means that the detector searchcoil can be used in wet grass or that it can withstand minor splashing, such as from rain water dripping from leaves, trees, and bushes. "Waterproof" means that during the worst rainstorm, or under similar moisture conditions, the searchcoil will continue to operate perfectly. "Submersible" means that the searchcoil can be submerged beneath the surface of water to a depth indicated by the manufacturer, generally to about twenty-four to thirty inches, or, to the cable connector.

MISCELLANEOUS HARDWARE

Detectors use dozens of kinds of miscellaneous hardware. Any particular detector may need a bolt, a lock washer, a flat washer and a wing nut to hold the searchcoil to the end of the lower connecting stem. There may be one or more screws to hold the battery door in position. Occasionally, screws and nuts hold the handle to the detector. When you lose or break a piece of hardware, always replace it with exactly the same type, whether purchased from the factory or a hardware store. Always use a replacement part made from the same type of metal. In other words, if the bolt and wing nut that attach the lower stem to the searchcoil are nylon (non-metallic), be certain to replace them with similar nylon hardware.

INSTRUCTION MANUALS

A great deal of forethought, and attention to detail and design should be put into every instruction manual. In many cases, the manual is the chief reference from which a detector operator learns to use his equipment. As important as it is, however, often it is the very last thing the new detector owner reads. As the saying goes, "When all else fails, read the instruction manual!"

The seller of the instrument should instruct the buyer in correct operating procedures; it then becomes the responsibility of the owner to learn how to use the detector, by paying careful attention to the manufacturer's instructions and what he has been taught. (Read Chapter 23.)

The manual should clearly identify and explain the function of each switch, knob, and major component. Full instructions should teach the owner how to test and replace batteries. It should give complete operating instructions, as well as a listing of precautions, and basic instructions on field usage. Each capability of the instrument should be explained. The instruction manual should also include field repair data, so that in the event of minor problems, the operator could run through a check list for a clue to the cause of the difficulty.

KITS

Metal detectors that need to be assembled from kits, probably will not use the latest detector technology. A well-constructed kit detector, however, will probably perform as it was intended, according to published specifications. Extra care should be taken in the construction of kit instruments; the builder should follow instructions exactly as specified. Should the completed kit not perform satisfactorily, the builder should have a source to take the detector for troubleshooting by a qualified technician.

CHAPTER 9 QUESTIONS

1. Rechargeable ni-cad batteries cost more than carbon zinc and alkaline batteries, therefore, rechargeables will give your detector more power.
   True _____   False _____
2. When rechargeable ni-cads are in a run-down condition, it's perfectly ok to wait to recharge them until just before you need your detector.
   True _____   False _____
3. If you have a "musical ear" it means that: (A) you have the ability to hear sounds coming from near-by metal detectors so you will know where the deep treasures are that others missed; (B) you can instantly tell what type of detector you are hearing just by

listening to the audio sound; (C) you can identify detected targets by listening to how the target "rings" when it is detected; (D) you have the ability to hear metal detector sounds that are extremely weak or are composed of harmonic frequencies that occur when the detector detects metal.

4. When selecting a metal detector, it is best to select the one that has the largest number of identical control knobs all lined up in neat rows.

True _____   False _____

5. Some manufacturers purposely leave knobs off control shafts to: (A) save money; (B) confuse the operator; (C) encourage you to set those controls one time and forget them; (D) to prevent those controls from wearing out prematurely because of too much knob twiddling.

6. The meter is the most common target response indication used.

True _____   False _____

7. Match up the following metal detector types with the correct audio sound system.

BFO _____ _____ ; TR and VLF _____
_____ ; PI (bell ringing).
(Volume change — frequency change) (Each Correct answer is worth 5 points)

8. Whenever you use your metal detector it is best to wear headphones.

True _____   False _____

9. Metal detector indicator lights are of great value because they illuminate the metal detector's fringe area.

True _____   False _____

10. A waterproof searchcoil can be submerged right up to the connector without any damage occurring to the searchcoil.

True _____   False _____

Each of the 10 complete questions, answered correctly, is worth 10 points. Perfect score is 100. Answers given in Appendix 2.

CHAPTER 10

Ground and Target Elimination, Target Classification, Tuning and Retuning, Pinpointing, Depth Measuring and More

In prior chapters you have learned about detection circuits and how metal and some minerals are detected. You have learned how searchcoil antennas are powered by circuit signal current. You have seen how an electromagnetic field is generated by the transmitter antenna, how the field radiates downward from the searchcoil, and how the field lines are crowded together inside and below the transmitter winding, and how this crowding produces the detection pattern. You have seen how eddy currents are formed, how the electromagnetic field is "warped," and how both of these phenomena cause metal detection and some mineral detection to occur.

You have seen how the ground "matrix" consists of minerals and other elements, some of which can be detected by a metal detector. You have seen how some of these elements have an adverse effect upon metal detection.

In this chapter, you will learn how metal detector manufacturers have overcome some of these problems. You will learn what ground elimination (canceling) is, and how it works. You will learn what discrimination and target elimination mean, and how these capabilities help you avoid digging worthless objects. You will learn the tricks of the trade when it comes to specialized searching, like target identification, reverse discrimination, Super Sniping, depth measuring and much more. This chapter concludes the theoretical aspects of metal detection. The next chapter explains the important functions and characteristics of searchcoils. Then, beginning with Chapter 12, you will begin to learn about the various kinds of metal detectors, how they work, what they are capable of and how to get the most from them all.

IRON MINERAL GROUND ELIMINATION

As explained, the majority of the earth's surface contains various densities of iron mineralization. You learned in Chapter 7 (Figure 7-3) how iron distorts the electromagnetic field so an imbalance occurs between the transmitter and receiver windings, causing the detector to detect the presence of the iron. This is a characteristic that caused difficulty for manufacturers (and metal detector users) until they finally utilized available circuit knowledge and techniques to overcome the problem.

During the late 1800s, electrical engineers discovered three main circuit components (characteristics): resistive, inductive, and capacitive. It was discovered that when an alternating electrical voltage was connected across a circuit containing these three elements, a phenomenon called phase shift occurred that caused the current to lag or lead the impressed voltage by ninety degrees.

Since most ground matrixes contain resistive, inductive, and capacitive elements, modern-day metal detector design engineers pondered the question, ''Does phase shifting occur across these elements, and could phase shifting be utilized to eliminate the troublesome aspects of ground minerals?'' The engineers worked on the problem and discovered, in fact, that phase shifting did occur, and that phase shifted voltages could be measured and used to build ground eliminating metal detectors.

Figure 10-1 illustrates the basic circuitry and components. With a simple manipulation of a detector ground eliminating control (some detectors adjust out ground minerals automatically), the effects of iron mineralization can be ''dialed out,'' resulting in mineral-free operation over most iron earth materials. Only detected metal target signals are amplified and conditioned to power the audio and visual indicators. Chapter 14 describes VLF Ground Eliminating detectors in considerable detail.

10-1 BLOCK DIAGRAM OF VLF GROUND ELIMINATION (CANCELLING) METAL DETECTOR

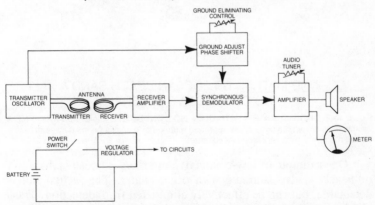

Figure 10-1: ELECTRONIC BLOCK DIAGRAM OF VLF GROUND ELIMINATION (CANCELLING) METAL DETECTOR. This is a block diagram of the VLF Ground Elimination (cancelling) type metal detector. The basic circuits and components and their interconnections are shown, as are the electrical phase relationship between metal and iron mineral targets. The phase shifting phenomenon allows ground elimination detectors to ignore the detection effects of iron earth minerals.

CONDUCTIVE MATRIXES

Most ground matrixes contain conductive minerals (those which will conduct eddy currents). Some ground contains more of these minerals than others. Conductive minerals tend to "mask" targets. That is, since the metal detector sees the ground as one large target (see MATRIX discussion, Chapter 7), a smaller target, say a coin, is not as easily "seen" by the detector, compared to when there are no conductive minerals at all. (See Figures 10-2 and 10-3.) The resultant effects of conductive matrixes and non-conductive iron mineral matrixes, upon metal detector operation, are about the same. While both effects can be "nulled out," electromagnetic field distortion can occur, which may result in decreased depth detection and poorer target identification. (See Figure 7-5 and 7-6.)

10-2 **GROUND MATRIX WITH COIN.**
NO CONDUCTIVE MINERALS PRESENT

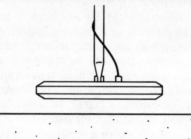

GROUND MATRIX: DRY OCEAN BEACH SAND & SALT
(NO CONDUCTIVE MINERALS)

Figure 10-2: GROUND MATRIX WITH COIN. NO CONDUCTIVE MINERALS PRESENT. A searchcoil is shown hovering above a ground matrix that contains no conductive minerals. The coin is obviously a very pronounced target.

One example of low-conductive matrixes is ocean (salt) water or beach sands, saturated with ocean water. The wetted salt is detectable, but can be effectively eliminated from detection. Trash eliminating detectors can "measure" the conductivity of detectable metals and minerals. A Trash Eliminator control (sometimes called the "Discriminator" control) lets the operator "dial out," or eliminate from detection, materials that have a low conductivity. Consequently, the control can be set to a point where ocean water is

**GROUND MATRIX WITH COIN.
CONDUCTIVE MINERALS PRESENT**

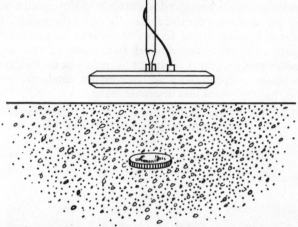

GROUND MATRIX : WET OCEAN BEACH SAND & SALT
(DENSE, HIGHLY CONDUCTIVE MINERALS)

Figure 10-3: GROUND MATRIX WITH COIN. CONDUCTIVE MINERALS PRESENT. A searchcoil is shown hovering above a ground matrix that contains a considerable amount of conductive mineralization. The conductive matrix produces a masking effect that reduces the ability (sensitivity) of the detector to detect the coin.

ignored. At this setting, most desirable metals will be detected as they have a higher conductivity.

TARGET ELIMINATION DISCRIMINATING METAL DETECTORS

A Trash Elimination metal detector is one that "tells" the operator whether the detected metal is desirable or not, depending on what the operator seeks. The detector gives the operator this information by increases or decreases in speaker or headphone volume, and by certain deflections on an indicator. Generally, good (or desirable) objects cause the audio and visual indicators to increase in amplitude; junk (undesirable) objects cause the indicators to decrease. Classifier and some bar graphs indicators relate additional target information to the operator.

For all practical purposes, the terms "Elimination" and "Discrimination" mean the same thing. The term "Elimination," however, is more easily understood because it more accurately describes the metal detector function. When the control is set to zero, no metal targets are eliminated from detection. The higher the setting, the more targets that are eliminated from detection.

CONDUCTIVITY

The term "conductivity" means how well any given metal

will conduct electricity as compared to some norm. You will remember, from our study of eddy currents in Chapter 7, that the electromagnetic field causes eddy currents to flow on the surface of metals (or in any conductive material). Since the various metals have different conductivity factors (resistance to current flow), (see Figure 10-4), eddy currents can flow easier on the surface of some metals than on others. Fortunately, the more desirable metals such as silver, copper, and gold have higher conductivities than iron, foil, tin, and other less desirable metals.

10-4 RESISTIVITY (microhm-cms) AND CONDUCTIVITY (mhos/meter) OF MATERIALS

	Resistivity	Conductivity		Resistivity	Conductivity
Silver	1.6	6250	Tin	11	909
Copper	1.7	5882	Lead	20.6	485
Gold	2.4	4167	Nickel Silver	29	344
Aluminum	2.7	3704	Cast Iron	67	149
Zinc	6.0	1667	Stainless Steel	72	138
Nickel	6.9	1450	Mercury	98.4	101
Brass	7	1429	Water of the		
Bronze	9.2	1087	Great Salt Lake	500	20
Iron	9.7	1031	Carbon	1375	7.2
Platinum	10.0	1000	Sea Water	2000	5
Carbon Steel	10	1000	Wet Soil	1,250,000	.008

Figure 10-4: RESISTIVITY (microhm-cms) AND CONDUCTIVITY (mhos/meter) OF MATERIALS. Each type of metal has its own conductivity factor as shown in this table. Eddy currents flow easier in the higher conductivity metals. Fortunately, desirable metals such as gold, silver and copper have higher conductivity than iron, foil, tin, and other less desirable metals. Since the amount of power expended in the generation of eddy currents can be measured, the detector can "tell" which metals are the better conductors and which are the poorer conductors.

Since metal detectors can "measure" the amount of lost power that is used to generate eddy currents, the detector can "tell" which metals are the better conductors.

Most detectors have a control that allows the operator to "dial in" the amount of desired discrimination or elimination. The illustration in Figure 10-5 is a Metal Detector Target Elimination Chart. The arrow is the knob's pointer. Detectable targets are positioned on the chart in order of conductivity, with the better conductive metals to the right. The metal detector measures the conductivity of each target and "compares" it to the setting the operator has "dialed in" with the control. All targets positioned to the left of the pointer are eliminated from detection; that is, the detector does not produce a positive audio or metal signal. All targets positioned to the right of the pointer are accepted.

This chart represents the conductivity positioning of one particular metal detector. Since conductivity is a function of the radio frequency of the detector's transmitted signal and other factors,

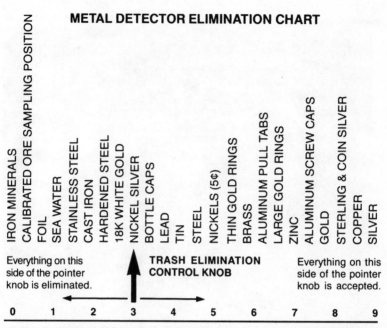

METAL DETECTOR ELIMINATION CHART

IRON MINERALS
CALIBRATED ORE SAMPLING POSITION
FOIL
SEA WATER
STAINLESS STEEL
CAST IRON
HARDENED STEEL
18K WHITE GOLD
NICKEL SILVER
BOTTLE CAPS
LEAD
TIN
STEEL
NICKELS (5¢)
THIN GOLD RINGS
BRASS
ALUMINUM PULL TABS
LARGE GOLD RINGS
ZINC
ALUMINUM SCREW CAPS
GOLD
STERLING & COIN SILVER
COPPER
SILVER

Everything on this
side of the pointer
knob is eliminated.

**TRASH ELIMINATION
CONTROL KNOB**

Everything on this
side of the pointer
knob is accepted.

0   1   2   3   4   5   6   7   8   9

Figure 10-5: METAL DETECTOR TARGET ELIMINATION CHART. Most metal detectors have a control that allows the operator to "dial in" the amount of desired target elimination (discrimination). This is an illustration of a metal detector target elimination control with various targets placed in the order of their conductivity. The arrow is the knobs pointer. (See Figures 10-4 and 10-6.) The metal detector measures the conductivity of each target and "compares" it to the setting the operator has "dialed in" with the control. All targets to the left of the pointer are eliminated from detection. All targets to the right of the pointer are accepted.

the exact position on the chart of each type may vary somewhat from detector to detector. You can develop a chart for your detector by testing differing targets and determining where, on your Trash Elimination control, the various targets are eliminated. The control setting at which any given target can no longer be detected, is that target's position on the conductivity chart.

To determine where salt water should be positioned on your chart, fill a gallon plastic container with water and one-half cup of salt. Mix the salt well and move the container toward the bottom of the searchcoil with the detector operating at number "1" on the Trash Elimination dial. If the detector detects the salt water, rotate the control to "2," retune the detector and test again. The point on the control at which salt water is no longer detected, is its "position" on the conductivity chart. Figure 10-6 shows where salt water elimination is positioned on one VLF metal detector control panel.

VARIOUS TYPE TRASH (TARGET) ELIMINATORS

As will be explained in Chapters 12 through 17, trash (target) elimination characteristics of the various kinds of detectors, may

95

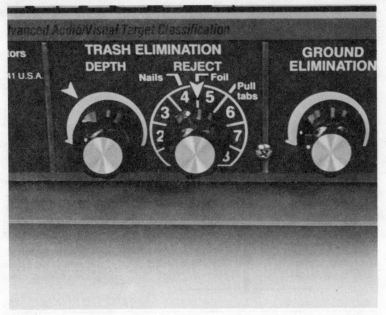

Figure 10-6: This photograph shows a detector's Trash Elimination control adjusted to the point where salt water is barely eliminated from detection. Compare this control setting with the control setting in Figure 10-5. Photo by Melvin Climer.

differ from each other.

BFO trash elimination circuitry is primarily of the metered type. BFO audio is an "all-metal" indicator only. BFOs do not ignore iron mineralization while operating. Salt water cannot be eliminated. Metered trash elimination is very good.

TRs are very accurate trash eliminators. Salt water interference can be eliminated, but iron earth minerals cannot. Consequently, when iron earth minerals are present, TR operation (and trash elimination) becomes more difficult.

VLF audio and meter trash eliminator circuitry does a very good job for the operator. Salt water and iron earth minerals can be eliminated. VLF's can reject foil, nails, pulltabs and screw caps quite well, but signals from bottlecaps may not be perfectly defined, depending upon the detector brand. Some brands do a much better job of eliminating bottlecaps than do others.

Pulse Induction eliminator circuits do a good job of rejecting junk targets. Iron nails, however, tend to be accepted. Pulse detectors ignore iron earth minerals and salt water automatically; no operator control adjustments are necessary. Just turn a Pulse detector on, adjust the audio threshold to the desired level, and start hunting. The Trash Elimination control can be set where desired.

TRASH ELIMINATION AND DISCRIMINATION
CIRCUITRY IS NOT PERFECT

In addition to eddy current measuring, there are other factors involved in trash elimination circuitry. The size, mass (volume), thickness, shape, and proximity to the searchcoil, must be considered. Consequently, detectors can accurately classify small, coin-sized objects, but larger targets cannot be accurately classified. Large objects such as cans, buckets, sheet metal, etc., may read as "good."

The major factor, however, is conductivity. The intrinsic value of a target is not a consideration. For instance, an extremely valuable platinum diamond ring may read "poor" because platinum is a relatively poor conductor compared to copper, silver and gold. Most rings and jewelry items are alloys. That is, the metal contains several metals. An alloyed gold ring could conceivably be rejected if the metal alloyed with gold is a poor conductor.

Since eddy current generation is a prime factor, very small jewelry items such as gold and silver chains, fine wire bracelets, thin rings, etc., may be rejected because there is no flat surface where eddy current generation can take place. Aluminum pulltabs read about the same as most rings. Consequently, at pulltab rejection, some rings may be rejected. United States pennies dated prior to 1983 will read "better" on classifier meters than 1983 and newer pennies, because more copper was used in the manufacturing of pre-1983 pennies. (See "AN IMPROVED TONAL SYSTEM," this chapter.)

The conductivity of United States nickels is relatively poor, which may cause them to be rejected when pulltab elimination is used. An exception to this is World War II United States nickels which contain about one-third silver. Some tinfoil, when crumpled, has a large volume compared to surface area. These crumpled tinfoil balls may then read "good." Small steel pieces, when bright and shiny, may read good because the surface tends to be a good conductor. When rust sets in, the surface becomes current resistant resulting in rejection.

BACK-READING

Back-reading produces false signals that occur when a "reject" target is brought closer than one inch from the bottom of some searchcoils. This occurs in the discrimination mode. The signal, even though it is positive, is easily recognizable as back-reading. If you suspect you have a back-reading signal, raise the searchcoil one inch above the ground, press the retune button, and scan back over the spot. If the target is a junk target, you will hear a positive indication only if the target is "good."

97

OVERSHOOT

Overshoot is a phenomenon that occurs when TR discrimination and the automatic mode are used. It does not occur in any other mode. When a detector's discrimination control is adjusted to reject a given target, the audio (and standard indicators) decreases whenever that target is detected. This decrease occurs when the target is directly below the center of the searchcoil bottom. When the detector is operated in the automatic tuning mode (explained later in this chapter), overshoot occurs. Here's what happens.

As the searchcoil moves clear of the target the audio suddenly increases to a loud sound (Figure 10-7(A)). The same thing occurs when the searchcoil is scanned in the opposite direction. Thus, a loud audio "overshoot" occurs on both sides of the detected target (Figure 10-7(B)). Overshoot occurs when TR discrimination circuits electronically "pull" the audio "down" into the null zone when the searchcoil is directly above the target. When the searchcoil passes beyond the target, the circuit "releases" the "pull" causing the audio to swing back toward threshold. This "swing," however, has nothing to stop it, and the audio shoots up above threshold, causing the audio overshoot sound. This phenomena is analogous to a coil spring when depressed. When the depressing force (the target being rejected) is removed, the spring (audio) springs back, but instead of slowly moving back up to its normal height (the audio threshold level), it rapidly "overshoots" before it finally returns to its normal, relaxed height. Most detector users soon learn these characteristics and pay the phenomenon little mind.

HOW MUCH TRASH ELIMINATION TO USE?

So, then, how much trash elimination do you use? Well, it's up to you. One method is to scan an area without eliminating anything. After you have dug a few targets, you'll be able to decide the amount and kind of junk present in the ground. Then, adjust the control to reject targets you don't want to dig. If there are only a few bottlecaps and pulltabs, set the control to eliminate only small nails, foil, etc.

A factor which obviously must not be overlooked, is that you must be certain the items you want to recover are not eliminated. For instance, in many coin sites along the United States/Canadian border, coins of both countries may be in the ground. Some Canadian coins have poorer conductivity than United States coins. In ghost towns, tokens are oftentimes plentiful. Many tokens, however, were made of poorer conductive metals. Consequently, they will classify as "poor" on the conductivity chart. In very old areas, old coins are waiting to be found. Some old coins have relatively poorer conductivity than modern ones. Also, patina may decrease

10-7   TR DISCRIMINATION OVERSHOOT AND ALL-METAL RESPONSE CURVES

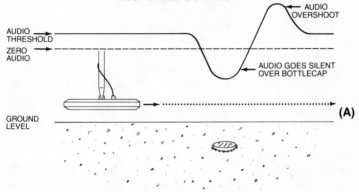

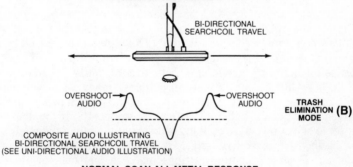

TRASH ELIMINATION AUDIO RESPONSE. BOTTLE CAP TARGET

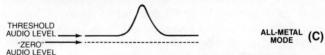

Figure 10-7: TR DISCRIMINATION OVERSHOOT AND ALL-METAL RESPONSE CURVES. These audio response curves illustrate the "overshoot" phenomenon that occurs when TR discrimination is used in the automatic mode. The (A) response curve shows how the audio level increases as the searchcoil moves clear of a reject target. This same phenomenon occurs when the searchcoil is scanned in the opposite direction. Thus, there is an audio "overshoot" that occurs on both sides of the detected target, as illustrated in (B). (C) illustrates normal all-metal detection.

99

a coin's conductivity. It may pay you to be aware of these situations and adjust your elimination control so no desirable objects are rejected. Sure, this takes time and effort, but nevertheless, it's true that your coin hunting and metal detecting success will be in proportion to your efforts.

TARGET MASKING

There are several reasons why trash elimination, or discrimination, (whichever you prefer to call it) is not a perfect method of eliminating undesirable, or "trash" metal objects, from detection. First, a masking effect causes some good targets to not be detected, because trash target negative signals cancel desirable target positive signals. Second, heavy patina, corrosion of the target's surface, and other factors, reduce conductivity of desirable targets, causing them to be rejected. Third, the earth's minerals upset a detector's "air" settings causing good targets in the ground to be missed. And, there are also some lesser effects.

The more elimination you have dialed in, the greater will be the problem of target masking. In other words, the more elimination you use, the more good targets you will miss. So, use target elimination, sparingly!

THE PULLTAB DILEMMA

There is a tendency for some manufacturers to overstate pulltab elimination capability. Claims are made that you do not "lose" rings when pulltab rejection is used. These claims are based upon precise setting, of controls; by careful monitoring of meter deflections; and by computer circuits that "identify" pulltabs.

There are several styles of pulltabs, many of which have different characteristics. Sometimes, there are broken pulltab pieces which have peculiar characteristics. Consequently, if the detector is set to reject one style pulltab, what about the other styles? Also, an earth mineral matrix may look entirely different than an air matrix. Trash elimination settings made in air, may be thrown completely off when the metal detector is scanned over the ground. So, if you fine tune the metal detector to ignore pulltabs and give good signals on certain rings, how do you know all rings will be accepted? And, the problem of good target cancellation by the negative effects of junk target rejection (target masking), is still present, and is worsened by the greater target elimination dialed in when the detector is set to pulltab rejection.

And, because there are so few places where pulltabs are a bother, pulltab rejection is not nearly as big a problem as detector users are encouraged to believe.

Consequently, I continue to stress, use as small amount of trash elimination as possible, preferably no higher than iron bottlecap rejection, and dig some pulltabs and other trash. Wouldn't you like to discover that valuable ring you are about to miss because you have too much trash elimination dialed in?

CLASSIFIERS, METERS AND BAR GRAPHS

There seems to have always been signal-strength indicator meters. The meter pointer gives a visual indication, in syncronism with the audio, that a target is detected. Trash elimination meters deflect upward for "good" targets and downward for "reject" targets.

Some manufacturers install classifier meters, and liquid crystal bar graphs, on detectors. These devices indicate target identification probabilities. While most manufacturers don't describe their visual readouts as probability indicators, to some extent that's what they are. On several meter scales various data is printed (see Figure 10-8) of several "good" and "not-so-good" targets including gold, silver, copper, iron and United States coinage, as well as nails and other targets. When detection occurs, the meter pointer (or bar graph) indicates probable target identity.

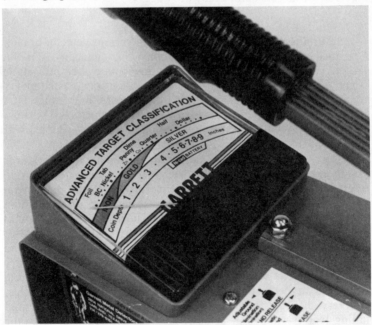

Figure 10-8: When target classifier detectors determine the conductivity of detected targets, the intelligence information is used to drive a meter pointer. The pointer swings upward a distance proportional to the conductivity of the detected target. Since silver has the highest conductivity, silver (and clad) coins read higher than copper coins. Since the conductivities of metals is easily determined, pure metals can be readily identified by reading the IRON-GOLD-SILVER scale.

There are numerous targets that may read the same. If the pointer or bar graph swings up to "rings" it may be an aluminum pulltab. Pulltab pieces and nickels may read the same. On some detector brands, bottlecaps often don't read "bad." Near by trash can cause erroneous readings. Target depth often causes errors. Large pieces of metal may also "fool" classifier meters and bar graphs.

Almost all targets fall into one of three categories: POOR, FAIR or GOOD. "Poor" targets are usually bottlecaps, iron, and some foil. "Fair" are usually gold, rings, nickels, pulltabs, and other medium conductivity metals. "Good" are usually silver, coins, and other high conductivity metals. Certain objects like tiny platinum rings and some alloy jewelry, don't correctly categorize themselves, but the majority of targets likely to be found, do accurately fit into one of the three categories. Target I.D. meters do not identify targets as deeply as audio circuits can detect them.

All things considered, very accurate indicators can be built that greatly improve the operator's efficiency by properly classifying detected targets before they are dug.

TONE INDICATIONS

Several tonal systems are available on various detector brands. One method depends upon the "quality" or conductivity of the target. The audio tone varies in pitch: low-range pitch indications occur when targets are "poor" conductors; mid-range pitch indications occur when targets are "fair" conductors; high-range pitch indications occur when targets are "good" conductors. This tonal identification method, or some variation of it, when coupled with an accurate indicator meter, improves operator efficiency.

A problem with this type audio tonal system is: the operator is usually not sure which pitch the detector is producing. There is no reference tone or discrete brackets in relation to the three main target classifications. Also, this type system sounds something akin to one of the old Ford Model "A" horns that sounds something like this — Ahhhhhhhh...Ooooooooo...Gaaaaaaaa! After several sweeps over the target, the sounds usually level out, and with experience, the operator can generally decide which category the tonal system is indicating. There are, however, no discrete steps, and targets that have conductivities that fall between ranges, are very difficult to interpret. Also, the constantly rising and falling tone is annoying, at best. Another drawback of this type tonal system is that reject targets, which should not be dug, do not have a fixed, definite, "no" sound.

AN IMPROVED TONAL SYSTEM

The ideal system is one that instantly, with one searchcoil

sweep, alerts the operator to the type target detected. But, who is the operator and for what is he or she searching? Cache hunters search for money caches; prospectors search for gold, silver, nuggets, veins, etc.; relic hunters search for relics; coin hunters search for coins. Can there be distinct tonal sounds for each category? No, it would not be practical, or possible, for that matter.

One solution to the problem, that helps the greatest majority of searchers, is to design a system to help the coin hunter find coins. Since about ninety-five percent of all field type detectors in use are employed to search for coins, at one time or another, a "coin" circuit is the most practical.

The illustration shown in Figure 10-9 describes this new circuit. Each time the instrument detects a coin, the operator hears a bell ringing sound. The sound is unmistakable. There is no need to look at the classifier meter to know that a coin has been detected. The operator simply digs at the point where the bell sound is the loudest.

But, what about targets that are not coins? How are they distinguishable? The answer is simple. All other category sounds are exactly the same as metal detector operators have heard for years. Reject targets cause the audio level to decrease to silence. Mid-range targets cause the audio level to increase in loudness (not a bell ringing sound but a normal VLF audio sound). Reject and accept target ranges are determined by where the operator sets the Trash Elimination Control. So, in effect, the operator has complete control over the detector's Trash Elimination circuitry. The audio tells, instantly, with one searchcoil sweep, the type target detected.

The bell tone is caused by targets that have conductivity within the silver or higher range. All targets (including silver, clad and copper coins) with a conductivity higher than United States zinc pennies, cause the bell tone sound. Since some valuable targets (nickels, rings, high patina coins, etc.) may fall in the mid-range category, whenever the mid-range sound is heard, the operator takes a quick glance at the classifier meter to identify the detected target.

CLASSIFIER INDICATOR/TONAL SYSTEM ADVANTAGES

There are many advantages to this system. The operator's efficiency greatly improves. One argument against these new audio/visual systems is that good targets will be dug anyway, so why bother to identify them as to type? That's a good argument, but with the proper audio/visual system, more valuable targets will more quickly be located and recovered. For instance, as explained in this chapter, good targets buried in close proximity to reject targets, may be rejected by the detector. The above described

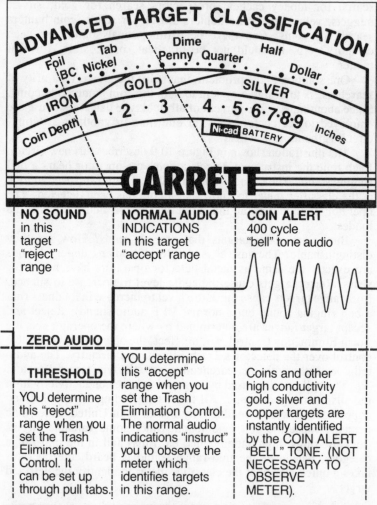

Figure 10-9: BELL TONE COIN ALERT/AUDIO/VISUAL TARGET CLASSIFICATION SYSTEM. This composite drawing illustrates a unique meter/audio target classification system. A coin-alert audio "bell" tone, indicates the presence of coins and upper-range, high-conductivity targets. A standard audio tone alerts the operator to the presence of mid-range targets that are then identified by the meter. Lower range reject targets do not produce an audio tone but cause the audio threshold to decrease to silent.

The coin-alert range is factory preset. All coins that have conductivities of United States one-cent copper and higher, cause the bell tone to sound. With a single adjustment of the Trash Elimination control knob, the operator sets the mid and lower ranges. In the illustration, the point between these two ranges is set at foil (bottlecaps). This system allows the operator to adjust the detector's computer circuitry to achieve maximum detection efficiency regardless of the nature of the targets in the ground.

classifier meter and/or a tonal system, however, operates even though "zero" trash elimination is dialed in, a far better probability of not rejecting these good targets is possible. The overall trash elimination circuit does not reject any targets WHILE THE METER AND/OR AUDIO SYSTEM ACCURATELY IDENTIFIES TARGETS. The bell tone is heard regardless of where the trash elimination circuit is set. Thus, operators can work (and rework) high trash areas and not miss coins that less capable detectors miss.

Just knowing what a target is, prior to digging, has a certain psychological value that keeps one's interest extremely high. Detectors that feature only classifier meters, are not as efficient as the combination audio/visual systems, because operators must visually observe the meter each time a target is detected if they wish to know the target's identity. This reduces speed and efficiency. If the detector has an accurate tonal system, the operator knows instantly that, if it is a coin, it is to be dug. It is not necessary to view the meter to learn target identity.

VLF DETECTION DEPTH CONSIDERATIONS

Does detection depth remain constant, or does it vary depending upon where VLF Ground and Trash Elimination Controls are set? Mid-range detection depth is better than at the extremities of the control range. In other words, VLF detectors tend to detect deeper when these controls are adjusted near mid-range. How can this help you? This pecularity provides you with a means whereby, under some circumstances, you can detect slightly deeper.

The illustration (Figure 10-10) is a plot of detection depth versus the adjustment range of ground and target elimination controls. Zero target elimination and negative (-) rotation of the ground control are positioned on the left side. The numbers indicate two metal detector control features: (1) zero to ten on the Trash Elimination Control and (2) the ten rotational turns of a ten-turn Ground Elimination Control. If your Ground Elimination Control is single-turn, each chart number represents one-tenth of one full rotation.

You will notice that maximum ground elimination mode depth occurs in the mid-range area. Certain iron earth minerals, however, may prevent you from setting the ground control in the mid-range area to achieve this slight extra detector depth. Certainly, for the least erratic operation, the control must be properly adjusted to eliminate detection of iron earth minerals. To locate mid-range on a ten-turn control, rotate the knob ten-turns in either direction. This will insure that the control is at the "end." Then, rotate the knob in the reverse direction five turns. This will be your midpoint, but, of course, it may not be the optimum setting for your particular ground mineral situation.

105

DETECTION DEPTH VS *VLF ALL-METAL & •VLF ELIMINATION ADJUSTMENT RANGE

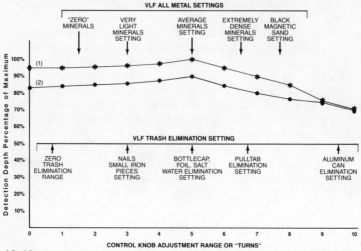

10-10

Figure 10-10: DETECTION DEPTH VS VLF ALL-METAL AND VLF ELIMINATION ADJUST-MENT RANGE. This illustration is a plot of Detection Depth versus the Adjustment Range of Ground and Target Elimination controls. The numbers represent: (1) zero to ten on the Trash Elimination control and (2) the ten rotational turns of a ten turn Ground Elimination control. Zero Target Elimination and fully negative rotation of the ground control are positioned on the left side. Notice that maximum detection depth occurs in the mid-range areas. Detection depth decreases slightly as you rotate the controls in either direction. Study the text to determine the optimum settings for your particular metal detector.

Maximum detection depth in the trash elimination mode occurs near bottlecap rejection. The best way to locate your detector's maximum depth points is to calibrate your detector using the following method.

Lay the detector on a table so that you can measure detection distances from the searchcoil. Set the Trash Elimination Control at zero (0) and select Manual tuning. Measure how far you can detect a coin and make a note of the distance. Rotate the control to number one (1) and again check the detection distance. Continue until you have reached the highest number and have recorded the results on graph paper.

VLF Trash Elimination and Automatic Ground Elimination modes are "automatic," so, you will have to quickly scan the coin across the searchcoil while watching the meter. This will be easier if you have someone to help you. Testing automatic mode detectors may be difficult, and the true shape of the detection depth curve may not be obtainable. When making detection distance tests in the Ground Elimination mode, start by rotating the knob fully toward the negative (-) end. Make a measurement for each turn of ten-turn controls or one-tenth turn for single-turn controls.

To achieve the extra margin of depth from your detector, operate with the controls set as near the "peak" as possible. Of course, ground minerals and your operating preferences may prevent your achieving these maximum detection depth settings.

REVERSE DISCRIMINATION

An accurate form of trash elimination discrimination over mineralized ground is reverse discrimination. A thousand people may take the credit for this one, but Roy Lagal should be credited with the discovery. For years, I have traveled to the northwest, especially to Idaho. Idaho has some of the toughest iron minerals found anywhere in the United States.

On one trip in the mid-'70s, Roy and I were faced with the "hot rock" problem which is common to all VLF detectors. Rocks that contain a certain composition of minerals, different from the surrounding ground to which VLF detectors are adjusted, produce detector signals that sound like those from metal. To check whether the detector had detected a hot rock or a piece of metal, Roy developed the "reverse discrimination" technique which allowed him to identify targets quickly and correctly. It was also discovered that this method could be used to identify all detected targets correctly, whether metal or hot rocks.

Primarily, you need reverse discrimination because TRs cannot discriminate efficiently when used over iron minerals. As discussed earlier, iron minerals interfere with detector operation, thus masking detector signals, especially the weaker discrimination ones. Consequently, the operator sometimes cannot tell if detector signals are due to iron minerals or targets. So, reverse discrimination is a method which greatly increases the operator's ability to identify detected targets correctly, in heavily mineralized ground. Reverse discrimination is not needed when there are no ground minerals present in the search matrix.

HOW TO REVERSE DISCRIMINATE USING THE
TR DISCRIMINATING MODE

To reverse discriminate, you must use the MANUAL TR discrimination mode. It is difficult to reverse discriminate in the AUTOMATIC mode. The discrimination control must be adjusted to reject items you do not want to dig.

TO REVERSE DISCRIMINATE, TUNE TO THE OBJECT AND SCAN THE SEARCHCOIL IN THE REVERSE DIRECTION. Here's how you do it: (1) Pinpoint the detected target using the "X" scan method in the non-discriminate mode. (2) Place the searchcoil ON THE GROUND directly above the target. (3) PRESS the retuning button (or switch) which tunes the detector in the discrimination mode and to the target. In other words, retune the detector to threshold while the searchcoil is directly above the target. Keep the searchcoil still. You will hear the threshold sound. (4) Smoothly, move the searchcoil either to the left or right, completely clear of the target (Figure 10-11), and listen for the sound change. If the sound DECREASES OR DOES NOT CHANGE, DIG the target! If the sound INCREASES, DON'T DIG the target.

Figure 10-11: This photograph shows the scanning procedure to use when you reverse discriminate to identify detected targets. To take a "reading" after you have pinpointed the target and detuned the detector, move the searchcoil either to the left or to the right completely clear of the target. If the sound decreases, or does not change, dig the target. If the sound increases, don't dig the target. Refer to the text for a full explanation of the reverse discrimination procedure.

ILLUSTRATIONS WILL HELP

To understand exactly what is happening, refer to Figures 10-12 and 10-13. During normal discrimination (Figure 10-12), when the searchcoil APPROACHES a good target, the audio increases to a peak directly over the target. In reverse discrimination, when the searchcoil MOVES AWAY FROM a good target, the audio DECREASES. You will note that the forward and reverse audio profiles are exactly the same. In both cases, the sound is highest DIRECTLY OVER THE TARGET. If the audio does not change when you move the searchcoil away from the target, it means that the target was too deep for the discrimination circuit to read.

The difference between normal and reverse discrimination

10-12 REVERSE DISCRIMINATION — GOOD TARGET

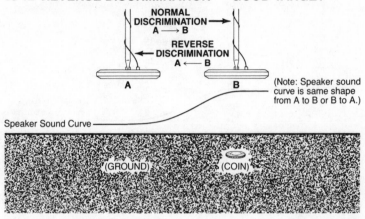

Figure 10-12: REVERSE DISCRIMINATION-GOOD TARGET. This illustration shows the audio response curve produced when the searchcoil approaches a good target. In reverse discrimination, when the searchcoil moves away from a good target, the audio decreases or does not change. Note that the forward scan and reverse discrimination scan curves are exactly the same.

methods is that you simply reverse the direction of searchcoil travel. This method works quite well because what you do is prevent iron mineral signals from interfering with discrimination signals. If you jerk the searchcoil, or do not keep it flat upon the ground as you move it, ground mineral signals will prevent your getting a good discrimination signal. This method may sound difficult, but it is really very simple. Just try it a few times and you'll soon see how easy it becomes.

Refer to Figure 10-13 and you'll see what happens when the target is junk. As you approach a junk target in normal scan, the signal DECREASES, but when you reverse discriminate and move the searchcoil away from the target, the signal will INCREASE. If you will study the illustration you will see that the signal profiles are exactly the same; you have merely REVERSED THE DIREC-TION OF SEARCHCOIL TRAVEL.

Use reverse discrimination whenever you want to doublecheck a target. You may be engaged in electronic prospecting and want to check for hot rocks, or you may be coin hunting and not sure about the target you just detected.

NUMEROUS OTHER METHODS

There are numerous other methods that help detector operators determine the identification of buried targets. When some nails and elongated iron objects are detected, a "blip-blip" audio sound will be heard. This double sound can also occur when coins are standing on edge. I have also noted it when nugget hunting, so, use

10-13 REVERSE DISCRIMINATION — REJECT TARGET

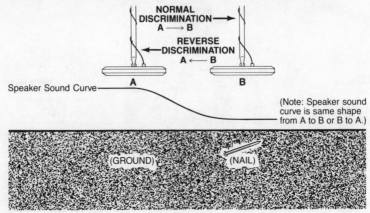

Figure 10-13: REVERSE DISCRIMINATION-REJECT TARGET. During normal scanning when the searchcoil approaches a reject target, the signal decreases (see audio response curve). In reverse discrimination, when the searchcoil moves away from the reject target, the audio increases. In studying the illustration you will see that these two signal profiles are exactly the same. When you reverse discriminate, you simply reverse the direction of searchcoil travel.

the method with caution.

Ferrous (iron) targets produce a much wider detection width than do coins when the VLF Ground Elimination mode is used (Figure 10-15). Figure 10-14 illustrates electromagnetic field reactions which cause wide responses on ferrous targets and narrow response on non-ferrous ones. There are various methods for using the phenomena but you are advised to be cautious when using this method. Deep targets are not as subject to this phenomenon, as shallow ones. As you scan, say, from left to right, notice the point on the ground (at the right edge of the searchcoil) where audio begins to increase. Scan on across and notice the ground point (at the left edge of the searchcoil) where the sound returns to threshold. If the audio returns to threshold at roughly the same point where it increased, the target is probably non-ferrous. If the audio returns to threshold at a point that is obviously to the right of where it first increased, the target is probably ferrous. Coin-sized targets produce narrow response; large non-ferrous ones do not.

Refer to Figure 10-15 which illustrates "double blip" response as well as audio response signals when several common targets are detected. Detuning by minerals is also illustrated.

Various methods have been worked out by coin hunters to distinguish between rings and pulltabs. The methods use both audio and meter indications. Most of them involve setting trash elimination to the exact point where pulltabs are accepted with a positive signal when the pulltab is about one inch from the bottom

ELECTROMAGNETIC FIELD REACTIONS ON FERROUS AND NON-FERROUS TARGETS

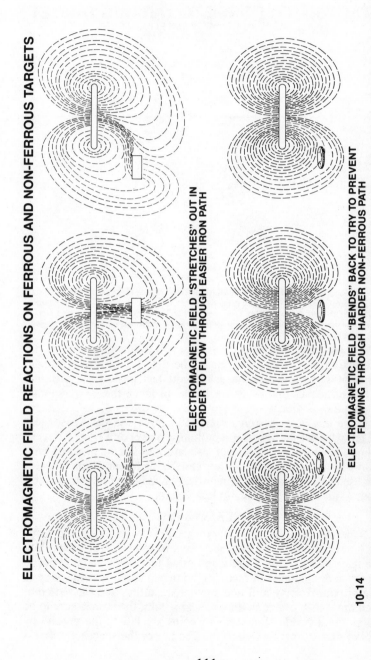

ELECTROMAGNETIC FIELD "STRETCHES" OUT IN ORDER TO FLOW THROUGH EASIER IRON PATH

ELECTROMAGNETIC FIELD "BENDS" BACK TO TRY TO PREVENT FLOWING THROUGH HARDER NON-FERROUS PATH

10-14

Figure 10-14: ELECTROMAGNETIC FIELD REACTIONS ON FERROUS AND NON-FERROUS TARGETS. This illustration shows the electromagnetic field reactions which cause wide audio response on ferrous targets and narrow response on non-ferrous targets.

111

AUDIO RESPONSE CURVE ILLUSTRATING DETECTOR RESPONSE TO VARIOUS TARGETS
ALL METAL MODE. NO TRASH ELIMINATION.

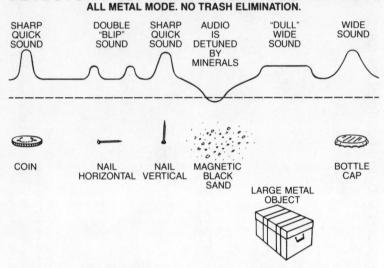

Figure 10-15: AUDIO RESPONSE CURVE ILLUSTRATING DETECTOR RESPONSES TO VARIOUS TARGETS. The audio response when a metal detector reacts to various targets is illustrated in this drawing. Note the "double blip" response over elongated ferrous objects, the narrow response on coins, and the wide response on ferrous and deeply buried targets.

of the searchcoil. The detector is operated in the automatic mode. Nickels and most rings then cause the detector to produce audio overshoot signals when the searchcoil has passed on over the target. Bottlecaps and other trash also produce these overshoots, but the audio is louder.

Some operators watch meter deflections and can reasonably well tell whether the signal is a pulltab, a nickel or a ring. All these methods have some merit, but you are advised to proceed with caution because response in air can be different from detector response to buried targets. Mineralization may foul the most exacting air adjustments resulting in lost targets.

SUPER-SNIPING

Super-Sniping is one method that is very exacting and helps coin hunters to recover coins and rings from high junk areas. You have learned that junk targets and good targets produce opposite polarity audio signals. In fact, one bottlecap and one coin, lying in close proximity, may null one another, resulting in a missed coin. When more than one junk item is near a coin, the coin is sure to be missed. As a result, thousands of coins are left in the ground by users of discriminating detectors. The larger the searchcoil that is

112

AUDIO RESPONSE CURVES
ILLUSTRATING DETUNING OVER TARGET

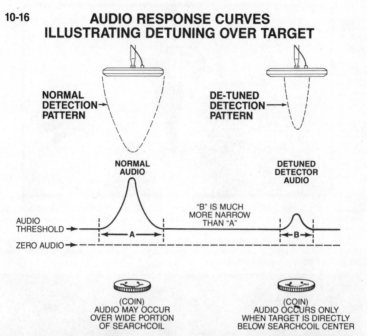

Figure 10-16: AUDIO RESPONSE CURVES ILLUSTRATING DE-TUNING OVER TARGET. This illustration compares normal audio response to de-tuned audio response. You will notice the detection pattern is reduced in size when the detector is de-tuned.

used, the more coins that are left, especially in junky areas, because more items can be beneath the searchcoil at the same time. The more junk metal there is in the ground, the more coins that will be left unrecovered.

Consequently, some way to pick out individual targets is needed. One extremely productive method is to use a Super-Sniper type searchcoil. Certain small three-inch to four-inch diameter searchcoils have an extremely intense electromagnetic field that "shoots" down past junk items to reach individual coins. (See Figure 10-17.) Small searchcoils of this type have become very popular, because users are finding large amounts of coins and rings in junky areas, parks, and other recreational sites that were long since thought "worked out."

Super-Sniper searchcoils won't penetrate as deeply as will larger ones but they will produce more shallow coins that have been previously missed. Also, Super-Sniper searchcoils can be used quite effectively near metal fences, buildings, parking meter posts, playground equipment (Figure 10-18) and adjacent to side-walks that have metal reinforcements. If you haven't used a Super-Sniper type searchcoil, you will be in for a pleasant surprise when you try one.

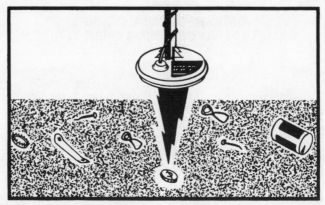

Figure 10-17: SUPER-SNIPING IN HIGH JUNK AREAS. Super-Sniping is an efficient way to recover the maximum number of coins in high junk areas. The Super-Sniper penetrates down past junk targets to detect individual coins and other high conductivity targets. The negative response of near by junk targets is reduced or eliminated. The Super-Sniper searchcoil also operates effectively near metal fences, buildings, parking meter posts, playground equipment and sidewalks.

Figure 10-18: When the Super-Sniper searchcoil is used, the metal detector can be de-tuned slightly if extremely close scanning adjacent to metal objects is desired.

TUNING/RE-TUNING

Metal detector tuning is one of the most misunderstood detector adjustments. Tuning is nothing more than adjusting a knob to achieve the optimum audio threshold level (see Figure 10-19).

Figure 10-19: Correct tuning is simply adjusting a knob to achieve the optimum audio threshold level. The optimum level, for most detectors, is the lowest possible sound level that the operator can hear. If the threshold is set down in the silent zone, or set too loud, detection depth and sensitivity will be reduced. Photo by Melvin Climer.

This optimum level is, on most detectors, the lowest possible sound level that the operator can hear. If the threshold is set down in the silent zone or, conversely, set too loud, detection depth can suffer.

On most models, this level is set when the operator first uses his detector. The audio is adjusted to the lowest sound level that can be heard. This is called the THRESHOLD. This knob is never adjusted again, provided the detector is equipped with a flip switch or push button "retune" switch. Most detectors have this switch. These "retune" switches instantly reset the audio to the operator's preset threshold whenever it needs resetting, as may occur during temperature changes and battery drift.

Instructors sometimes feel like pulling their hair out when they are teaching students how to tune their detectors. There is something about human nature that causes some people to start manipulating all knobs each and every time the detector is turned on. Once you have set your threshold, FORGET IT! Even if you change searchcoils or batteries, or let the detector sit in the closet for a month, all you have to do to regain threshold is to turn the metal detector on and PUSH THE RETUNE BUTTON! An exception to this "set and forget" advice is that the threshold level may be different depending upon whether you are using the speaker or headphones. Headphones generally require a lower threshold, so

115

the TUNING knob (called AUDIO on some detectors) may require a slight INITIAL readjustment. Lower cost detectors may not have the "set and forget" feature just described.

MANUAL VERSUS AUTOMATIC TUNING

Tuning can be further confusing, especially when one tries to learn the difference between MANUAL and AUTOMATIC tuning. Some detectors have a switch that can be placed in the MANUAL or AUTOMATIC tuning position. When the MANUAL position is selected, the handle-mounted retune switch (or push button) must be MANUALLY PRESSED momentarily to return the audio to threshold. When AUTOMATIC tuning is selected, the retune switch does not have to be pressed; the detector AUTOMATI-CALLY and ELECTRONICALLY keeps the audio level at the preset threshold. When anything (target detection, drift, etc.) causes the audio threshold to change, the automatic circuit "pulls" the audio back to preset threshold. That is why the detector searchcoil must be kept in continuous motion, and why the searchcoil cannot "hover" or be held stationary over a target. When automatic tuning is used, detection depth capability and sensitivity may be reduced, and the overshoot problem (Figure 10-7) may be present. Some operators, however, prefer automatic tuning. You should judge for yourself.

TARGET PINPOINTING

Detector operators should strive to develop accurate pinpointing methods. The more precisely the target is pinpointed before digging, the faster will be recovery, and the less damage there will be to sod and grass. It is especially important that all coin hunters who work in parks and recreational areas learn good pinpointing and recovery methods. Laws have been enacted to keep coin hunters out of city-owned parks because of a few people who leave gapping holes. The well-being of the coin hunting hobby depends upon YOU!

DETUNING

It is quite easy to pinpoint by sight. You develop the ability to discern the point on the ground where maximum audio occurs. By noticing where maximum sound occurs, and drawing an imaginary "X" (Figure 10-20) with the searchcoil, you can precisely pinpoint buried targets. One method that makes pinpointing more precise is DETUNING. To detune, first locate maximum sound as precisely as you can by drawing on the ground an imaginary "X." Then, set the searchcoil upon the ground directly above "X." Press the retune switch momentarily and release. This operation tunes the detector TO THE TARGET. (To detune, the MANUAL tuning mode must be used.)

Figure 10-20: By noticing where maximum sound occurs, and drawing an imaginary "X" with the searchcoil, you can quickly pinpoint buried targets. Electronic Pinpointing, and detuning of the detector's audio, gives you additional measures of pinpointing accuracy.

Now, slide the searchcoil back and forth, over the ground, keeping it in contact with the ground. Each time the target center of your searchcoil is directly over the target, you will hear a slight "blip" audio sound. (Study Figure 10-16.) This method is performed easiest in the VLF Ground Eliminating all-metal mode.

Target center of a searchcoil may be at the exact physical center, or it may be slightly forward of center toward the "toe" of the searchcoil. Determine your instrument's target center by placing a coin directly on the searchcoil bottom near the center. Press the retune button momentarily, then slide the coin around on the bottom of the searchcoil. The point where audio is loudest, will be your target center. (See also, Chapter 11, DETERMINING TARGET CENTER.)

ELECTRONIC PINPOINTING

Electronic pinpointing is a noteworthy metal detector circuit development that greatly enhances the ability of the detector to pinpoint targets. When the electronic pinpointing switch is pressed an automatic gain circuit comes into play that narrows the audio response. The audio becomes a much more noticeable and discernible "blip" whenever the searchcoil is directly above the target. (See Figure 10-21 which illustrates electronic pinpointing detection pattern narrowing, and compares it with detuning.)

117

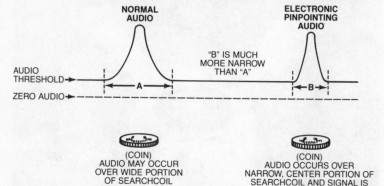

Figure 10-21: AUDIO RESPONSE CURVES ILLUSTRATING ELECTRONIC PINPOINTING. When electronic pinpointing circuits are activated, the audio is a more noticeable and discernible "blip" whenever the searchcoil is directly above detected targets.

COIN DEPTH MEASUREMENT

Coin depth measurement circuitry is also a noteworthy development. When a switch is pressed, the meter pointer indicates approximate coin depth whenever coins are detected. Meter scales are usually calibrated in inches and millimeters. The circuits are calibrated for coin-sized objects only; objects larger than coins cause the meter to read more shallow than the true depth of targets. Targets smaller than coins cause the meter to read deeper.

Some depth detection meters are "reversed" to a person's normal way of reading a meter. Deep coins read toward the left side of the scale and shallow coins read toward the right. This "reversed" reading method uses circuitry that is cheaper to construct than meters that read deeper coins to the right. The "right-hand" depth meters (Figure 10-8) begin "zero" depth on the left and indicate increasing depth as the pointer swings toward the right.

Some detectors must be hovered above the target while the operator reads the meter. Other meter circuits "lock in" on the reading with just one pass over the coin; the reading holds steady until a handle-mounted switch is released. Other detectors require several passes over the target before an accurate reading is obtained.

Coin depth measuring circuitry is a desirable feature and supplies the coin hunter with valuable data. Coin retrieval is simplified when approximate depth is known. Keep in mind that depth measuring circuits are calibrated for a given size searchcoil, usually a seven-inch to eight-inch diameter searchcoil. The searchcoil must be in contact with the ground for the most accurate reading. Some coin depth measuring circuits are more accurate than others.

MODE SWITCHING

Some detectors feature electronic mode switching. A momentary pressing of a switch causes modes to change instantly. As many as six modes have been controlled by one switch. Usually, whenever a mode switch is pressed, the detector retunes to audio threshold.

Often, I receive questions like, "Which mode do I use?", and "How do I know when to change modes?" In response to these questions, I have listed below all modes that your detector (regardless of type) may have. I have not listed any manufacturer's trademarked mode designations.

AUTOMATIC (TUNING): Recommended when drift becomes a problem and when you prefer to use it. Compare MANUAL and AUTOMATIC operating characteristics (detection depth, discrimination, etc.) before using.

AUTOMATIC (VLF TYPE DETECTOR): This newest type detector is recommended for coin hunting only. It can perform other tasks, but with reduced capability.

BFO DISCRIMINATION: Use when coin hunting or ghost towning for coins, tokens, etc. Do not use when cache, relic, nugget or vein searching.

BFO METAL ZONE: Use, when searching for metal and when ore sampling.

BFO MINERAL ZONE: Use when searching for black magnetic sand (magnetite).

COIN DEPTH MEASURING: Use when you wish to know approximate coin depth.

DE-TUNING: Use when you wish the most precise pinpointing, and when you are searching only for very shallow targets.

ELECTRONIC PINPOINTING: Use for fast, quick pinpointing that is more accurate than regular pinpointing.

PULSE INDUCTION-ALL-METAL: Use when you wish to dig every target.

PULSE INDUCTION-TRASH ELIMINATION: Use when you do not wish to dig every target.

RETUNING: Any time the audio drifts away from your preset threshold, simply push a buttom or flip a switch to restore threshold. Retune as often as necessary to maintain threshold.

REVERSE DISCRIMINATION: Use primarily when you are using a TR over heavy ground mineralization and you wish to identify targets, hot rocks, etc.

SILENT (NO AUDIO) TUNING: Use only when you do not wish to hear the steady tone of audio threshold. You will lose some detection depth and sensitivity. The newer, Automatic VLF Ground Elimination detectors can be operated silent, but a very slight amount of detection depth and sensitivity will be lost.

THRESHOLD (AUDIO) TUNING: Use slight audio sound (threshold) when you desire the greatest detection depth, sensitivity and detector efficiency.

TR ALL-METAL: Use when you wish to dig every target. Mineralized ground may necessitate use of VLF ALL-METAL mode (detector).

TR DISCRIMINATION: Use when coin hunting, and you do not wish to dig "trash" targets. Mineralized ground may necessitate use of VLF TRASH ELIMINATION mode (detector).

VLF ALL-METAL: Use when you wish to dig every target; when gold (precious metal) searching; when cache and relic hunting and when you wish to detect to maximum depth. Use over mineralized or non-mineralized ground.

VLF CALIBRATED (GROUND, TRASH ELIMINATION OR HIGH GRADE MODE): Use when ore sampling (high grading mine dumps, etc.)

VLF TRASH ELIMINATION (DISCRIMINATION): Use when you do not wish to dig every target. Do not use when cache and precious metal searching. Use over mineralized or non-mineralized ground.

CHAPTER 10 QUESTIONS

1. The reason why VLF ground eliimination type detectors are so good, is that they eliminate from detection all ground minerals.
   True _____ False _____

2. Some earth materials are actually conductive matrixes. Consequently, detection capability may be reduced.
   True _____ False _____

3. Some metal detectors can be adjusted to "ignore" ocean water because salt water is a highly conductive matrix.
   True _____ False _____

4. A target elimination discriminating metal detector eliminates from detection undesirable metal objects.
   True _____ False _____

5. A metal detector "rejects" undesirable targets because these targets have a very high conductivity.
   True _____ False _____

6. The target elimination control allows you to select the range of conductive targets that you are interested in locating.
   True _____ False _____

7. Pulse Induction metal detectors cannot be designed to "reject" undesirable low conductivity metal targets.
   True _____ False _____

8. Perhaps the major fault of target elimination discrimination circuitry is that: (A) you may occasionally have to dig an aluminum pulltab; (B) junk targets can mask good targets; (C) a lot of good targets are left in the ground so that you will have a productive place to hunt next year; (D) the circuits inhibit eddy current generation thus greatly reducing depth detection.

9. It's good practice to never dial in aluminum pulltab rejection because the higher the trash elimination control is set, the more good targets that are rejected.
   True _____ False _____

10. Classifier meters will sometimes give the same reading on both desirable and undesirable objects. Why?

11. The conductivity of almost all targets falls into one of three categories. Poor, _____ and _____ . (Each correct answer is worth 2 points)

12. Fortunately, most desirable targets have better conductivity than most undesirable targets.
    True _____ False _____

13. Classifier meters are better than indicator meters because targets can be more accurately identified.
    True _____ False _____

14. Using reverse discrimination will: (A) give greater detection

depth; (B) drain batteries rapidly; (C) reduce ground mineralization; (D) identify detected targets accurately.

15. When you reverse discriminate, the main thing you accomplish is: (A) reverse direction of searchcoil travel; (B) reverse audio sound; (C) minimize ground mineral interference; (D) eliminate "hot rocks" from detection.

16. One detecting method that is very exacting and helps coin hunters to recover coins and rings from high junk areas is _____ _____ .

17. You can find more coins especially in high trashy areas when you use the detecting method described in question 16, because the masking effect of reject targets is greatly reduced.
    True _____   False _____

18. Once you set the tuning (audio) threshold, about the only time you may need to reset it is when you change from _____ to _____ and vice-versa. (Each correct answer is worth 2 points)

19. A retune push button or flip switch instantaneously retunes your detector to your preset audio threshold.
    True _____   False _____

20. When automatic tuning is used, _____ _____ and _____ may be reduced. (Each correct answer is worth 2 points)

21. Detuning is done primarily because it is a very precise way of tuning the audio down into the silent zone so you do not have to listen to the audio sounds.
    True _____   False _____

22. Electronic pinpointing "sharpens up" detection signals so that you can pinpoint detected targets easier.
    True _____   False _____

23. Coin depth circuits measure very accurately the distance of coin size targets from the very bottom of the searchcoil.
    True _____   False _____

24. When using a metal detector's electronic coin depth measuring circuit, objects smaller than coins will cause the coin depth meter to indicate the object is deeper than it actually is.
    True _____   False _____

25. A coin standing on edge, will cause a coin depth measuring circuit meter to indicate the coin is more shallow than it actually is.
    True _____   False _____

Each of the 25 complete questions, answered correctly, is worth 4 points. Perfect score is 100. Answers given in Appendix 2.

CHAPTER 11

Metal Detector Searchcoils

You can think of detector searchcoils as having the same function as the wheels on an automobile; wheels make the car go. Wheels take power from the motor via the transmission and drive shaft. Wheels are the interface between the automobile and the ground; they roll along and take the bumps, grinds and shocks, and they get you to your destination. Searchcoils take power from the oscillator via the searchcoil cable. They are the interface between the electronics and the ground. They scan along and take the bumps, grinds, and shocks, and they get you to your destination . . . the target.

SHAPES AND SIZES

There are many shapes and sizes of searchcoils. They range in size from about three-quarter-inch up to the very large Depth Multiplier size (Figure 11-1). Roughly speaking, the smaller the searchcoil, the smaller the object that can be detected. The larger the searchcoil, the deeper the detection, but the larger the object must be. There are reasons all sizes are needed. One size searchcoil cannot perform every task. Consider, for instance, coin hunting. Most searchcoils, from about seven inches in diameter up to about ten inches, make good general purpose coin hunting searchcoils. You may often search for long hours. This criteria calls for light-weight searchcoils. The smaller the searchcoil, the better the detection of small objects. But, the smaller the searchcoil, the less depth penetration, so there must be a compromise somewhere between the smallest and the largest sizes.

For cache and money hunting, and large object hunting, large searchcoils are needed. The most popular are the twelve-inch to fourteen-inch sizes. These are large enough to give excellent depth but small enough to be reasonably lightweight. The larger the searchcoil, the more difficult it becomes to maneuver around trees and rocks, and to pinpoint targets.

All the various types of land and underwater searchcoils will be discussed in this chapter. Each manufacturer designs and produces searchcoils for its own brand of detector. Searchcoils of one detector when used on another brand, may not produce optimum results. Well-meaning people who recommend searchcoil swapping between detector brands, may be making misleading statements. Searchcoils are built with varying degrees of waterproofness.

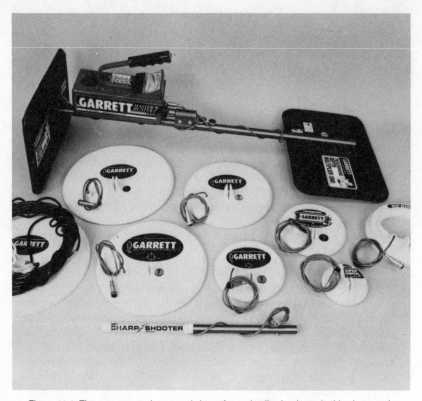

Figure 11-1: There are many shapes and sizes of searchcoils. As shown in this photograph, they range from three-quarter-inch diameter up to the large Depth Multiplier size. The smaller searchcoils are used for locating small and large objects at shallow depths; the larger searchcoil sizes are primarily used for locating larger objects buried deeply. Since one size searchcoil cannot perform every task, many different sizes are needed. True universal detectors, that can perform a large number of tasks, require many different size searchcoils. Photo by Melvin Climer.

Splashproof means that if a little water occasionally gets on the searchcoil, as when you move it through wet grass, the moisture will not affect operation. Waterproof means that the searchcoil can be operated in a downpour, and the rain will not affect operation. Submersible means that the searchcoil can be submerged up to the cable connector without affecting the operation of the detector. Submersible searchcoils can be submerged about thirty inches under water. All manufacturers may not agree to the above searchcoil descriptions, so it is best to check with your metal detector manufacturer if you are in doubt.

SEARCHCOIL DESIGN

Searchcoil windings are transducers (commonly called antennas) that convert the transmitter oscillator signal into an electromag-

124

netic field which penetrates or "illuminates" the area or object being scanned. Searchcoils, depending upon the type of detector, will have from one to several windings, clustered together in a meaningful pattern, and rigidly encased in a plastic housing. This complete assembly is most often referred to as the searchcoil, but is occasionally referred to as the coil, loop or antenna. Detector types such as the Beat Frequency Oscillator (BFO) and Pulse Induction (PI) use only one winding. VLF type detectors use two or three windings. "Two-box" type detectors use two searchcoils: the rear searchcoil houses the transmitter winding and the front one houses the receiver winding.

The design and construction of searchcoils is very critical. A large portion of a manufacturer's design budget is allocated for searchcoil design. Since wire and plastic expand and contract with temperature changes, the electrical parameters of searchcoils can change unless care is taken in manufacturing. This change causes detector instability and drift, and sometimes erratic operation.

Searchcoils withstand the greatest abuse that detector components are subjected to, as they are constantly being slid across the ground, bumped into rocks and trees, submerged in water, and generally banged around unmercifully. Consequently, great care must be taken in searchcoil construction.

ELECTROSTATIC SHIELDING

There are two types of field potentials, electromagnetic and electrostatic. Throughout the first part of this book, electromagnetic fields and detection signals have been discussed.

An electrostatic field potential is primarily one that has constant voltage. This electrical phenomena occurs when two objects come in close proximity to each other. When wet grass or other substances come close to a searchcoil antenna, a detector signal may occur. This is an unwanted "false" signal. Fortunately, in well engineered detectors, the problem has been solved. Manufacturers can construct what is called a Faraday-shield that "shields" the windings from near by objects.

You are advised against purchasing a detector that does not have an electrostatic shield on each searchcoil. To test a detector, pull a handful of weeds and thoroughly wet them with water. Turn the detector on and adjust to threshold. Drag the weeds across the bottom of the searchcoil. If very noticeable changes occur in the threshold sound, the searchcoil does not have effective shielding. Slight audio changes are not objectionable when the grass is passed over the top of the searchcoil.

PULSE INDUCTION AND BFO SEARCHCOILS

Pulse Induction and BFO searchcoils (Figures 11-2 and 11-3)

125

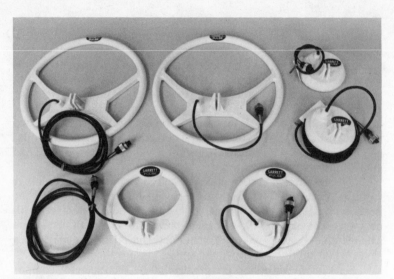

Figure 11-2: The most popular Pulse Induction searchcoils are shown in this photograph. The three-and-one-half-inch, the eight-inch and the twelve-inch diameter searchcoils are selected depending upon the needs of the operator. Photo by Melvin Climer.

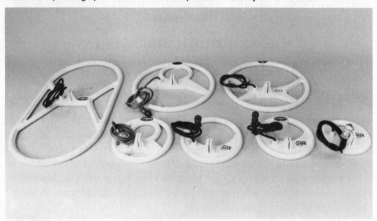

Figure 11-3: Almost as wide a range of searchcoils were available in earlier BFO days as are available today for VLF type metal detectors. The most popular BFO searchcoils have, for many years, been the independently-operated dual searchcoils, two of which can be seen in the photograph. Photo by Melvin Climer.

are the easiest to manufacture. They are generally perfect circles of some number of wire turns. The problem of expansion and contraction with temperature changes, however, is more critical in BFO searchcoil construction than in that of Pulse Induction. Pulse Induction and BFO searchcoils have uniform response to targets with no dead spots within the detection pattern. Life is somewhat easier for the producer of Pulse Induction and BFO equipment,

126

since only one type configuration is suitable for all types of searching. This is not necessarily so for VLF, VLF/TR and TR detectors.

VLF, VLF/TR AND TR SEARCHCOILS

Since VLF, VLF/TR and TR detectors operate almost identically, they use the same types of searchcoils (Figure 11-1). These contain both transmitter and receiver windings and configurations. The following searchcoil descriptions apply to these three types of detectors. Refer to the Glossary for definitions of VLF, VLF/TR and TR detector designations.

CO-PLANAR SEARCHCOILS

In co-planar searchcoils, the transmitter and receiver windings are lying in the same plane (Figure 11-4). The co-planar configurations have one or two transmitter windings and one receiver winding. The transmitter winding (antenna) transmits an electromagnetic field into the medium surrounding the searchcoil. The receiver searchcoil is so positioned that the smallest possible amount of electromagnetic field energy is induced in the winding. Whenever certain detectable targets enter the strong electromagnetic field detection area (Figure 7-3), searchcoil "balance" is upset causing an induced voltage to appear in the receiver winding. This signal is amplified and conditioned to power a speaker, meter and headphones, thus alerting the operator to the target's presence.

ILLUSTRATION OF CO-PLANAR SEARCHCOIL WINDINGS (SAME PLANE)

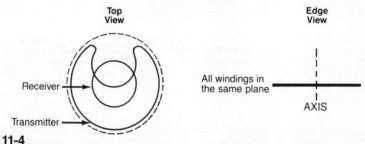

11-4

Figure 11-4: ILLUSTRATION OF CO-PLANAR SEARCHCOIL WINDINGS (SAME PLANE). This illustration of co-planar searchcoil construction shows that the windings are placed one on top of the other and lie in the same plane. Co-planar searchcoils have been in use for several decades.

Co-planar searchcoils are one of the preferred types because they produce very sharp, quick target response characteristics. These characteristics result in excellent coin and small object metal detection capabilities. Co-planar searchcoils have more or less uneven response patterns, which can result in dead spots.

Generally, however, since system power of VLF type detectors is so great, dead spots are of no consequence because they tend to disappear unless the detector is detuned far down in the null or quiet tuning zone. (See DETUNING, Chapter 10.)

Co-planar searchcoils have the problem, "back-reading". Back-reading occurs in the discrimination mode when "reject" targets come within one inch of the bottom of the searchcoil. Within this one inch, positive signals occur on targets that the detector is set to reject. To the untrained ear, these signals may appear the same as "good" target signals. To circumvent the problem, the searchcoil can be held at least one inch above the ground. One-inch-high elevated searchcoil skid plates can also be used. Whatever method is used, most operators find back reading to be of no consequence whatever.

CO-AXIAL SEARCHCOILS

Co-axial searchcoil construction can be extremely precise, resulting in a uniform and predictable response pattern. In Figure 11-5, it can be seen that all windings are the same diameter, and "stacked," or positioned, exact distances apart. The transmitter winding is positioned between the two receiver windings. This construction method is precise because the wire of the three windings is wound in "grooves" on a spool. The spool is then encapsulated within the searchcoil housing.

ILLUSTRATION OF CO-AXIAL SEARCHCOIL WINDINGS (SAME AXIS)

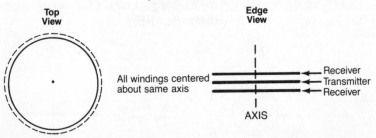

11-5

Figure 11-5: ILLUSTRATION OF CO-AXIAL SEARCHCOIL WINDINGS (SAME AXIS). Co-axial searchcoil windings are placed one above the other with one transmitter winding sandwiched in between two receiver windings. This type winding placement gives the most uniform detection pattern of all VLF and TR detector types and is affected the least by outside electromagnetic field interference.

Co-planar and concentric searchcoil windings are wound on mandrels. They are then removed, positioned by hand as accurately as possible, and bonded in position. If perfect nulls are not achieved by the mechanical positioning, then capacitors, inductors, and other electrical components are hooked on in order to achieve a better null.

Of all searchcoils built, co-axial searchcoils give the best performance in areas of high voltage powerlines and electromagnetic interference. Also, co-axial searchcoils (Figure 11-6) do not have the back-reading problem. They are, however, slower response searchcoils. That is, they produce a slower detector audio "turn on" time when targets are detected.

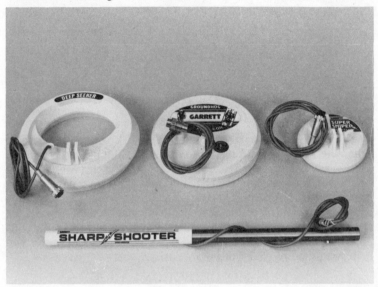

Figure 11-6: This photograph shows the majority of co-axial searchcoil sizes that are currently being manufactured. The most popular is the three-and-one-half-inch Super-Sniper searchcoil. The eight-inch diameter searchcoil is popular with beachcombers and prospectors. The small diameter probe is used for probing into cracks and crevices and other small areas. Photo by Melvin Climer.

CONCENTRIC SEARCHCOILS

Concentric searchcoils are constructed with the transmitter and receiver windings lying in the same plane, centered about the same axis (Figure 11-7). Concentric searchcoils have basically the same response as do co-planar. The number of turns in the receiver windings is more critical than in co-planar windings, but the physical placement is not as critical. A study of co-planar types will also give you a basic understanding of concentric types. Concentric searchcoils have dead spots near the outer rim that extend the full distance around the searchcoil. This, however, is a minor problem.

DETERMINING TARGET CENTER

Any given searchcoil may or may not produce maximum audio when small coin-sized targets are directly beneath the exact center of the searchcoil. To determine target center of detection, place a

ILLUSTRATION OF CONCENTRIC SEARCHCOIL WINDINGS
(SAME PLANE AND AXIS)

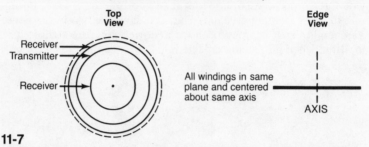

11-7

Figure 11-7: ILLUSTRATION OF CONCENTRIC SEARCHCOIL WINDINGS (SAME PLANE AND AXIS). Concentric searchcoil windings lie in the same plane and are centered about the same axis. This newer type searchcoil is operationally equivalent to co-planar searchcoils.

small coin directly on the bottom of your searchcoil, near the center. Retune the instrument to threshold. Slide the coin around. The target center is the place where you hear maximum audio sound. On co-axial and concentric types, the target center is the center of the searchcoil. On co-planar types, the target center may be slightly forward of the searchcoil housing center, toward the "toe" of the searchcoil. Place an "X" with a felt tip pen at this point on the searchcoil bottom and top. Knowing target center will help you pinpoint your finds more easily.

DYNAMIC DETECTION RANGE

The dynamic detection range of a searchcoil means how wide a range of target sizes a given searchcoil can detect to a practical depth. Some examples will show more clearly the meaning of dynamic detection range. A twelve-inch VLF searchcoil can detect objects from BB shot size up to very large targets, and detect this wide range of sizes to practical depths. This searchcoil, then, has a wide dynamic detection range.

A twelve-inch BFO searchcoil can detect a very large target to a practical depth, but the smallest target it can detect to this depth, is a large coin. Thus, the BFO searchcoil has less dynamic detection range than does a comparable size VLF searchcoil.

BFO searchcoils have the smallest dynamic detection range of all metal detectors. VLF searchcoils have the widest dynamic detection range. In between are TR and Pulse Induction searchcoils. For all practical purposes, the dynamic detection ranges of TR; Pulse Induction, and VLF, are quite acceptable. In the following metal detector chapters, you will find charts which describe the applications of different sizes of searchcoils. A few minutes study of these charts will clearly reveal the relative dynamic detection ranges of the various types and sizes of searchcoils.

130

You may believe that if searchcoil size is doubled, detection depth is doubled. This is not the case. If a seven-inch searchcoil detects a coin to, say, ten inches, a fifteen-inch searchcoil will not detect the same coin to twenty inches. Figure 11-8 shows SEARCHCOIL DETECTION DEPTH VERSUS SEARCHCOIL SIZE.

11-8   SEARCHCOIL SIZES vs DETECTION DEPTH OF VARIOUS TARGETS

Searchcoil size	Round non ferrous flat metal targets			Large 12" dia.
	25¢ Coin	4" dia.	14" dia.	iron bucket and lid
3½"	7"	14"	23"	25"
7½"	9"	22"	36"	38"
10"	11"	27"	48"	50"
12"	12"	29"	50"	56"
14"	14"	31"	55"	59"

Figure 11-8: SEARCHCOILS SIZE VERSUS DETECTION DEPTH OF VARIOUS TARGETS. A study of this table will reveal much to you about searchcoil characteristics. For instance, an eight-inch-diameter searchcoil cannot detect objects twice as deeply as a four-inch diameter searchcoil.

SEARCHCOIL TYPE AND SIZE DESCRIPTIONS

As stated earlier, searchcoils are manufactured in various sizes and types from the three-quarter-inch probe to the "two box" Depth Multiplier. Beginning with the smallest and proceeding to the largest, we will discuss the features and applications for which the various searchcoils are intended.

THREE-QUARTER-INCH PROBE

This is the smallest searchcoil manufactured for hobbyist equipment. This size is usually called a probe because that is its main function. This small diameter construction (Figure 11-9) creates an extremely intense electromagnetic field, permitting the detection of very small particles of gold, silver and other metals. Most probes have a detection area (Figure 11-10) that permits slight detection along the sides but mostly out from the end a few inches.

Probes are used primarily to search for small objects, especially when the area to be searched is small, and physical contact or close proximity searching is desired. Prospectors use probes to scan beneath boulders and in bedrock cracks, in their search for nuggets and placer deposits. Ghost-towners probe into walls, behind partitions and chimneys, and in other tight quarters, to locate relics and caches. Probes are used in medical applications to locate pins and small objects in the body.

THREE-INCH TO FOUR-INCH SEARCHCOILS

The three-and-one-half-inch searchcoil (Figure 11-11) is trade-

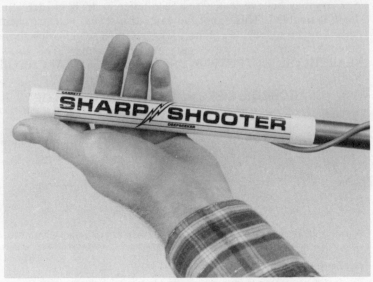

Figure 11-9: This small three-quarter-inch diameter probe, while not in everyone's arsenal of searchcoils, is nevertheless important to electronic prospectors and others who search for tiny objects, and other objects buried, hidden, or concealed in small places. Photo by Melvin Climer.

11-10 THREE-QUARTER-INCH SEARCH PROBE DETECTION PATTERN

Detection Pattern

¾" Probe

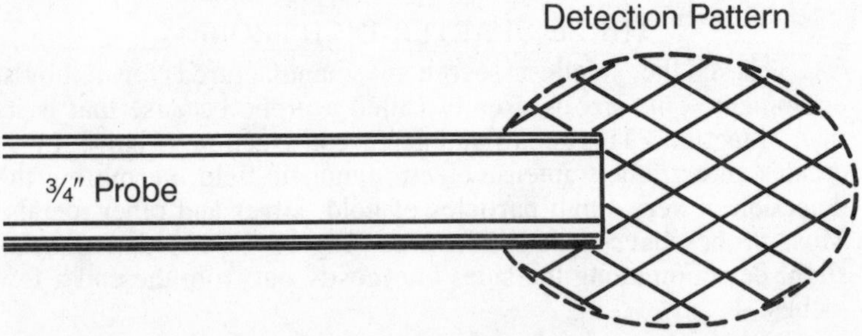

Figure 11-10: THREE-QUARTER-INCH SEARCH PROBE DETECTION PATTERN. This illustration shows that the detection distance out from the end of small diameter search probes is very short. Because the electromagnetic field intensity is so great, gold nuggets as small as pin head size can be detected. Note, the lateral detection along the sides of the probe.

named the Super-Sniper. Searchcoils this size have a very intense electromagnetic field which gives good detection to small objects. The narrow detection pattern permits excellent isolation and pinpointing of detected targets. This is where Super-Sniping gets its name. (See SUPER-SNIPING, Chapter 10.)

Three-inch to four-inch searchcoils scan a more narrow width

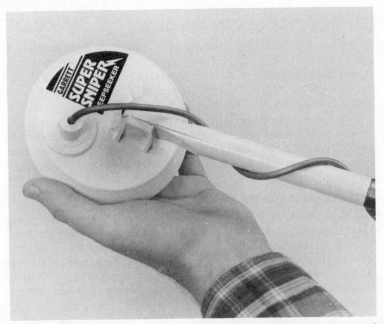

Figure 11-11: The Super-Sniper type searchcoil is very popular among coin hunters and electronic prospectors. The small diameter searchcoil has excellent sensitivity, pinpointing characteristics, and detection depth. Photo by Melvin Climer.

than do larger searchcoils and they do not scan as deeply. Since most searchcoils this size use co-axial windings, the search pattern is uniform.

The narrow search width allows close proximity scanning adjacent to metal buildings, fences, and sidewalks with rebar (reinforcing rods). This size searchcoil is used to locate, trace, and count, rebar in concrete roads, driveways, walls and structures of all kinds.

As an accessory, small searchcoils rate very high. Not all detectors are capable of using small searchcoils, nor do all manufacturers provide them for their customers. If they are available for your detector, the purchase and use of one is suggested, especially if you hunt in "worked out" high junk areas.

SEVEN-INCH TO EIGHT-INCH SEARCHCOILS

Most detector types and brands are sold with seven-inch to eight-inch diameter searchcoils as standard equipment. This is the best general purpose size for most forms of detector usage. The searchcoils are lightweight, have good scanning width, and are sensitive to a wide range of target sizes. Objects as small as a BB shot can be detected. Good ground coverage can be obtained with shallow scanning width equal in most cases to the width of the

133

diameter of the searchcoil. Of course, scanning width becomes narrow toward the bottom of the detection pattern.

Since the detection patterns of all sizes of searchcoils are cone-shaped, overlapping of each detector sweep is necessary to lessen the possibility of missing targets. Pinpointing is good, but made even better by electronic pinpointing and "detuning" to target center. (See Chapter 10.)

Seven-inch to eight-inch searchcoils can be constructed using co-planar, co-axial and concentric configurations. As explained earlier, co-planar and concentric searchcoils have quicker response detection times, but co-axial searchcoils have a more uniform detection pattern.

TEN-INCH TO TWELVE-INCH SEARCHCOILS

Searchcoils of this size, while still able to detect small coin-sized objects to great depths, are classified as the smallest searchcoil sizes to be used for cache and relic hunting. Pinpointing is slightly more difficult, and the extra weight requires the use of an armrest or hipmounted control housing, especially if the detector is to be used for long periods of time. Accurate pinpointing can be achieved, however, by using the "detuning" method. (See, also, ELEC-TRONIC PINPOINTING, Chapter 10.)

When coin or nugget hunting, how do you know when to use a ten-inch or twelve-inch size? Just use a little reasoning. Suppose, when using a seven-inch or eight-inch searchcoil, you are finding targets in the fringe area of detection. Weak audio signals indicate that you are reaching the outer detection limits of the searchcoil you are using. By using the next larger size, you will be able to detect deeper. Of course, there are limitations on object size. You may not find a BB shot size nugget with a fourteen-inch searchcoil. You will stand a better chance of finding nuggets that size with a three-and-one-half-inch, seven-inch, or eight-inch searchcoil. Practically speaking, a ten-inch searchcoil is the largest practical size to use when coin hunting.

If you are relic hunting where targets are deeply buried, or if you are searching for a money cache, use the larger searchcoils. As my good friend, Roy Lagal, advises, "If you go hunting for elephants, take an elephant gun!"

One disadvantage of using large searchcoils when searching for money caches in junk areas (around farmhouses, etc.), is these searchcoils will detect small bits of ferrous metal at extreme depths. Since you should never search for caches using trash elimination (discrimination), you may spend considerable time digging lots of trash. A solution to this problem is given in the section, DEPTH MULTIPLIER ATTACHMENTS, later in this chapter.

134

FOURTEEN-INCH AND LARGER SEARCHCOILS

It's unfortunate that in the metal detecting business, competitors often promote the idea that "Bigger is better!" This is certainly not true. Close examination will reveal flaws in that thinking.

Fourteen-inch and larger searchcoils are offered by several manufacturers. These large searchcoils may (if correctly designed) detect large objects to greater depths than will smaller searchcoils but the depth difference may be so small that often the extra trouble of lugging a larger one around is just not worth it. The depth detection difference between twelve-inch and fourteen-inch searchcoils, and between fourteen-inch and sixteen-inch searchcoils, is very small, indeed. And, when you learn first-hand that tennis elbow, strained muscles and ligaments, and sore backs can result from swinging the large searchcoils around, you'll begin to more critically select the size searchcoil you need.

The larger the searchcoil, the wider the scan area that should be achieved. Before purchasing the largest searchcoil you can find, however, try to get a first-hand demonstration. If you are searching for, say, an iron pot, check various size searchcoils in an air test using an iron pot. If you are looking for a gold bar, check the searchcoils using a gold bar (a silver, or copper bar will do). Unless you can see, first hand, an obviously greater detection distance with the largest searchcoil, purchase a smaller size.

Coin and small object hunting should not be attempted with searchcoils larger than about twelve inches in diameter. Possibly one exception to this is in the field of battlefield relic hunting. EXTREME DEPTHS on Civil War Minie balls is achieved regularly with searchcoils in the twelve-inch to fourteen-inch size category. Two-foot and greater depths are commonly reached for these small targets.

DEPTH MULTIPLIER ATTACHMENT

Last in searchcoil examination, but certainly not least, is the Depth Multiplier attachment. The Depth Multiplier attachment does just as the name implies; it multiplies the depth that VLF detectors can detect large objects. The larger the object, the greater will be the depth multiplication. Depth multiplication factors, on the order of two or three or more, can be obtained. For instance, if a large safe can be detected to a depth of seven feet with a twelve-inch to fourteen-inch searchcoil, the Depth Multiplier can locate it maybe to twice that depth.

A battlefield searcher, using a Depth Multiplier, found a three and one-half inch diameter, seven inch long iron projectile at a depth of four feet. A treasure hunter found a pint jar of pre-1930 pennies to a measured depth of twenty-seven and one-half inches. While a twelve-inch or fourteen-inch searchcoil would have found this jar, no junk items like nails were found with the Depth Multiplier. Also, this find shows that Depth Multiplier attachments can find small targets, even though, to be on the safe side, they are not recommended if the sought-for target is less than quart size.

A large, round, corrugated culvert was easily detected to a depth of twelve feet to the top of the culvert. A law enforcement agency located several automobile engines to a depth of better than ten feet. The engines were removed from stolen automobiles and buried because they were too "hot" to sell.

The Depth Multiplier, as shown in Figure 11-12, is easy to use. It is attached to the control housing in a matter of about two

Figure 11-12: The Depth Multiplier as shown in this photograph lives up to its name, a true multiplier of metal detection depth. It will detect money caches, ore veins, trash dumps and large metal objects to depths of several feet. Maximum depth capability of the Depth Multiplier is thought to be about twenty feet. Several unique features of the Depth Multiplier are: (1) ground minerals are ignored; (2) consequently, no ground elimination adjustments are necessary; (3) very small targets are ignored; (4) large areas of ground can be covered very quickly. The Depth Multiplier is highly recommended.

minutes. No tuning or Ground Elimination adjustments are required. Simply turn the detector on and select the VLF Ground Elimination mode. Do not use the Automatic Tuning mode. Press the retune switch to achieve threshold sound and begin searching. Walk straight ahead with the "nose" of the Depth Multiplier held as close to the ground as possible.

Figure 11-13 shows operating stance and the electromagnetic field and detection patterns. When a signal is first heard, make a mark on the ground. Walk on across the target. Turn around and walk back. When a signal is heard, make a mark on the ground. The target will lie directly below the centerpoint between the two marks.

The Depth Multiplier is recommended when searching for money caches, large relics, safes, cannon, ore veins and mineral structures. The Depth Multiplier takes no more battery power than smaller searchcoils, but the depth multiplication capability is one that no detector owner should be without.

Figure 11-14 illustrates recommended searchcoil sizes for optimum results. Note the overlapping capabilities of all the searchcoils. The wide dynamic range of several searchcoils is obvious. Figure 11-15 is a searchcoil selection table. Recommendations are the same as in Figure 11-14, but specific applications are more clearly defined.

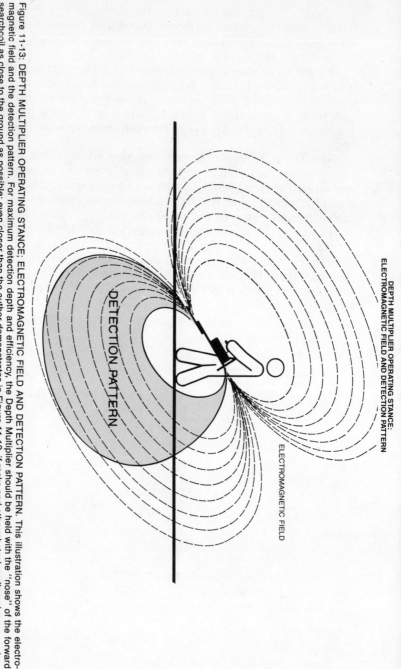

DEPTH MULTIPLIER OPERATING STANCE:
ELECTROMAGNETIC FIELD AND DETECTION PATTERN

DETECTION PATTERN

ELECTROMAGNETIC FIELD

Figure 11-13: DEPTH MULTIPLIER OPERATING STANCE, ELECTROMAGNETIC FIELD AND DETECTION PATTERN. This illustration shows the electromagnetic field and the detection pattern. For maximum detection depth and efficiency, the Depth Multiplier should be held with the "nose" of the forward searchcoil as close to the ground as possible; even closer than the author demonstrates in Figure 11-12, if rocks and other obstacles allow close scanning. Precise pinpointing, as explained in the text is easy.

138

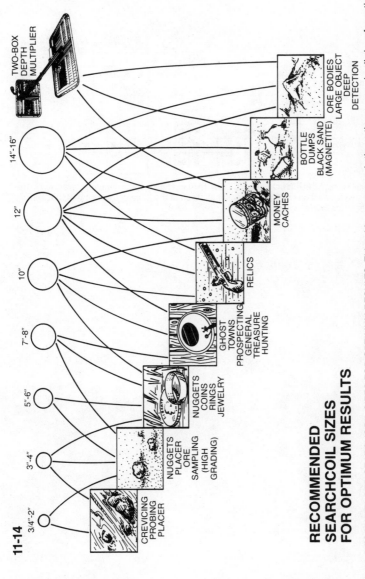

11-14

TWO-BOX DEPTH MULTIPLIER

3/4"-2" 3"-4" 5"-6" 7"-8" 10" 12" 14"-16"

CREVICING PROBING PLACER

NUGGETS PLACER ORE SAMPLING (HIGH GRADING)

NUGGETS COINS RINGS JEWELRY

GHOST TOWNS PROSPECTING GENERAL TREASURE HUNTING

RELICS

MONEY CACHES

BOTTLE DUMPS BLACK SAND (MAGNETITE)

ORE BODIES LARGE OBJECT DEEP DETECTION

**RECOMMENDED
SEARCHCOIL SIZES
FOR OPTIMUM RESULTS**

Figure 11-14: RECOMMENDED SEARCHCOIL SIZES FOR OPTIMUM RESULTS. This table recommends the optimum searchcoil sizes for optimum results. Note the overlapping capabilities of all the searchcoils. The wide dynamic range of several of the searchcoils is obvious.

139

SEARCHCOIL SELECTION CHART

COIL SIZES	BEGINNER	GENERAL COIN HUNTING	SUPER SNIPING	EXTRA DEPTH (COINS)	BEACH HUNTING	RELIC HUNTING	BUILDING SEARCHING	GHOST TOWNING	BOTTLE DUMPS	CACHE (MONEY) HUNTING	MAXIMUM DEPTH HUNTING (OUTHOUSES)	PLACER SNIPING	ORE SAMPLING (CREVICING) LARGE OBJECTS	NUGGET HUNTING	BLACK SAND	MINE DUMPS (DREDGE PILES)	ORE BODIES (VEINS)
3/4″-2″										*		*					
3″-4″	*		*								*	*					
5″-6″	*	*			*		*					*					
7″-8″	*	*			*		*	*				*	*	*			
10″				*	*	*	*	*		*				*			
12″				*	*	*			*	*			*	*	*	*	
14″ (and larger)					*				*	*				*		*	
BLOODHOUND DEPTH MULTIPLIER					*				*	*	*						*

Figure 11-15: SEARCHCOIL SELECTION TABLE. Note the recommendations given in this searchcoil selection table are the same as given in the table in Figure 11-14, but specific applications are more clearly defined.

CHAPTER 11 QUESTIONS

1. The most commonly used coin hunting searchcoil sizes range from seven inches to _____ inches in diameter.

2. Using smaller searchcoils will: (A) find deeper targets; (B) give better battery life; (C) give a sharper, more pronounced signal on individual targets; (D) increase mineralization effects.

3. Using larger searchcoils will: (A) give improved target elimination; (B) make tuning easier; (C) give better performance in grass; (D) give greater detection depth especially on larger targets.

4. Correctly designed searchcoils have _____ shielding.

5. The main problem when searchcoils are not correctly shielded is that they will detect _____

6. Which two of the following searchcoil types are the most popular: co-planar, concentric, co-axial or ferrite core? (Each correct answer is worth 3 1/2 points)

7. Co-axial searchcoils will (select two): (A) give more detection depth; (B) eliminate ground minerals; (C) reduce all "back-reading" effects; (D) eliminate electromagnetic field interference. (Each correct answer is worth 3 1/2 points)

8. Describe dynamic detection range.

9. The most popular application of three-inch to four-inch diameter searchcoils is _____ _____ .

10. The largest practical size searchcoil to use when coin hunting is the _____-inch size.

11. When coin or nugget hunting how do you know when to use a larger searchcoil?

12. When using very large searchcoils you should very definitely use a _____ kit or an _____ . (Each correct answer is worth 3 1/2 points)

13. A Depth Multiplier (two-box) type searchcoil attachment will: (A) provide you with two boxes for storing your finds and your lunch; (B) eliminate detection of deep objects so you won't have to dig so deeply; (C) a device that measures the depth of money caches; (D) a searchcoil attachment that multiplies the detection depth of large objects.

14. Searchcoils are like automobile wheels, they are the interface between the metal detector (the automobile) and the _____.

The correct answers to Questions 8 and 11 are worth 8 points each.

All other questions are worth 7 points each if all answers are given correctly.

Perfect score is 100. Answers given in Appendix 2.

BFO Metal Detector Short Course

While it is generally true that BFO circuitry and searchcoil construction are technically simple compared to other types of detectors, it is not true that top quality, all-purpose BFO detectors are any cheaper to construct. Quality equipment of any kind costs more to build than does cheaply built equipment, even of a more complex type. Much care and skill goes into the production of stable, sensitive BFO equipment.

The block diagram in Figure 12-1 shows the various BFO circuits and how these circuits are interconnected with the power supply, searchcoils and other components.

A BFO consists of two electronic radio frequency oscillators that are designed to oscillate at the same frequency. The REFERENCE oscillator is generally controlled by an electronic crystal and other stable components and, consequently, cannot (or should not) change its frequency. The SEARCH oscillator is constructed using two variable type components and, consequently, its frequency can change if one or both components change their "value." Thus, the search oscillator's frequency is controlled by two variable components: the tuning control and the searchcoil. The tuning control is generally a variable capacitor. This variable capacitor is indicated by the letter C and the searchcoil is indicated by the letter L in the following equation:

$$fs = \frac{1}{6.28\sqrt{LC}}$$

where
fs = frequency of search oscillator

L = inductance of searchcoil

C = tuning capacitance (tuning control in search oscillator circuit).

A change in L or C produces a change in fs. Whenever the tuning control (C) is turned, its value changes, which results in a corresponding change in search oscillator frequency (fs). Thus, whenever an amount of capacitance is reached that causes the search oscillator frequency to be identical to the reference oscillator frequency (fr), no sound is heard from the BFO speaker. That is, the NULL point has been reached. The NULL is the TRUE CENTER POINT, the true METAL/MINERAL point between the detection of conductive metal and non-conductive ferrous (iron) mineral.

142

12-1 BLOCK DIAGRAM OF BFO METAL DETECTOR

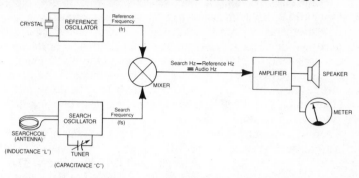

Figure 12-1: ELECTRONIC BLOCK DIAGRAM OF BFO METAL DETECTOR. This block diagram of a crystal controlled BFO metal detector illustrates circuit connections and electronic oscillator mixing to produce an audio Beat Frequency tone.

To further illustrate, refer again to Figure 12-1. A mixer circuit is connected between the reference and search oscillators. Whenever the oscillating output voltages of these two oscillators is fed into the mixer, one usable output frequency of the mixer is equal to the difference between these two frequencies. For example, if the reference oscillator is operating at 100,000 Hertz per second and the search oscillator is oscillating at 100,060 Hertz per second the mixer output will be 60 Hertz per second. The 60 Hertz signal is fed into amplifiers and a speaker (or headphones) so that it can be heard by the BFO operator. This 60 Hertz audio tone is the threshold sound.

Let's say that a coin (conductive metal) is buried in the ground and you are detecting it. The coin causes the inductance (L) of the searchcoil to decrease. From the equation, you can see that the frequency of the search oscillator, fs, increases. As a result, the speaker output will change from the 60 Hertz tone to a higher frequency.

Let's take another example. Assume you are scanning the detector along and you encounter a nail that has turned completely to rust (non-conductive iron minerals-equivalent to black magnetic sand— magnetite). The iron rust causes the inductance, L, of the searchcoil to increase, and from the equation, you can see that the frequency of the search oscillator now decreases. Thus, the 60 Hertz tone now decreases to some level less than 60 Hertz.

From the above discussions, you can see that BFO circuitry is basically simple and straightforward. Nevertheless, BFO operating characteristics can provide the operator with a wealth of information that can be put to good use. All of this information is basic to the understanding and operation of the BFO in metal detection, prospecting, metal/mineral ore sample identification (high grading), black magnetic sand (magnetite) hunting and iron identification.

During the '70s, one by one, detector manufacturers stopped producing BFOs. BFO production has almost ceased, primarily because better instruments for most metal detector applications have been designed and developed. Need for the BFO continues, however, in certain applications, especially in prospecting for black magnetic sand. There are many BFO detectors still in operation. Most professional treasure hunters and electronic prospectors probably own at least one, and it's not likely you would ever be able to buy one unless you offered a great amount of money.

There is something about a BFO that makes you fall in love with the instrument. The audio is especially pleasing. You respect it for its all-purpose capability, extreme reliability, and field ruggedness. That's not to say that other types of detectors are not rugged or field-worthy. It's just that back during the days when so many new and different types of detectors were coming on the market there were abnormally high failure rates. When the new what-you-may-call-it detector failed, the BFO was used while the new what-you-may-call-it detector was being repaired.

A BFO can perform most treasure hunting tasks. In fact, there is very little a BFO can't do, especially once the operator has mastered its capabilities. A BFO can search for coins, money caches and relics. It can search ghost towns and structures of all types. The BFO is right at home while performing every prospecting task. (See Figure 12-2.)

The limits of the BFO are that it does not have the depth capability nor the ground canceling ability of VLF types. It does not have the ability to neutralize salt water effects. While these detectors may not probe as deeply as other types, nor cancel iron minerals, there are BFO experts who have mastered these instruments and can literally make these detectors "talk" to them in such a way that they can probably outperform the average detector operator who is using even the very latest of the new types of detectors.

Let's say, for instance, a BFO can detect, through air, a given coin to eight inches. A BFO trained expert could find that same coin to ten inches, maybe twelve inches in the ground. Skilled operators have learned to detect even whispers of sound that detectors produce in the fringe area of detection. (See Chapter 7, Figure 7-9.) These whispers are oftentimes called "skips" or "hesitations" in the BFO audio tone. But the purpose of this chapter is not to make BFO experts of you, so let's get on with the basics.

The accompanying chart (Figure 12-3) will help you decide which BFO searchcoil you should use for the type of hunting you are planning. For all types of hunting, with the exception of searching for black magnetic sand concentrations, use the metal mode. Turn the detector on, hold the searchcoil at the desired height above the ground, (two-inches to four-inches or higher to clear rocks, etc.) and

Figure 12-2: In times past, before the advent of VLF detectors, the BFO was the only all-purpose metal detector manufactured. It was called the "work horse" of the industry. It could perform almost every metal detecting task with great efficiency. The superior performance of modern-day VLF's, however, has caused the BFO to lose popularity.

tune the instrument to a 40 to 60 Hertz (cycles or beats per second) "motorboating" sound. If the ground is heavily mineralized, searchcoil operating height should probably be, maybe as high as four inches or higher. The larger the searchcoil diameter, the higher it can be held. Scan the searchcoil side-to-side in front of you in a straight line as described in Chapter 23. Scan at a rate of about two feet per second or slower, use headphones, and be very attentive. The obvious increases in BFO beat notes, of course, signal the presence of metal. If you want to be more proficient, and reach the deepest possible depth, train yourself to listen for "skips" or "hesitations" in the sound that occur when the searchcoil passes over an extremely small or deeply buried target. Concentrate on the threshold frequency and listen for any slight variation of the signal. If you are not sure on the first pass, stop, go back, and make several more passes over the same spot. If you continue to hear this faint hesitation or skip in the sound, dig. Dig for sure if you see the meter pointer deflect, however slightly, even if you don't hear an audio indication.

In highly iron mineralized ground, or when operating over salt water, three techniques will help you get better performance from your BFO. Hold the searchcoil slightly higher above the ground than you normally would. Tune the detector to a slightly higher beat note and scan the searchcoil a little faster than normal. These techniques

	Probing	Super Sniping	Coin Hunting	Cache Hunting	Relic Hunting	Ghost Towning	Nugget Hunting	Vein Locating	Ore Sampling	Black Sand Locating	General Purpose Hunting
¾" to 2"	10						8				
3" to 4"	8	10	8				10		10		
5" to 6"		7	10		8		10		10		9
7" to 8"			7		10	10	8				10
10" to 12"				8	8		10		8		
13" x 24"				10			10		9		
24" x 24"				10			10		10		

BFO SEARCHCOILS VS APPLICATIONS

The scale of numbers, "0" to "10", represent the relative capabilities of the various BFO searchcoil sizes with "10" being the maximum capability. Do not compare capabilities, using these numbers, with other similar tables in this book. A BFO rating of "10" may be more or less capable than a "10" rating of another type metal detector.

Figure 12-3: BFO SEARCHCOILS VERSUS APPLICATIONS. This table will help you decide which BFO searchcoil you should use for the type of hunting you are planning. For all types of hunting, with the exception of searching for black sand concentrations, tune the BFO to the metal mode.

have the effect of smoothing out the erratic signals received from ground minerals, while allowing the individual target signals to come through.

If your BFO is equipped with discrimination, by all means use it when coin hunting, or perhaps when searching an old house and do not wish to detect nails, iron construction staples, etc. Be careful not to adjust discrimination to a higher level than necessary, and keep in mind, as with all discriminators, you are probably going to lose an occasional good target because it will be masked by the negative signals caused by junk targets.

If you want to go prospecting with your BFO, go ahead. It just might be that you will find more gold, silver, platinum or copper than the guy right next to you with a VLF who has not mastered his detector. Since most prospecting sites contain considerable amounts of iron minerals, you may need to use the above mentioned techniques. Use no discrimination when looking for nuggets and ore veins, and be prepared to dig lots of iron junk metal if it is present in the ground. Your chances of missing valuable nuggets are good if you use discrimination.

146

To high grade a mine dump, use a three-inch to six-inch diameter searchcoil (see SEARCHCOIL SELECTION CHART, Figure 12-3). Hold the searchcoil from two to four inches above the ore. Tune the detector to approximately 60 Hertz in the metal mode. Scan slowly. Investigate the area under the searchcoil when the audio frequency increases. Check all ore in the detected area. Bring individual ore specimens directly in toward the bottom center of the searchcoil and take home all that cause the audio tone to increase. Remember, the BFO has an inherent metal/mineral null point and it won't lie to you. It will always, with one hundred percent accuracy, give you a reading indicating whether the predominant element is conductive or ferrous non-conductive.

It's a good idea to check each specimen several times as you rotate the piece. An iron ore sample with a thin gold vein running through it may give you both positive and negative readings, depending upon the orientation as you bring it up toward the searchcoil. (See Chapter 22, SCANNING MINE DUMPS AND DREDGE PILES for a discussion on how to use the Gravity Trap gold pan in conjunction with your metal detector.)

To locate black magnetic sand, use the largest searchcoil possible, as indicated by the chart. Hold the searchcoil at a height of about four inches above the ground, and tune to a 40 to 60 Hertz audio in the mineral side of null. Hold the searchcoil in front of you; do not scan it from side-to-side. Walk in a straight line, pointing the searchcoil straight ahead. When you get to the end of the search path, move over a foot or two and walk a parallel return path. Continue this procedure until you cover the desired area. When you begin to cross over a black sand concentration, the audio frequency beat note will increase. Do not readjust the tuning. Continue walking; when you clear the black sand concentration, the tone will return to its normal or preadjusted frequency level.

When detecting black sand concentrations in the mineral mode, the BFO will increase in audio beat note. Because conductive metal will cause the beat note to decrease, you must be very observant. Let's say you are scanning along, tuned to the mineral side of null searching for black sand concentrations. Suddenly, the detector threshold increases slightly (or even very sharply), then after a few steps the signal returns to preset threshold. "Oh, boy!" you say; you have found a black sand concentration! You begin digging and you find a deeply buried fender that once was attached to a Model A Ford. What happened? The answer is very simple. The strong metal target overrode the mineral setting (see Figure 12-4,) and was sufficiently strong to drive the BFO circuits down out of the mineral zone, through the null zone, into the metal zone, thus giving you a positive sound. However, had you been carefully listening to the sound, you would have noticed that the sound first decreased, went quiet, and then

BFO OPERATION: METAL TARGET OVERRIDING MINERAL THRESHOLD TUNING

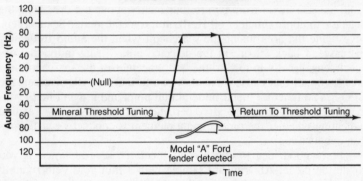

12-4   Mineral Tuning and Metal Target Detection

Figure 12-4: BFO OPERATION: METAL TARGET OVERRIDING MINERAL THRESHOLD TUNING. It is important that you understand how metal and mineral targets cause the BFO to react. This illustration shows how a metal target can override the mineral threshold tuning. When you are scanning with the tuning set to the mineral threshold, you must pay particular attention to the audio. Otherwise, a metal target can cause the detector to produce a signal that you would mistake as being a mineral target, as illustrated.

increased. That increase, you thought, was caused by black sand. So, when searching in the mineral mode, pay particular attention to the audio sound fluctuations. Scan slowly over the suspect area several times to determine the full characteristics of the sound response.

Failure to pay attention is one reason why many "false" holes have been dug. As an example, an operator scans with the detector tuned to the metal side of null. Suddenly, the detector sounds off with a sharp positive increase in beat notes. "Oh, boy, there's my treasure!" So, he digs, and digs, and digs, and continues to dig, but finds no metal. Had he been paying strict attention, he would have noticed that there was, perhaps, a quantity of red or black sand that he removed from the hole. He could have rubbed a magnet into the dirt to attract black iron mineral particles. He would have then known he had detected a mineral pocket. Here's what happened:

The concentration of non-conductive iron minerals was sufficiently strong to drive the BFO circuits down out of the metal setting, through the null and into the mineral zone, thus producing a positive sound (Figure 12-5). This is the reverse of what happened when he found the Model A Ford fender (Figure 12-4) when he thought he had found a black magnetic sand concentration.

Alas, the days of the BFO are essentially over. It has gone the way of the manual typewriter, the pinball machine, and the push-type lawnmower. If you own a BFO, occasionally turn it on, check it out, replace weak batteries, and spend a little time working with it and learning a little bit more about its capabilities. Take it along on a

BFO OPERATION: MINERALS OVERRIDING METAL THRESHOLD TUNING

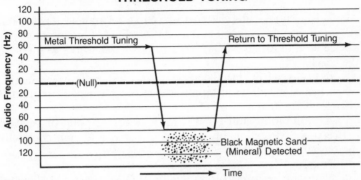

12-5   **Metal Tuning and Mineral Detection**

Figure 12-5: BFO OPERATION: MINERALS OVERRIDING METAL THRESHOLD TUNING. This illustration shows how minerals can override a metal audio threshold setting. In most operating situations, the BFO is adjusted to audio threshold on the metal side of null. As illustrated, large shallow buried mineral deposits can cause the detector to produce a positive audio sound that you would mistake as being metal. If you will study this curve, and the curve in Figure 12-4, you will be prepared in the event overriding minerals and metals are detected.

Figure 12-6: Charles Garrett received this photograph through the mail. There was no sender's name or return address included. The author knows as much about this story as you. Draw your own conclusions.

treasure hunting or prospecting excursion. Someday that detector may pay for itself many times over, if it hasn't already!

149

CHAPTER 12 QUESTIONS

1. A BFO type metal detector is: (A) an instrument for dowsing; (B) an all-purpose detector best used in the field of prospecting; (C) a device used to locate UFOs; (D) a detector that works well only on the beach.

2. Basically, a BFO metal detector changes its audio _____ when metal and mineral targets cause the reference oscillator to change its frequency.

3. A BFO tuning null-point is the true center-point of detection between the detection of conductive metal and non-conductive ferrous (iron) mineral.
    True _____   False _____

4. Name two reasons (uses) why a BFO is a very popular prospecting instrument. (Each correct answer is worth 4 points)

5. Name two limitations of the BFO. (Each correct answer is worth 4 points)

6. To improve your performance when using your BFO, you must learn to detect the "skip" and "hesitation" sounds produced when targets are in the _____ area of detection.

7. When operating over highly mineralized ground, or over salt water, there are _____ (quantity) techniques that will help you get better performance.

8. When checking ore samples, why is it a good idea to check each specimen several times as you rotate the specimen?

9. When ore sampling, the metal detector audio readings indicate the _____ element in the sample.

10. Magnetic black sand concentrations can be located to what approximate maximum depth?

11. When checking ore samples with a BFO, tune to the mineral mode.
    True _____   False _____

12. When searching for black sand concentrations with a BFO, you tune to the mineral mode.
    True _____   False _____

The correct answers to Questions 11 and 12 are worth 10 points each. All other questions are worth 8 points each if all answers are given correctly. Perfect score is 100. Answers given in Appendix 2.

TR Metal Detector Short Course

The history of Transmitter Receiver (TR) metal detectors follows a parallel path with BFO detectors. Both types were developed during the same time period; together, they rose to the pinnacle of popularity and then fell from prominence as VLF's became popular. TRs continue to be manufactured as low-cost coin hunting detectors. Improvements in TR design and construction make today's models better than TRs of the popular years.

The electronic circuit design and construction of TRs is based upon electronic parameters different from BFOs. From your study of BFOs in Chapter 12, you learned that the presence of conductive metal and non-conductive iron mineral within the detection pattern caused the antenna inductance to change. A search oscillator frequency change resulted.

TR detector reaction, due to the presence of metal or mineral within the detection pattern is caused by two phenomena: eddy current generation on the surface of conductive targets, and inductive imbalance between the transmitter and receiver antennas. For a better understanding of these phenomena, let's study TR circuitry and searchcoil antenna construction.

The name transmitter-receiver is not fully descriptive because a phenomenon called Induction (searchcoil) Balance (IB) "magnifies" the effects of target detection by the Transmission/Reception (TR) method, thus improving sensitivity and detection depth. Depending upon how long you have been using metal detectors, you may recall either using or hearing about TR or IB detectors; however, the terms stand for the same type metal detector.

Even though TR and IB detectors are one in the same, in the course of time, the designation TR simply "won out" or became more popular than IB. "TR" stuck, and continues to be used today; the term "IB" is history.

The simplified block diagram illustrated in Figure 13-1 shows a transmitter oscillator connected to a transmitter antenna. The oscillator feeds a radio frequency signal current into the antenna. The current, circulating in the winding, generates an electromagnetic field that flows out away from the antenna in all directions. It resembles the electromagnetic field as illustrated in Chapter 3 (Figure 3-2). An amplifier boosts any detection signal that is sensed by the receiver antenna. The amplified signal is fed into a speaker, or

13-1 BLOCK DIAGRAM OF TRANSMITTER-RECEIVER METAL DETECTOR

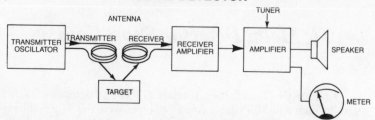

Figure 13-1: ELECTRONIC BLOCK DIAGRAM OF TR METAL DETECTOR. This simplified block diagram of a Transmitter-Receiver (TR) metal detector illustrates the major circuits and interconnections. The transmitter oscillator feeds a radio frequency signal current into the transmitter antenna. This current, circulating in the winding, generates an electromagnetic field that flows away from the antenna in all directions. Within the area called the detection pattern, metal and mineral objects will disrupt the electromagnetic field causing the detector to produce an audio indication.

earphones, and suitable indicators, which alert the operator to the presence of the target.

To understand how TR models detect the presence of targets, bring a metal object within the detection pattern beneath the searchcoil as shown in Figure 13-2.

The eddy current generation phenomenon takes place on the surface of the metal. The eddy currents require a power source, and that source is the electromagnetic field. The metal detector senses power being taken from the field, and alerts the operator by producing audio and visual indications.

The second detection phenomenon takes place according to Induction Balance (or Imbalance) principles.

To understand how metal targets cause the windings to become "imbalanced," it must first be understand why and how the windings are "balanced."

In Figure 3-2, Chapter 3, you can see that the transmitter antenna transmits radio frequency electromagnetic field energy in all directions. Any metal that comes within this primary energy field, has eddy currents generated on its surface. Another way of explaining this phenomenon is to say that metal targets absorb some of this primary field energy. Since the receiver antenna is constructed of metal wire, it can very effectively "absorb" energy. If this were allowed to happen, metal detection would not occur because the amount of direct absorption would be many times greater than the small amount of secondary (or target) field absorption. Primary field absorption would completely "mask" the secondary field (electromagnetic field generation by eddy currents) as well as the small "imbalance" caused by targets interacting with the electromagnetic field.

We now come to the explanation of why the term Induction Balance (sometimes referred to as searchcoil antenna balance) is used

EDDY CURRENT GENERATION ON METAL SURFACE

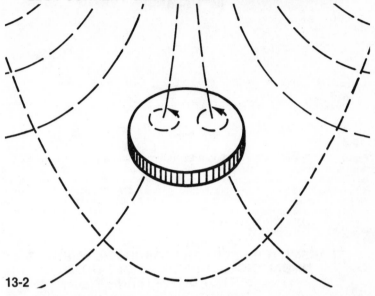

13-2

Figure 13-2: EDDY CURRENT GENERATION ON METAL SURFACE. This illustration shows a representative sample of the electromagnetic field lines generated by the transmitter current flowing in the antenna windings. As electromagnetic field lines penetrate the surface of metal, eddy currents flow on the metal's surface. Eddy current generation uses some of the electromagnetic field's power. This power loss is detected by the metal detector circuitry. Audio and visual signals alert the operator to the presence of the detected metal target.

to describe the operation of this type detector. To understand how primary field energy is prevented from being absorbed by the receiver antenna, refer to Figure 13-3. This illustration shows the shape and placement of a co-planar searchcoil's transmitter and receiver windings. You will note that the transmitter antenna (which was originally constructed perfectly round) is reformed, with a section of the wires reshaped within the center portion of itself. The receiver antenna, which is perfectly round, is placed directly in contact with the transmitter antenna, as shown.

Because the receiver antenna is precisely positioned with respect to the transmitter antenna, equal amounts of energy are absorbed by the receiver antenna at points "A" and "B".

The two equal amounts of absorbed energy oppose each other in the receiver antenna, resulting in ZERO ABSORBED ENERGY. Now, it will be shown how very tiny amounts of imbalance between the two windings can occur, resulting in "detection" of metal targets.

We have shown in Figure 7-3 how an electromagnetic field penetrates metal objects, and how the field can be "warped" by these metals. Figure 13-4 illustrates how this warping upsets the energy

153

TRANSMITTER-RECEIVER SEARCHCOIL WINDINGS IN "BALANCE"

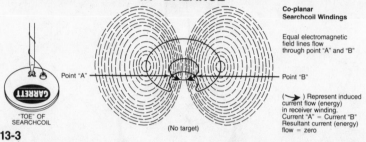

Co-planar Searchcoil Windings

Equal electromagnetic field lines flow through point "A" and "B"

Point "A"

Point "B"

(➤) Represent induced current flow (energy) in receiver winding. Current "A" = Current "B" Resultant current (energy) flow = zero

"TOE" OF SEARCHCOIL

(No target)

13-3

Figure 13-3: TRANSMITTER-RECEIVER SEARCHCOIL WINDINGS IN BALANCE. This illustration shows how primary field energy is prevented from being absorbed by the receiver antenna. Equal magnitude but opposite polarity currents are induced at points A & B. The resulting current flow in the receiver winding is zero. Whenever a target causes the field to become "imbalanced" the sum of currents A & B is no longer zero. A resulting current signal flows in the receiver winding. Audio and visual signals alert the operator to the presence of the detected target. Figure 13-4 illustrates how this warping upsets the energy balance at points A&B.

TRANSMITTER-RECEIVER SEARCHCOIL WINDINGS "IMBALANCED" DUE TO TARGET WITHIN DETECTION PATTERN

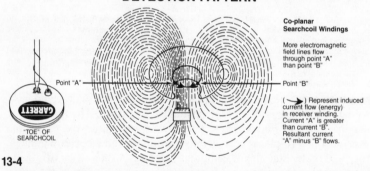

Co-planar Searchcoil Windings

More electromagnetic field lines flow through point "A" than point "B"

Point "A"

Point "B"

(➤) Represent induced current flow (energy) in receiver winding. Current "A" is greater than current "B". Resultant current "A" minus "B" flows.

"TOE" OF SEARCHCOIL

13-4

Figure 13-4: TRANSMITTER-RECEIVER SEARCHCOIL WINDINGS IMBALANCED DUE TO TARGET WITHIN DETECTION PATTERN. Figure 13-3 illustrates how the Induction (antenna winding) Balance principal is utilized in metal detectors. When the electromagnetic field is not warped by near by targets no signal is produced in the receiver winding. Whenever a metal target or non-conductive iron mineral target comes within the detection pattern of a searchcoil, the electromagnetic field is warped or "imbalanced." This imbalanced condition results in a signal current being caused to flow in the receiver winding. Electronic circuitry amplifies and conditions this signal to alert the operator to the presence of the near by target.

balance at points "A" and "B". The amount of primary field energy at the two points is no longer equal or "balanced." This results in a signal being induced in the receiver antenna. The detector then alerts the operator to the presence of the metal target.

The two phenomena, eddy current generation and antenna imbalance add together to produce one signal in the receiver antenna. The

154

operator cannot tell which was the greater or lesser effect, nor does it matter which effect was predominant. The important thing is that detection occurred.

You can see why TR searchcoils are more complex than, those of BFOs. That same complexity, however, is one reason that prevents the TR from being as capable an instrument as the BFO. An explanation of these differences is not within the scope of this book.

TR detectors can utilize target elimination (discrimination) technology as described in Chapter 10. TRs have fringe area detection (Figure 7-9) which results in that extra margin of depth that the trained operator can achieve.

Since TRs do not have ground elimination (cancelling) capabilities, the TR is, for all practical purposes, limited to operation over non-mineralized, or only moderately mineralized, soils. Several operational techniques, such as detection depth reduction, operating in the "quiet" zone (below audio threshold) and "scrubbing," are often used by TR operators when trying to achieve acceptable operation over ground mineralization. Since the TR is still a reasonably popular detector, these operational procedures will be presented.

HOW TO USE YOUR TR

TR use should be limited to coin hunting and building searching. Relic hunting, beachcombing (without a target elimination or discrimination circuit to eliminate salt water detection), and electronic prospecting, should not be attempted. Poor performance may result. Beach hunting with TRs on ocean beaches void of magnetic sand, can be very productive. On the dry areas, the TR performs beautifully at any trash elimination setting. Out over the wetted beach areas, the trash elimination mode will have to be set so the detector will ignore the conductive salt water. At this setting, however, most TRs produce maximum depth, increasing your chances of success.

Headphones should be used for maximum recognition of weak detection signals caused by very deep coins, coins standing on edge, etc. Seven-inch to eight-inch diameter searchcoils are the preferred type. Larger diameter searchcoils may be used, but extra weight and more difficult pinpointing are the disadvantages. The table (Figure 13-5), shows the various TR searchcoils and their applications.

If the ground is mineral free, operation will be relatively simple. To test for the presence of ground minerals, proceed as follows: hold the detector with the searchcoil positioned about four feet above the ground. Tune the detector (or adjust the AUDIO control) to achieve a very faint audio sound. This is the optimum TR threshold operating point. Lower the searchcoil to the ground. If there is no change in the threshold level, the ground contains no detectable minerals. If there is an increase in the audio level, you should perform this test at several different places, because you are probably detecting buried metal targets. If the ground contains wetted salt, the salt will produce an increase in sound loudness, also.

13-5

	Probing	Super Sniping	Coin Hunting	Cache Hunting	Relic Hunting	Ghost Towning	Nugget Hunting	Vein Locating	Ore Sampling	Black Sand Locating	General Purpose Hunting
¾" to 2"	10						NOT RECOMMENDED	NOT RECOMMENDED	NOT RECOMMENDED	NOT RECOMMENDED	
3" to 4"		10					NOT RECOMMENDED	NOT RECOMMENDED	NOT RECOMMENDED	NOT RECOMMENDED	
7" to 8"			10		10		NOT RECOMMENDED	NOT RECOMMENDED	NOT RECOMMENDED	NOT RECOMMENDED	10
10"			8	6	7	10	NOT RECOMMENDED	NOT RECOMMENDED	NOT RECOMMENDED	NOT RECOMMENDED	10
12"				10	10		NOT RECOMMENDED	NOT RECOMMENDED	NOT RECOMMENDED	NOT RECOMMENDED	
14" to 16"				10	10		NOT RECOMMENDED	NOT RECOMMENDED	NOT RECOMMENDED	NOT RECOMMENDED	

TR SEARCHCOILS VS APPLICATIONS

The scale of numbers "0" to "10" represent the relative capabilities of the various TR searchcoil sizes with "10" being maximum capability. Do not compare capabilities, using these numbers, with other similar tables in this book. A TR rating of "10" may be more or less capable than a "10" rating of another type metal detector.

Figure 13-5: TR SEARCHCOILS VERSUS APPLICATIONS. This table lists the various TR searchcoils and gives recommended applications.

If the sound decreases as you lower the searchcoil toward the ground, iron minerals are present in the soil. The closer you can move the searchcoil to the ground before the threshold sound begins to decrease, the fewer the iron minerals. Roughly speaking, if the threshold begins to decrease when the searchcoil is one foot above the ground, the ground should be considered highly mineralized. If the audio begins to change at a height of about three-inches to four-inches or less, the ground should be considered to be lightly mineralized. (Perform these tests with TR sensitivity set to maximum.)

If, when you scan the searchcoil across the ground at a two inch height, the detector operation is erratic (the audio threshold does not remain constant) then one or two, or perhaps all, of the following techniques may be needed to achieve satisfactory performance.

DETECTION DEPTH REDUCTION

If your TR is equipped with a detection depth control or switch, reduce the detection depth to minimum. This will greatly facilitate operation of the TR. Don't worry about the loss of depth; you will be able to hear signals much more clearly now that the detector is less sensitive to ground minerals. As you gain experience, you can gradually increase detection depth.

OPERATION IN QUIET ZONE

To operate in the quiet zone, hold the searchcoil about four feet above the ground. Adjust the tuning (AUDIO) control until you achieve "quiet" operation. Do not rotate the control any more than necessary to achieve the silent point just below threshold. Lower the searchcoil to the recommended two-inch operating height and press your retune button momentarily. This returns the audio to your preset "quiet" operating point. Scan the searchcoil over the ground, maintaining, as closely as possible, the two-inch height.

SCRUBBING

When the above two methods are not sufficient to achieve acceptable operation, you may employ also the "scrubbing" technique. Reduce detection depth and set the audio to the "quiet" point as described above. Place the searchcoil directly upon the ground. Press the retune button momentarily. Maintain light ground contact throughout your scanning. This has the effect of keeping the searchcoil at a constant "height" above the minerals, and the disturbing effects of the minerals do not permit the threshold to arise from "silent" operation. Targets, however, will force the audio out of the silent point into the zone of hearing. This method may seem awkward at first, but with practice it becomes easy. You should use a searchcoil skid plate to reduce searchcoil wear.

If, after using the above three techniques, you cannot achieve acceptable operation, you should consider using a VLF ground canceling detector which ignores the effects of iron soil minerals.

To recap: make detection depth and audio adjustments as you have learned from the above procedures. Wear headphones. Always press the retune button after making any detector adjustments and immediately before starting any searchcoil scanning. Occasionally, as you scan, press the retune button to insure the detector is properly tuned to your preset audio level at your preferred searchcoil height. Scan with the searchcoil in a straight line sweep. At the end of each sweep, advance the searchcoil ahead, from one-half to two-thirds the diameter of the searchcoil. Maintain level searchcoil scanning throughout each sweep.

If your TR is equipped with discrimination (or elimination), set the control no higher than necessary to reject junk items in the ground where you are searching. Remember, at pull tab setting, you may lose some nickels and rings.

BUILDING SEARCHING

If you wish to scan a building, hold the searchcoil about one or two inches from the wall and momentarily press the retune button to return the audio to threshold. Scan over the walls, and, when you receive a signal, make sure you are not detecting pipes, wiring, metal window sashes and other metal objects before you investigate the cause of the signal. If nails are a bother, you may dial in slight target elimination.

CHAPTER 13 QUESTIONS

1. The designations TR and IB actually mean about the same thing when they are used to describe a type of metal detector.

    True _____   False _____

2. TR metal detectors detect metal objects primarily because of two phenomena. What are they? (Each correct answer is worth 10 points)

3. Why is it that when the receiver winding is placed directly on top of the transmitter winding in a TR searchcoil, large amounts of power are not absorbed by the receiver winding?

4. The main disadvantage of TR metal detectors is that they: (A) are less sensitive than other types; (B) should be used only by beginners; (C) cannot be adjusted to ignore earth mineralization; (D) they work well only in the fields of prospecting.

5. TR detectors are primarily used in the field of _____ hunting.

6. If ground minerals disturb the operation of a TR metal detector, there are three things that can be done. Name two of them. (Each of the two answers given correctly are worth 10 points)

7. It's best not to use the TR metal detector when scanning a building because the wiring in the walls acts as a giant receiver antenna causing the TR to pick up distant radio and television stations.

    True _____   False _____

The correct answers to questions 2 and 6 are worth 20 points if all answers are given correctly. All other questions are worth 12 points each if answered correctly. Perfect score is 100. Answers are given in Appendix 2.

CHAPTER 14

VLF Metal Detector Short Course

This chapter is devoted to the history, theory, characteristics, and field applications of the VLF Ground Elimination (canceling) type metal detector. This type has been in use since the mid-'70s and is referred to as the MANUAL-ADJUST VLF. In order for the metal detector to "ignore," or eliminate from detection, iron earth minerals, the operator manually adjusts a control knob to achieve iron earth mineral elimination for each location where the metal detector is used.

The newer Ground Elimination metal detectors, called the AUTO-MATIC VLF GROUND ELIMINATION types, can be operated over the earth's iron minerals without any manual adjusting of a panel control knob. The detector continually analyzes the soil beneath the searchcoil, and automatically "adjusts" itself to "ignore" the minerals. Except, for a brief discussion in this chapter of Automatic VLF Ground Elimination types, the main discussion of this newer type metal detector is given in Chapter 15.

The Very Low Frequency (VLF) ground eliminating (canceling) type detector is today's most popular metal detector. The VLF derives its name from its radio frequency operating range which is within the Very Low Frequency radio spectrum of 3 to 30 kilohertz. Most VLFs operate no higher than about 15 with the majority operating near 5 kilohertz. The VLF is actually a transmitter-receiver (TR) type detector with two main differences: the VLFs operate at a much lower frequency than TRs (see RADIO FREQUENCY SPECTRUM TABLE, Figure 6-2), and VLFs cancel, or eliminate from detection iron soil minerals.

Because VLFs are not bothered by disturbing effects of iron minerals, circuit gain can be made higher; thus, improving sensitivity (smaller targets can be detected) and greatly increasing detection depth. Since the radio operating frequency is lower, eddy current generation will be greater. Since the depth to which eddy currents can be generated (skin depth) increases as the frequency of the electro-magnetic field source decreases, larger amounts of eddy currents are generated in a metal's surface. Thus, all targets can be detected deeper with VLFs.

Although early VLFs were also called GEBs (Ground Exclusion Balance), MFs (Mineral Free), etc., by various manufacturers, today, most are called VLF or VLF/TR detectors. The VLF/TR designation was made when an additional circuit was added. Trash target elimina-

159

tion was not accomplished simultaneously with iron mineral elimination. An additional trash target elimination circuit (TR discrimination) was added even though the earth's minerals could not, simultaneously, be eliminated from detection. Thus, a detector was created that had a VLF iron mineral elimination circuit mode and a TR discriminating circuit mode. Both circuits operated at the same VLF frequency, thus, was born the VLF/TR dual mode detector.

As the mid-'80s approached, acceptable ground/trash elimination circuits were developed. Since TR discriminating circuits had the disadvantage of not working well over mineralized ground, the new VLF detectors gained in popularity, VLF/TR detectors giving way to VLF Ground/Trash Discrimination types. Later, the word "Discrimination," began to be replaced with the more accurate term "Elimination."

Some manufacturers have developed a wide range of searchcoils and accessories for use with their VLFs. Searchcoils (Figure 14-1), that range in size from three-quarter-inch diameter probes to extremely deep seeking "two-box" type attachments, have greatly expanded the capabilities of VLF instruments. Improved accuracy depth meas-

14-1

	Probing	Super Sniping	Coin Hunting	Cache Hunting	Relic Hunting	Ghost Towning	Nugget Hunting	Vein Locating	Ore Sampling	Black Sand Locating	General Purpose Hunting
¾" to 2"	10					5					
3" to 4"	8	10	7			8		10			
7" to 8"		10		6	10	10			8		10
10"		10	7	8	10	10	8				10
12"		8	10	10		8	10			8	
14" to 16"			10	10			10		10		
Depth Multiplier			10				10				

VLF SEARCHCOILS VS APPLICATIONS

The scale of numbers "0" to "10" represent the relative capabilities of the various VLF searchcoil sizes with the "10" being maximum capability. Do not compare capabilities, using these numbers, with other similar tables in this book. A VLF rating of "10" may be more or less capable than a "10" rating of another type metal detector.

Figure 14-1: VLF SEARCHCOILS VERSUS APPLICATIONS. This table lists VLF searchcoils and applications. A large assortment of searchcoils is manufactured for VLF metal detectors. VLF searchcoils have a wider dynamic range than all other types.

160

uring circuits and target identification methods have been developed that greatly expand VLF capabilities.

THEORY OF OPERATION

VLF detectors are very similar in design to TR detectors (review TR theory, Chapter 13). The block diagram (Figure 14-2,) shows the main VLF circuits and components and how they are interconnected. An electronic oscillator feeds a signal into the transmitter antenna, extending the resulting electromagnetic field into the space that surrounds the searchcoil. The portion that extends below the searchcoil creates the detection pattern. Detectable metals and minerals have a disturbing effect upon the electromagnetic field.

14-2   BLOCK DIAGRAM OF VLF METAL DETECTOR

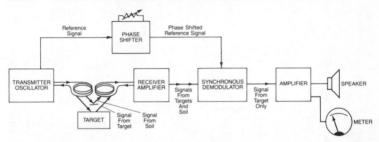

Figure 14-2: ELECTRONIC BLOCK DIAGRAM OF VLF METAL DETECTOR. This block diagram shows the main VLF circuits, components and interconnections. VLF metal detectors work almost identically to TR detectors in that the transmitter and receiver windings are electronically balanced until detectable targets upset this balance. The detector then produces signals which alert the operator to the presence of the targets.

At this point, similarity with TR detection ends, as VLF ground elimination circuits are brought into play. An electromagnetic signal transmission phenomenon called phase shift occurs. Phase shift refers to a time delay between electrical voltage and current signals, one occurring before the other. Phase shift has been known and used for many years, especially in military radar systems, (See Chapter 10, the discussion on IRON MINERAL GROUND ELIMINATION.)

Eddy current "loss" signals are ELECTRICALLY PHASE SHIFTED or TIME DELAYED (Figure 14-3) with respect to the transmitted electromagnetic field. The Synchronous Demodulator, "measures" this time difference, and separates the phase separated signals.

When purely non-conductive ferrous targets (iron minerals) cause field distortion, transmitter/receiver antenna imbalance occurs but there is no phase shift.

When a composite signal containing in-phase and phase shifted components is fed into the Synchronous Demodulator, the two phase related signals are separated. The earth iron mineral signal is discarded but the metal target signal is amplified to power the speaker or

VLF SIGNAL PHASE SHIFT CHARACTERISTICS

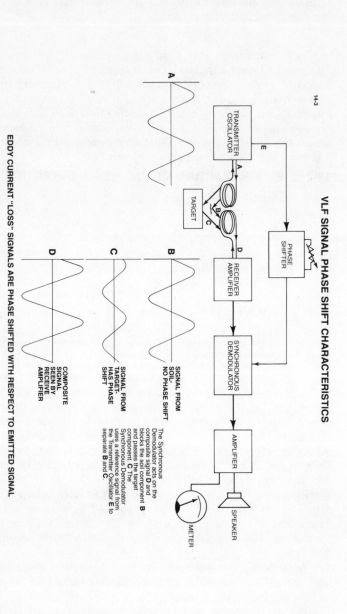

14-3

The Synchronous Demodulator acts on the composite signal **D** and blocks the soil component **B** and passes the target component **C**. The Synchronous Demodulator uses a reference signal from the Transmitter Oscillator **E** to separate **B** and **C**.

EDDY CURRENT "LOSS" SIGNALS ARE PHASE SHIFTED WITH RESPECT TO EMITTED SIGNAL

Figure 14-3: VLF SIGNAL PHASE SHIFT CHARACTERISTICS. Eddy current power "loss" signals are electrically phase shifted (time delayed) with respect to earth mineral signals. The synchronous demodulator determines time difference between the phase separated signals. The earth mineral signals are discarded and the metal target signals are amplified and conditioned to alert the operator to the presence of metal targets.

162

headphones and indicators. Thus, the effects of the earth's iron minerals are "eliminated" or "ignored."

A Ground Elimination Control is provided by the manufacturer so that the operator can adjust his detector to "match up" with almost any mineral matrix. When "match up" occurs, minerals are eliminated from detection and target signals alert the operator to the presence of metal.

WETTED SALT CANCELLATION

Wetted salt is electrically conductive (looks like metal to a metal detector) and cannot be eliminated from detection in the same manner that iron minerals are. It can be eliminated, however, because its conductivity can be determined the same as conductivity of any conductive (metal) element. Using the Trash Elimination mode, the operator can "dial out" ocean beach and other wetted salt. The Target Elimination Chart (Figure 10-5,) shows salt water in relation to conductive metals.

THE HOT ROCK PROBLEM

VLF detectors will respond "positive" to "hot rocks" (mineralized rocks that contain a highly concentrated magnetic iron/conductive element content differing from the matrix to which the VLF detector is adjusted.) Hot rock response is troublesome in some areas, but the VLF will not indicate its presence unless the hot rock is close to the searchcoil, a maximum distance roughly equal to the diameter of the searchcoil. If a detected target is "suspect," switch into the VLF Trash Elimination mode (set to "zero" elimination) and pass back over the target. If the sound decreases from the audio threshold level, the target is a rock or mineralized hot spot. If the audio remains the same or increases, investigate the target. It has some metallic content. You can use "reverse discrimination" to perform this test if your detector has a TR mode.

If you are prospecting, be certain the Trash Elimination control is set to "zero." Nuggets and ore samples may be rejected if greater elimination is used. Even the "zero" setting on non-calibrated detectors may result in rejected nuggets and ore. Consequently, always use the all-metal VLF mode.

SENSITIVITY PROBLEM

VLF detectors are very sensitive to iron, even small pieces, so, when operating in the all-metal mode, you will be digging extremely deep holes for bits and pieces of iron. When coin hunting, you can use trash elimination to remove most of the problem, but when you are cache hunting and don't want to use any amount of trash elimination, you will detect small, deeply buried targets. To be more efficient when hunting large caches you should consider using the Depth Multiplier "two-box" attachment which ignores small metal pieces.

DEEPSEEKING DETECTORS

VLFs are well known for their deep seeking capabilities, detecting all-metal objects to great depths. The availability of large searchcoils greatly extends the VLF's depth capabilities. They can ignore iron minerals and wetted salt, although not simultaneously. Detection depth through these minerals is superb, but, when they are present in the soil matrix at the same time, erratic operation may result. In these situations, Pulse Induction Trash Elimination detectors are generally recommended.

DEPTH MEASURING AND TARGET IDENTIFIERS

Many VLFs are equipped with coin depth measuring circuits and indicator meters that, to a certain degree, classify or identify, detected targets, increasing the operator's efficiency. (See Chapter 10.)

AUDIO THRESHOLD

Manual-Adjust Ground Elimination detectors give the greatest detection depth when set to minimum audio level threshold. When operated in the "silent" zone, some ability to detect in the fringe area is lost. Also, when the detector is operating "silent," it is difficult to know WHERE in the null zone the operating point is set. Certain signal strength meters do give a fair indication as to where this audio threshold is located.

Since a certain amount of detection signal is "used up" in bringing the audio out of the "silent" zone (Figure 14-4) to a level where it can be heard, some sensitivity (and detection depth) is lost. The further the detector is operated down into the null zone, the worse the problem. Thus, manufacturers stress that detector audio be set to the lowest possible threshold level that can be continuously heard.

AUTOMATIC VLF GROUND ELIMINATION DETECTORS

Manufacturers of Automatic Ground Elimination detectors state that their machines can be operated in the "silent" zone, some claiming that no sensitivity and detection depth is lost. Let's examine the characteristics of this type detector and compare them with manually adjusted ground eliminating detectors. Manually-adjusted VLF Ground Elimination detector circuits are called, in engineering jargon, "linear" circuits. Automatic VLF Ground Elimination circuits utilize "non-linear" circuitry. Figure 14-5 illustrates the audio sound characteristics of a manually-adjusted detector while Figure 15-2 illustrates those of an automatically adjusted one.

Automatic VLF Ground Eliminating circuitry results in the audio being either OFF or FULLY ON; there are very few "in between" signals. Whenever target signals of sufficient strength occur, the audio is driven from "silent" to full audio volume. Notice the word "sufficient." Some target signals are INSUFFICIENT, and do

14-4   AUDIO THRESHOLD AND SUB-THRESHOLD CHARACTERISTICS

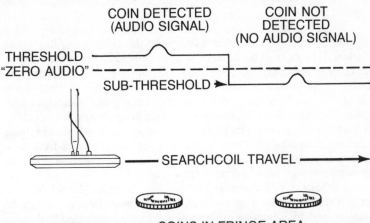

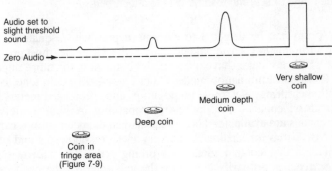

Figure 14-4: AUDIO THRESHOLD AND SUB-THRESHOLD CHARACTERISTICS. This illustration shows how fringe area coins (and deeply buried coins) can be missed when detector audio (tuning) is set in the null (silent) zone. The further down in the silent zone, the worse the problem. Automatic VLF instruments lose less silent zone detection "depth," however, than Manual-Adjust VLFs.

AUDIO RESPONSE CHARACTERISTICS OF MANUALLY ADJUSTABLE VLF GROUND ELIMINATION DETECTOR WHEN DETECTING COINS

14-5   Compare to Figure 15-2

Figure 14-5: AUDIO RESPONSE CHARACTERISTICS OF MANUALLY ADJUSTABLE VLF GROUND ELIMINATION DETECTOR WHEN DETECTING COINS. Manually-adjusted VLF Ground Elimination metal detector circuits are called, in engineering jargon, "linear" circuits; thus, linear audio signals are produced by VLF metal detectors. Linear circuit signals contain more information about the characteristics of targets than do non-linear circuit signals as illustrated in Figure 15-2 in chapter fifteen. In manually-adjusted VLF detectors, the audio signals become progressively louder as targets become larger or, are more shallowly buried. In Automatic VLF Ground Elimination metal detector non-linear circuits, almost all audio signals are produced at maximum volume.

165

not result in an audible alert. Consequently, SOME BURIED AND CONCEALED METAL TARGETS MAY NOT BE DETECTED WITH AUTOMATIC VLF GROUND ELIMINATION DETECTORS.

Precise contouring and subtle target characteristic determining capabilities may be lost. When the audio threshold is set to operate "silent," there may be no way of knowing WHERE in the null the detector is operating. Although manufacturers go to great lengths to build stable detectors with steady audio threshold, in improperly designed circuits it may drift from the preset point. Detectors with preset factory threshold settings may have no provision for adjusting the operating point. Since audio threshold location should be a concern of all who want to achieve maximum performance from their detector, perhaps operators should not consider purchasing preset instruments with no adjustment provision.

Automatic VLF Ground Elimination detectors should be used primarily for coin hunting and building searching. Prospecting, cache hunting and relic hunting, should be performed with standard, non-automatic ground elimination universal VLF instruments.

VLF VERSATILITY

The versatility of the VLF is legendary; there is not much it won't do. Formally, the BFO was the only all-purpose detector, and could be expected to perform just about every metal detecting job quite well. The VLF is more versatile because of its ground eliminating and extreme depth capabilities, and the availability of an extremely wide range of searchcoils and usable attachments.

COIN HUNTING

Coins can be detected to extreme depths with a quality VLF. Trash Elimination is available not only in the TR mode (most present-day VLF's no longer have a TR mode) but also in the more popular VLF Ground Elimination mode. Other features like coin tone, coin-depth measuring, electronic pinpointing, and specialized meters and indicators, enhance the operator's capability. A wide variety of searchcoils are available. Three-quarter-inch diameter probes can be used to search for shallow coins very close to sidewalks and other structures that contain metal reinforcing rods. The narrow-beam probe reaches primarily out along the axis (end) of the probe with only a very small portion of the electromagnetic field detection pattern extending laterally.

The three-and-one-half-inch "Super-Sniper" is the most popular optional detector searchcoil. With detuning (see Chapter 10), it can be operated extremely close to sidewalks, fences, etc. It efficiently permits the working of high trash areas (Super-Sniping) to recover coins that larger searchcoils cannot locate in the trash elimination mode.

Seven-inch to eight-inch diameter searchcoils are the most popular coin hunting sizes. Ten-inch to twelve-inch ones, however, are becoming increasingly popular, many professionals using the ten-inch for general coin hunting. Larger coils give greater depth and cover a wider sweep path, although their extra weight makes them more tiring to use. Pinpointing is slightly more difficult. These inconveniences are forgotten when deep and valuable coins are found. Fourteen-inch searchcoils can be used for coin hunting and are surprisingly sensitive to small coins. Pinpointing is difficult, but extra depth can be achieved.

The coin hunter has several mode options; he can search in the VLF Ground Elimination all-metal mode, the VLF Trash Elimination mode, or in the TR mode (if his detector is so equipped and ground minerals are minimal.) The VLF ground eliminating all-metal mode will find more and deeper coins, but every target will have to be dug. This can be a blessing in disguise, as sometimes valuable metal objects are rejected when target elimination is used.

COIN HUNTING TECHNIQUES

The smaller the searchcoil you use, the more efficient (coins/trash ratio) will be your efforts. You will dig more coins, but detection depth will not be as great as when using larger searchcoils, such as the ten-inch to twelve-inch sizes which should be a part of your coin hunting.

For instance, if a park is known as a good coin producer, but has been overworked, you may want to consider the larger searchcoils. Adjust the target elimination mode to reject the typical trash found in the area or set it to "zero." Adjust the detector to ignore iron mineralization and use one or more of the pinpointing methods explained in this book. As you retrieve coins and trash, notice their depth. If mostly junk is found in the first few inches, you may want to dig only the deeper targets.

If your detector is equipped with a depth measuring meter, dig only the targets beyond a predetermined depth. If yours is equipped with a detection depth control, set it to maximum. When you have pinpointed an object, rotate the control to minimum and recheck the target. If you don't detect it now, dig. It will be deep. (NOTE: When you change detection depth, it may be necessary to momentarily press the retune switch or button.) You may need to analyze detector operation using various detection depth control settings to find the optimum setting for any particular coin area.

SUPER-SNIPING

Another very efficient method of scanning "worked out" areas is Super-Sniping, the use of small three-inch to four-inch diameter searchcoils. Super-Sniping is a good way to have a successful coin hunting day!

CACHE HUNTING

When searching for caches, you should employ a VLF type detector; using the all-metal mode. Even though it responds to metal trash buried very deeply, it is still the best type detector for this purpose. It will not respond to subterranean water, moisture or mineralized ground. For cache hunting use large searchcoils. You get the benefit of the deepest possible penetration on big objects, and the larger the searchcoil the less you will be bothered by small metal trash. A very important accessory is the VLF Depth Multiplier (described in Chapter 11) which may be used when searching for quart-size and larger mass caches. Small trash will not be detected.

BUILDING SEARCHING

Use a three-inch to ten-inch diameter searchcoil. If necessary, use trash elimination to avoid detection of nails. Before extensively investigating a spot in a wall where the detector indicates the presence of metal, make sure the signals are not caused by pipes, wiring, window sashes and building materials.

RELIC HUNTING

Most relic hunters use deep seeking VLF detectors with twelve-inch or fourteen-inch searchcoils for maximum depth. Careful manual ground elimination adjusting is very important to achieve the greatest depth. Any amount of trash elimination may cause iron targets to be rejected. Slow methodical scanning with good searchcoil overlapping is important for best ground coverage. Use a hipmount detector or accessory if you scan for long periods of time with large searchcoils.

ELECTRONIC PROSPECTING

You can perform just about every electronic prospecting task with a quality built, universal type VLF. The automatic VLF types may not be suitable, depending upon the efficiency you demand. Study the material in this chapter and in Chapter 11 to learn which searchcoil to use for any given job. A good understanding of metals and minerals (see Chapter 10) is essential for the greatest success. The book, ELECTRONIC PROSPECTING, published by Ram Publishing Company, gives an explanation of the various facets of Electronic Prospecting with emphasis on the use of VLF Ground Eliminating detectors.

A Manual-Adjust VLF Ground Eliminating detector is best for most searching you may undertake. It cannot be overstressed that it is important to learn how to use the VLF correctly. At first it may seem difficult, but as time passes you'll find it becomes easier to use and your success will increase. There will be times when it doesn't seem to be operating smoothly. Check out the detector to make sure it is working correctly, then analyze the problem. Start by reducing detection depth. You may find that you are working in an extremely junky area and the mass of jumbled targets (metal and/or ore) is preventing the detector from reading individual ones. In that case, detection depth reduction and the use of a smaller diameter searchcoil may eliminate most of the problem. (See Chapter 25 for additional ELECTRONIC PROSPECTING INSTRUCTIONS.

THE LITTLE IRON KETTLE

In Chapter 3 a hypothetical situation was described where a little iron kettle filled with gold coins was buried beneath a large rock lying in a field. Unfortunately, there were nine hundred ninety-nine other flat rocks in the field and many of them were highly mineralized. From the discussions already given in this book you should be able to locate that pot of gold without overturning every rock in the field. How?

Use a VLF Ground Elimination detector equipped with one of the larger searchcoils. Use the all-metal mode, tuning out ground minerals. Use headphones and maximum detection depth and scan the rocks one at a time. With luck, you might get a positive signal over the very first rock. Raise the rock and dig down a few inches to find the gold! But, what if you dig and find nothing?What happened? The rock is a hot rock! Do you dig beneath every rock? No, set the trash elimination control to ''zero,'' and scan over the rocks one at a time using the VLF all-metal mode. When you get a positive response, pinpoint where the loudest signal occurs. Place the searchcoil directly upon the rock. Press your mode change switch to activate the trash elimination mode. Maintain searchcoil contact with the rock as you slide the searchcoil to one side. According to Reverse Discrimination procedures (Chapter 10, Figures 10-12 and 10-13), if the signal does not change or it decreases, dig the target. You have located metal and, hopefully, the little iron kettle!

Another, easier way to locate the kettle if it is large enough (about quart-size) is to scan with the Depth Multiplier attachment. Minerals and hot rocks do not create false signals. The Depth Multiplier detects only metal!

Spend the contents of the kettle wisely!

1. Today's most popular type metal detector is the: (A) BFO; (B) Pulse Induction; (C) TR; (D) VLF.

2. The designation VLF means _____ _____ _____ .

3. The Very Low Frequency designation means that the audio detection signal operates in the very low frequency radio spectrum.
   True _____ False _____

4. The word elimination describes the ability of VLF detectors to _____ iron minerals from detection.

5. The main reason why the VLF types are the most popular is because they can be adjusted to ignore _____ earth minerals.

6. Early-day VLF's could not eliminate iron earth minerals and _____ targets simultaneously.

7. Since eddy current "loss" signals and non-conductive ferrous targets (iron minerals) signals do not occur at the same electrical _____ the non-conductive ferrous targets can be ignored.

8. Wetted salt cancellation can be accomplished the easiest in the ground elimination mode.
   True _____ False _____

9. The cancellation of wetted salt occurs near the trash elimination point where iron bottlecaps are eliminated from detection.
   True _____ False _____

10. VLF detectors are well-known for their _____ _____ capabilities.

11. Manual-Adjust VLF ground elimination detectors give maximum detection depth when the audio is: (A) set to operate in the silent zone; (B) set to a very loud obvious sound; (C) set to the minimum audio level that you can hear; (D) set to coincide with indicator signals.

12. An Automatic VLF Ground Elimination detector is one that does not have to be _____ adjusted to eliminate iron earth minerals from detection.

13. For all practical purposes it is O.K. to adjust the Automatic VLF Ground Elimination detector audio to operate at silent threshold.
   True _____ False _____

14. When operating an Automatic VLF Ground Elimination detector at the silent threshold point the targets you miss will be those that come within the _____ area.

15. Since there is not much that Manual-Adjust VLF Ground Elimination detectors won't do, they are called _____ .

16. An extremely wide range of available _____ are manufactured for some brands of VLF detectors.

17. The most popular size VLF searchcoil is the seven-inch to _____ -inch diameter size.

18. You generally get more detection depth when using larger searchcoils but _____ is more difficult.

19. You can use searchcoils as large as the _____ -inch size when coin hunting.

20. When using the VLF Depth Multiplier to search for caches an important feature is that small metal trash will not be _____ .

21. Relic hunters have found VLF deepseeking instruments to be the preferred types. They generally use _____ searchcoils when relic hunting.

22. Many relic hunters prefer not to use much, or any, Trash Elimination because they may miss valuable _____ targets.

23. Some VLF metal detector types are called universal application types because they are designed to do just about every metal detecting and electronic _____ task.

24. How would you go about locating the little iron kettle buried in a field beneath a large flat rock as described in Chapter three?

The correct answers to questions 1 through 23 are worth 4 points each. The correct answer to question 24 is worth 8 points. Perfect score is 100. Answers given in Appendix 2.

Figure 14-A: Everyone is thrilled at the thought of finding an honest-to-goodness ghost town untouched by the treasure hunter. In this beautiful Colorado ghost town, Terry Kilcoyne and members of his family search for lost coins, jewelry, treasure and relics. Generally, in areas like this, metal trash abounds but the patient treasure hunter reaps the rewards.

171

Figure 14-B: Robert Marx searches with his Sea Hunter for sunken shipwreck coins. Robert Marx is a world renowned underwater archaeologist.

Figure 14-D: Members of a Colorado Search & Rescue Team search for a skier lost in an avalanche. Research proved that most skiers wear numerous metal articles that can be located with a deep seeking metal detector; consequently, many Search & Rescue Teams now include metal detection equipment in their search & rescue arsenal. The motorized vehicle is a product of (Jim) Cross International Research and Development, Incorporated. Numerous photographs of Jim and his work will be found throughout this book. Jim's father, John Cross, and several of the Cross brothers have spent their lifetime in the great outdoors following adventureous pursuits. Photo by Dave Loveless.

172

Figure 14-E: Richard Graham of the FBI (center-background wearing cap) instructs a group of El Paso FBI and Law Enforcement personnel in the use of VLF instrumentation. These classes create a great demand upon Richard's time as requests from Law Enforcement Agencies and cities throughout the United States come into the FBI Office in Salt Lake City, Utah, on a regular basis. There is never a lack of students as practically every class is filled to maximum.

Figure 14-F: Roy Lagal and Virgil Hutton gleefully discuss a gold nugget found with a VLF Deepseeker detector in one of the twin drifts shown in the photograph. When you view Garrett's WEEKEND PROSPECTING video presentation, you will recognize this scene. Nineteenth century Chinese tunneled their way into this ancient river bed following traces of gold. They did not, however, have the eye of the modern metal detector.

173

Figure 14-G: Jack Hube of Suffield, Connecticut, prepares to dig for the chunk of silver he has just located along a roadbed in the famous Cobalt, Ontario, silver mining districts. Thousands of pounds of silver have been located with detectors by modern-day electronic prospectors. Chunks of silver weighing more than one hundred pounds and worth in excess of $10,000 have been found near Cobalt. In Chapter 25, ELECTRONIC PROS-PECTING CREATES GOLD RUSHES, you will find a photograph of a $5,000 chunk of silver ore that the author located not far from this spot where Jack prepares to dig yet another specimen.

Figure 14-H: Virgil Hutton scans for a buried cache using a Deepseeker and a Depth Multiplier attachment. This attachment is a regular part of the professional cache hunter's arsenal of detecting accessories. The Depth Multiplier requires no tuning or ground elimination adjustments. It ignores background mineralization, moisture and subterra-nean water. Also, the Depth Multiplier ignores small metal objects while detecting only metal objects larger than approximately quart size.

Figure 14-I: This safe is one of two that a group of treasure hunters located in a northeastern state. They used Deepseeking instruments equipped with large deepseeking searchcoils. Safes can readily be detected to depths of six to eight feet with the type searchcoil as shown in the photograph and to depths double that distance with the Depth Multiplier attachment.

Figure 14-J: The VLF Groundhog is Rene LeNeve's choice of instruments. In the Bloomington, Illinois, area where he resides, he has proved many times that research pays off. His research and recovery efforts extend mainly into two fields, outlaw loot and valuables lost at swimming areas. Photos of Rene and his treasure finds are seen at a regular basis in various treasure hunting publications. Photo courtesy Rene LeNeve.

The Automatic VLF Ground Elimination Metal Detector Short Course

Before beginning this discussion of Automatic VLF Ground Elimination metal detectors, I wish to explain the difference between AUTOMATIC TUNING circuits and AUTOMATIC VLF GROUND ELIMINATION METAL DETECTOR circuits. These two circuits are entirely different and achieve different things.

Automatic tuning circuits simply keep the detector's audio threshold set to your pre-determined point. The circuits do this automatically, without you having to push any buttons or twist any knobs, that is, AFTER YOU HAVE MADE THE VERY FIRST MANUAL ADJUST OF THE TUNING (AUDIO) CONTROL TO ACHIEVE YOUR DESIRED AUDIO THRESHOLD. Automatic tuning circuits have been in use since the '70s and are employed in TR, as well as VLF, type metal detectors. Automatic tuning has nothing to do with ground mineral elimination except, perhaps, mineral disturbances might be "smoothed out" somewhat by the action of the automatic tuning "stabilization" effects of the circuit.

Automatic VLF Ground Elimination metal detectors, on the other hand, continually monitor the minerals in the earth beneath the searchcoil and make internal circuit adjustments automatically, as needed, to eliminate, from detection, the disturbances the minerals would otherwise have on the detector.

See how the two differ? Automatic tuning circuits keep the detector in "tune" by preventing audio threshold drift. Automatic VLF Ground Elimination circuits eliminate the disturbing effects of iron earth minerals. It just so happens—and I hope this is not confusing— that Automatic VLF Ground Elimination metal detectors also utilize automatic tuning circuitry. Not only do the Automatic VLFs "automatically" ignore ground minerals, they also maintain your pre-determined audio threshold automatically.

If these discussions have not made it clear to you the difference between the two circuits, re-read these previous paragraphs as well as the MANUAL vs AUTOMATIC TUNING section in Chapter 10.

The Automatic VLF Ground Elimination Detector (Figure 15-1) is actually a VLF type instrument; it operates in the very low frequency spectrum. It differs from the VLF types described in the previous chapter in its automatic and continuous evaluation of the

Figure 15-1: This Automatic VLF Ground Elimination detector, the Freedom 2, differs from the manually-adjustable VLF types in that the earth's mineralization is automatically eliminated from detection. The detector automatically and continuously evaluates the earth's mineral matrix beneath the searchcoil and eliminates iron minerals from detection.

ground mineral matrix beneath the searchcoil, and the adjustment of its circuitry to eliminate detection of the iron earth minerals present. There is no manually adjustable VLF ground elimination control; that function is performed automatically and electronically for you.

On some detectors there is a manually adjustable ground elimination control, not needed when the Automatic VLF mode is in operation, but provided so you can improve Electronic Pinpointing accuracy over highly mineralized ground. Also, some instruments feature both the Automatic VLF Ground Elimination mode and the Manual-Adjust VLF mode. Thus, when the Manual-Adjust VLF mode is used, this same control is adjusted to achieve iron mineral elimination.

Most all earth matrixes contain varying quantities of iron minerals. The VLF type detectors as described in the previous chapter have a ground elimination control knob that can be manipulated to adjust the detector to ignore iron earth minerals. The electronic circuitry of the Automatic VLF Ground Elimination type detector performs this manipulation for you automatically. As the electromagnetic field radiates downward from the searchcoil into the ground matrix, the iron minerals interact with the electromagnetic field. This interaction is analyzed internally, and the resulting data is used to electronically adjust the detector so that it continuously ignores the iron earth minerals in the matrix beneath the searchcoil.

178

WIDE OPERATING LATITUDE

Correctly designed detectors have an extremely wide adjustment latitude. Zero ground minerals, or any magnitude of iron minerals up to the greatest density that a metal detector operator is likely to encounter, will be eliminated from detection. There is nothing the operator can do to effect this operation as there is no control knob provided.

You must remember that these instruments operate continuously in an automatic "tuning" mode. You can prove this to yourself by stopping or hovering the searchcoil directly above a metal target. The signals will die out, indicating that the detector's functions are controlled automatically. While this may seem like a disadvantage, it is not. Since most people use these detectors for coin hunting only, there is generally no need to hover the searchcoils. A good percentage of users do report difficulty in pinpointing. This disadvantage is overcome by models that feature an electronic pinpointing mode.

The first time you use an Automatic VLF Ground Elimination detector you will notice that the audio signal, when a coin is detected (Figure 15-2) is generally much more quick and sharply pronounced than the manually adjustable type VLF. Most coin hunters have no difficulty in getting accustomed to this different audio sound, many preferring it.

DESIGNED FOR ANALYZING COIN-SIZED TARGETS

Automatic VLF Ground Elimination detectors, especially when some amount of target elimination is used, are most efficient when detecting coin-sized targets. They are not recommended for cache hunting, relic hunting and electronic prospecting. As you gain experience with this type detector you will learn that, often, the detector doesn't correctly analyze large and irregular shaped targets which cause the signals to break up or be erratic.

DUAL TARGET ELIMINATION MODES

Some models are manufactured with dual target elimination modes, Figure 15-3. Depending upon the model, both modes can be fully adjustable or, one can be adjustable and one fixed. The fixed mode can be all-metal or it can have some given amount of trash rejection, such as rusted metal or bottlecap rejection. The dual modes provide the user with a convenient means of obtaining additional data about detected targets. With one mode set at bottlecap rejection and one set at pulltab rejection, the operator can program the detector to classify most targets within meaningful categories. "Windows" of detection can be programed into the metal detector's circuits.

With the detector set as described, scanning in the bottlecap mode causes bottlecaps and poorer conductivity items to be rejected. When a positive sound is heard, the operator can press a switch

179

AUDIO RESPONSE CHARACTERISTICS OF AUTOMATIC VLF GROUND ELIMINATION DETECTOR WHEN DETECTING COINS

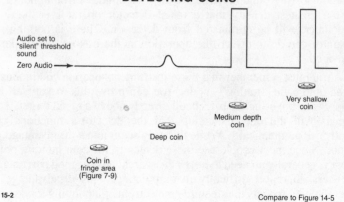

Audio set to "silent" threshold sound

Zero Audio ⟶

Very shallow coin

Medium depth coin

Deep coin

Coin in fringe area (Figure 7-9)

15-2

Compare to Figure 14-5

Figure 15-2: AUDIO RESPONSE CHARACTERISTICS OF AUTOMATIC VLF GROUND ELIMINATION DETECTOR WHEN DETECTING COINS. Note the audio response is fully "on" when targets are detected. Targets near and in the fringe area produce no (or very small) audio responses. Many coin hunters prefer the "Freedom" type metal detectors.

Figure 15-3: Some Automatic VLF Ground Elimination detectors are manufactured with dual Target Elimination modes. This dual mode capability provides the user with additional target data. The operator can program the detector to classify most detected targets within meaningful categories. "Windows" of detection can be programmed into the metal detector's circuits. Photo by Melvin Climer.

180

(Figure 15-4) causing the pulltab elimination mode to be activated. If no sound is heard as the searchcoil is scanned over the target, the operator knows the target lies within the bottlecap to pulltab range.

Figure 15-4: This is a Freedom 2 three-position mode selector switch. Two Target Elimination modes and an Electronic Pinpointing mode can be selected. This switch allows almost instantaneous target identification and precise pinpointing. Photo by Melvin Climer.

If, however, a positive sound is heard, the operator knows the target has conductivity of pulltabs or better, such as clad and silver coins have.

Various other settings are possible. Some operators claim they can reject pulltabs while accepting nickels and rings. Certainly the dual scan mode capability has positive aspects.

Before purchasing one of these types get a demonstration. Listen to the audio and check trash elimination. Some do a poor job of rejecting bottlecaps.

SILENT VERSES THRESHOLD AUDIO

All Automatic VLF Ground Elimination detector manufacturers state that their machines can be operated silent with no audible sound emanating from the speaker or headphones except when a target is detected. Some claim that no sensitivity or detection depth is lost in the silent mode. Let's analyze silent versus threshold operation.

In other chapters in this book, threshold operation is clearly defined and the metal detection process is described. Whenever a detector is adjusted to operate with slight audio threshold, the least disturbance of the electromagnetic field by a metal target can be heard in the headphones. This is fringe area detection. Whenever the operator is intently listening to audio threshold these very slight perturbations can be heard.

In silent operation, the detector is now operating in a null or quiet zone (see Figure 14-4). In all but the most extremely precise audio adjustments, there is a finite difference, electronically speaking, between the silent audio level and threshold audio level. In other words, when the detector is operating silent, it takes some definite amount of signal power to move the audio from silent to the point where the audio can just be heard. As long as the detected target is large enough or buried shallow enough to drive the audio from the silent point into the discernible range, the target can be located. But if the target is extremely small or deeply buried, it is possible that it cannot produce sufficient drive to cause the audio to break into this range. Thus the presence of the target is not revealed to the operator.

The sensitivity or detection depth that is lost with the Automatic Ground Elimination detector at silent, rather than at slight threshold, is often referred to as the lost fringe area detection. (See Figure 15-2).

Admittedly, the amount of loss could be very small, especially if the silent operating point is set very close to the "break point" into threshold audio. Each individual must decide if the lost detection depth is of any consequence.

ELECTRONIC PINPOINTING

As previously stated, these instruments may do a less-than-desirable job of pinpointing targets. The problem is because these instruments operate in an automatic mode. The operator must continually move the searchcoil and cannot hover above targets to pinpoint.

The metal detector shown in Figures 15-1 and 15-4, features three-step pinpointing capability. Scanning speed is extremely slow, almost to the hovering point, because the circuits permit almost as wide a range of scanning speeds as a standard Manual-Adjust VLF. If the operator wishes more precise pinpointing, two additional pinpointing methods, electronic pinpointing and de-tuning—can be brought into play.

To activate electronic pinpointing, the handle switch is held in the upward position. This mode sharpens detection signals and activates a non-automatic manual all-metal mode. The detector can be hovered and detection signals are sharpened. Thus, the target can be more accurately pinpointed. If even more precise pinpointing is needed, de-tuning (tuning to the target) can be brought into play. The operator draws an imaginary "X" on the ground, and determines the area where maximum signal occurs. The searchcoil is placed directly upon the ground. The switch is released, momentarily, and then depressed and held. This switching action tunes the detector to the target. As the searchcoil is scanned over the target, a sharp audio sound will be heard when the target is directly below the center point of the searchcoil.

SEARCHCOILS

Almost a full range of searchcoils can be used with some models of Automatic VLF Ground Elimination detectors (Figure 15-5). There are, however, practical limitations. Very few people go coin hunting with a fourteen-inch diameter searchcoil! And since these detectors are not recommended for prospecting, the small three-quarter-inch diameter probes may have very little application.

15-5

	Probing	Super Sniping	Coin Hunting	Cache Hunting	Relic Hunting	Ghost Towning	Nugget Hunting	Vein Locating	Ore Sampling	Black Sand Locating	General Purpose Hunting
¾" to 2"	NOT RECOMMENDED			NOT RECOMMENDED			NOT RECOMMENDED	NOT RECOMMENDED	NOT RECOMMENDED	NOT RECOMMENDED	
3" to 4"		10	8								
7" to 8"		10	10		8	10					10
10"		8	8		8	8					8
12"		6									
14" to 16"											

AUTOMATIC VLF SEARCHCOILS VS APPLICATIONS

The scale of numbers "0" to "10" represent the relative capabilities of the various VLF searchcoil sizes with the "10" being maximum capability. Do not compare capabilities, using these numbers, with other similar tables in this book. A VLF rating of "10" may be more or less capable than a "10" rating of another type metal detector.

Figure 15-5: AUTOMATIC VLF SEARCHCOILS VERSUS APPLICATIONS. This table lists various available searchcoils and gives recommended applications.

The Bloodhound Depth Multiplier attachment is not recommended with this type detector since it requires a slower walking (scanning) speed than regular searchcoils. The automatic function of this type detector prevents the Depth Multiplier from being used efficiently. Three-inch to ten-inch searchcoils are the most popular.

TRASH ELIMINATION

Trash elimination is very good. As stated, this type detector often has difficulty in analyzing large targets and reads most of them as "good". Iron bottlecaps present problems to some models.

COIN HUNTING

The Automatic VLF Ground Elimination type detector quickly acquired a top ranking status with many coin hunters. This occurred because it is very easy to use, and coin response is superb. Battery life of some models is much better than others. Even though many coin hunters know they aren't getting as great a depth as they could with the manually-adjustable VLF types, they prefer the automatic machines.

OPERATION IS EASY

To operate one of the automatic types simply turn the detector on and start scanning. There are no ground elimination adjustments. You can set the audio to either silent or threshold and you make the desired adjustment to the trash elimination modes. If you need more precise pinpointing you can use electronic pinpointing or the de-tuning method if your detector is equipped with these circuits. Wear headphones for improved efficiency. Scan the searchcoil in front of you in the side-to-side motion as explained in this book. Keep in mind that you cannot hover the searchcoil over a target; just scan as you normally would at a rate of about one to two feet per second, and you will get good depth.

Although these detectors do not shape up for electronic prospecting, cache and relic hunting, they do a superb job in coin hunting, and you can count on them to produce quite well in most phases of ghost-towning.

CHAPTER 15 QUESTIONS

1. Automatic tuning circuits keep VLF and TR detectors in "tune" by preventing audio threshold _____ .
2. Automatic VLF ground elimination circuits automatically eliminate the disturbing effects of iron earth _____ .
3. Since automatic VLF metal detectors operate continuously in an automatic "tuning" mode, you can actually hover searchcoils directly above metal targets while pinpointing the target.
   True _____   False _____
4. Automatic VLF metal detectors are recommended primarily for _____ hunting.
5. Since some automatic VLF metal detectors are manufactured with dual target elimination modes you can actually detect and analyze two individual targets simultaneously.
   True _____   False _____
6. Dual target elimination modes allow you to actually program "windows" of detection.
   True _____   False _____

7. When operating a metal detector with "silent" audio, some detection depth AND sensitivity will be lost especially when targets come within the _____ area of detection.

8. All types of metal detectors can be operated at "silent" threshold but the _____ types lose the least amount of depth detection and sensitivity.

9. Since automatic VLF type metal detectors operate normally in an automatic tuning mode, pinpointing may not be precise as when using Manual-Adjust VLF metal detectors.

True _____   False _____

10. To improve pinpointing, when using automatic VLF type detectors, two additional pinpointing methods are used by some manufacturers. These more precise pinpointing methods are called electronic _____ and de- _____ . (Each correct answer is worth 5 points)

Each of the 10 complete questions, answered correctly, is worth 10 points. Perfect score is 100. Answers are given in Appendix 2.

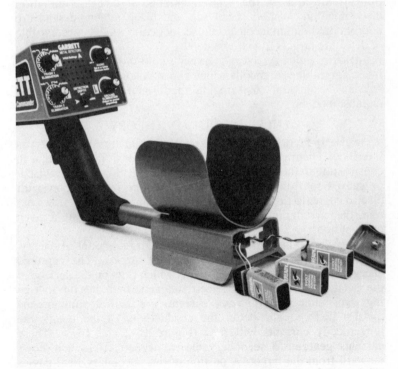

Figure 15-A: This Freedom 2 Coin Commander battery compartment is O-ring sealed to keep out moisture when the detector is placed upon the ground.

CHAPTER 16

Pulse Induction Metal Detector
Short Course

Pulse detectors came into their own during the '80s. Their tremendous value to the ocean beach hunter became apparent soon after the first Trash Elimination models became available. Several characteristics not only set them apart from other detector types, but result in superior performance during extremely adverse conditions.

Pulse Induction detectors are very easy to use. Just set the audio to your preferred threshold level and start scanning. No adjustments are required as these detectors ignore practically all types of minerals. If your detector is equipped with a trash elimination circuit, dial in the desired amount of target elimination discrimination. Wetted ocean salt and black magnetic sand are both ignored simultaneously. Pulse Induction models are capable of detecting targets to extreme depths.

Quality Pulse detectors are very stable. Some models feature interchangeable searchcoils which expand their capabilities. Some have a very pleasant "bell ringing" audio sound. Meters are found on most models.

PULSE INDUCTION THEORY

Pulse Induction detectors are intermittent transmission types (see Block Diagram, Figure 16-1). They use searchcoils similar in construction to those of BFOs. A large electrical current is pulsed, or caused to flow, in the winding. A very intense, powerful, electromagnetic field is generated which illuminates, or flows out into, the surrounding matrix for a very short time during a given cycle period.

The electromagnetic field contains a large amount of energy, some of which is "captured" by metal targets. The captured energy is in the form of eddy currents which flow on the surface of the metal. When the primary electromagnetic field dies out following transmitter shutoff, eddy currents are still flowing on the metal's surface. The better the conductivity of the metal, the longer eddy currents will flow (Figure 16-2 and 16-3). These currents generate a secondary electromagnetic field that flows outward from the target. A portion of this secondary field passes through the pulse antenna winding where some of its energy generates a signal in the winding. During the sample "window"

16-1 BLOCK DIAGRAM OF PULSE INDUCTION METAL DETECTOR

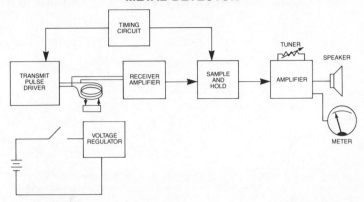

Figure 16-1: ELECTRONIC BLOCK DIAGRAM, PULSE INDUCTION METAL DETECTOR. This block diagram shows the basic circuitry, components and wiring inter-connections of a Pulse Induction metal detector.

PULSE INDUCTION ENERGY (EDDY CURRENT) ABSORPTION AND DECAY IN TARGETS

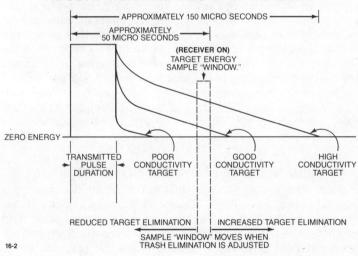

16-2

Figure 16-2: PULSE INDUCTION ENERGY (EDDY CURRENTS) ABSORPTION AND DECAY IN TARGETS. This illustration shows the decay curves of various metal targets. High intensity electromagnetic field pulses, cause eddy currents to flow on the surface of near by targets. As these eddy currents are flowing, secondary electromagnetic field lines are generated. As the eddy currents die out, corresponding reduction in the secondary electromagnetic field strengths occur. This decaying characteristic is plotted in this illustration. Note, that higher conductivity metals sustain eddy current generation longer than lower conductivity metals.

187

PULSE INDUCTION OPERATION
EDDY CURRENT FREQUENCY DECAY COMPARISON

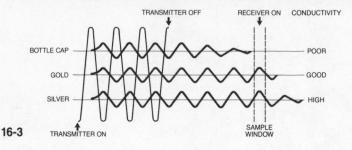

Figure 16-3: PULSE INDUCTION METAL DETECTOR OPERATION, EDDY CURRENT FREQUENCY DECAY COMPARISON. This is a simplfied illustration showing that higher conductivity metals permit eddy currents to flow for the longest periods of time. The lower conductivity metal eddy currents die completely out prior to the receiver circuitry turning on to receive desirable target signals.

period, this signal is amplified and conditioned to drive the "bell ringing" audio which alerts the operator to the presence of metal.

As stated earlier (in Chapter 10), wetted salt and most earth materials are somewhat conductive. The primary field power causes eddy currents to flow in wetted salt and soil mineralization, but the conductivity is so poor that they die out quickly; thus wetted salt and soil mineralization is not detected. In other words, when the transmitter circuit shuts off power to the searchcoil, the receiver circuits "wait" past the time needed for wetted salt and ground mineral eddy currents to die out. Then, the receiver circuits "turn on" and receive the metal target signals. Therefore, conductive ground minerals are ignored and only metal targets are detected. Also, since iron mineralization is not conductive, nor does iron affect the antenna circuits, it is not detected.

PULSE INDUCTION CHARACTERISTICS

Pulse detector circuitry is different from all detector types discussed in this book. BFO, TR and VLF types use a continuous wave type circuit. That is, they transmit the electromagnetic field continuously. Any metal or mineral that sufficiently interrupts the transmitted field produces a signal alerting the operator to the presence of the target.

Pulse detectors are slow response: the target detection process is slower than that of BFO, TR and VLF types. Consequently, target pinpointing is slightly more difficult. Pulse detectors require more battery power. They have an affinity for elongated iron objects; these are detected even in Trash Elimination modes. Eliminator Pulse Induction detectors, however, do an excellent job of eliminating foil, iron bottlecaps, small rusty iron pieces and

188

aluminum pulltabs. At pulltab setting, some rings and nickels may be eliminated.

Eliminator Pulse detectors are popular beach and underwater instruments. It is imperative that they be used on ocean beaches that contain magnetic black sand. VLF and BFO detectors cannot cope with magnetic black sand and salt water simultaneously, whereas a correctly designed pulse detector can. In fact, countless beach swimming areas that have never been scanned adequately are now being worked very efficiently. Coins, rings and jewelry that could not be detected by other types, are now being found.

UNDERWATER HUNTING

Several underwater models, and convertible types that can be used both on land and underwater, are available. Pulse detectors have long been popular with the diver, but Pulse popularity was limited in early years because of high market prices. Modern technology has resulted in greatly reduced production costs and Pulse detectors are now priced very reasonably and competitively.

The availability of various size searchcoils has improved the underwater searcher's capabilities. The depth detection selector, installed on some models, improves diver efficiency and speeds up target recovery time.

In Chapter 17, expanded underwater metal detector operating characteristics and procedures are discussed. Study through the chapter to become better acquainted with Pulse Induction metal detectors.

PULSE AUDIO

Pulse detectors should be tuned for faint threshold sound. The "bell ringing" audio sound is different from VLF and TR detectors. Not all pulse detectors feature this "bell ringing" sound, however. Whatever the characteristics, the audio should not be scratchy or irritating. The special "bell ringing" tends to prevent outside interference noise from masking detector target response, especially when underwater where its sound is especially pleasing.

SEARCHCOILS

Various sizes of searchcoils are being manufactured for certain models of Pulse units (Figure 11-2). The most popular sizes are in the seven-inch to ten-inch category. There is not a great amount of difference between these as far as depth capability is concerned. Ten-inch searchcoils scan a slightly wider area but require more pinpointing expertise. Consequently, the smaller size searchcoils are the most popular.

Small, specialty type, searchcoils such as the three-and-one-half-inch size are very good in small, confined areas. They are good for Super-Sniping and will detect coins (and rings, etc.) close to metal fences, sidewalks, cannon and other near by large objects. Large Pulse searchcoils, such as the twelve-inch size, produce greater depth. Larger searchcoils are heavier and more difficult to use in wooded areas, on rocky lake bottoms and among ocean coral and other growth.

The accompanying chart (Figure 16-4) lists the various uses to which Pulse detectors are suited and the optimum size searchcoils to use.

16-4

	Probing	Super Sniping	Coin Hunting	Cache Hunting	Relic Hunting	Ghost Towning	Nugget Hunting	Vein Locating	Ore Sampling	Black Sand Locating	General Purpose Hunting
3″ to 4″	7	10	8								
8″ to 10″		10		8	NOT REC	NOT REC	NOT REC	NOT REC	NOT REC		10
12″ to 14″		8	10	8							8
LARGER			10								

PULSE INDUCTION SEARCHCOILS VS APPLICATIONS

The scale of numbers "0" to "10" represent the relative capabilities of the various PULSE searchcoil sizes with "10" being maximum capability. Do not compare capabilities, using these numbers, with other similar tables in this book. A PULSE rating of "10" may be more or less capable than a "10" rating of another type of metal detector.

Figure 16-4: PULSE INDUCTION SEARCHCOILS VERSUS APPLICATIONS. This table will help you select the proper searchcoils for all Pulse Induction metal detector applications.

APPLICATIONS

Pulse detectors readily penetrate layers of black magnetic sand and wetted salt to locate coins, rings, and other metal objects to extreme depths. In fact, detection through beach mineralized sand can be greater than detection through air. Reports of single rings and coins being detected twelve to eighteen inches and deeper are often reported.

Cache and relic hunting with large searchcoils produces good results. Pulse detectors can be used in building searching, but nails may be a problem. Pulse detectors can be used for any type coin hunting applications, but where small iron trash abounds, VLF types may have to be used.

Pulse detectors are not recommended for any form of electronic prospecting. The form factor of nuggets and veins prevents good detection. ''Hot rocks'' respond and appear as metal targets.

190

Pulse Induction detectors fill a very important slot in the field of metal detection, without the Pulse, much treasure and other searched-for metals would not be found. Without hesitation, you should acquire a quality Pulse if your search for treasure takes you to the beach, especially salt water beaches. Deeply buried coins, gold and silver rings, and other jewelry you should find, will quickly pay off the investment. (See Chapter 13 for discussion of BEACH HUNTING WITH TRs.)

CHAPTER 16 QUESTIONS

1. One of the reasons why Pulse Induction type metal detectors are extremely easy to use, is because wetted ocean salt and black magnetic sand are both ignored automatically, and simultaneously.
   True _____ False _____

2. The reason why these instruments are called "Pulse Induction" is because they intermittently pulse (or transmit) a large amount of electromagnetic field energy into the matrix (especially metal targets) beneath the searchcoil.
   True _____ False _____

3. When eddy currents start flowing on the surface of metal targets, a secondary electromagnetic field is generated which travels upward and intersects the Pulse Induction searchcoil.
   True _____ False _____

4. Since ground minerals and low conductivity (reject) targets do not generate eddy currents, they are not detected by Pulse Induction detectors.
   True _____ False _____

5. Immediately, after the Pulse Induction detector transmits a large burst of electromagnetic field energy into the matrix, all circuits "shut-down." The receiver circuitry turns on: (A) when the operator pushes a button at the right time; (B) when enough secondary electromagnetic field signal is received at the antenna; (C) after a pre-determined amount of time has passed; (D) when the operator has rested enough to want to dig another target.

6. Pulse Induction type metal detectors are called "slower response" detectors because: (A) the target detection process is slower than other detector types; (B) of the extra battery power required; (C) the detector has only one antenna that acts both as a transmitter and receiver winding; (D) the Pulse Induction detector detects only metal.

7. It's a proven fact that Pulse Induction detectors operate easier than other types in most salt water environments, especially, when black magnetic sand is present in the soil.
   True _____ False _____

8. The most popular Pulse Induction searchcoils are the eight-inch to ten-inch diameter sizes.
   True _____   False _____
9. Because Pulse Induction detectors work so well both on the beach and in the water, convertible types have been built that allow both wet and dry hunting.
   True _____   False _____
10. You can improve your pinpointing capabilities with Pulse Induction detectors by using which two of the following techniques: (A) scanning at a slightly slower than normal speed; (B) using more powerful batteries; (C) by using smaller searchcoils; (D) hovering over each target and counting to ten before taking a reading. (Each correct answer is worth 5 points)

Each of the 10 complete questions answered correctly, is worth 10 points. Perfect score is 100. Answers given in Appendix 2.

Figure 16-A: This is just a few of the many rings and jewelry items that a New England couple have found during their water searches. Beginning in the early '80s, surf hunting and beachcombing began a remarkable and almost meteoric rise to popularity. For several years, many professional beachcombers have made a living working the beaches, but only recently has beach hunting become popular among the hobbyist.

Figure 16-B: Young Sally Blue searches Padre Island with her Pulse Induction detector, locating coins and jewelry items lost by surfers.

Figure 16-C: Professional treasure hunter, Eleanor Hube, during the past several years, has turned her attention to the lucrative surf. Formally, she was a coin hunter who searched mostly parks, playgrounds and other dry areas. Because of her water hunting success, she now devotes most of her time searching for treasure lost by swimmers and those who love the ocean's popular beach areas. Here are several finds she made, during one outing, on a beach in Connecticut.

Figure 16-D: Artist Melvin Climer recreated an underwater salvage success story, which you see here in the above drawing. Melvin created this scene after viewing the film TREASURES OF THE INDIAN OCEAN starring Robert Marx. This 16 mm and video cassette film is available, on a loan basis, from Garrett Electronics, to all outdoor groups and clubs.

Figure 16-E: Ciro Plebe, Garrett Electronics' Italian distributor, searches for sunken treasure off the coast of Italy. Ciro has a unique arrangement worked out with the Italian government. He works designated sites for a percentage of his finds. He has turned over many priceless objects and treasures to the Italian government.

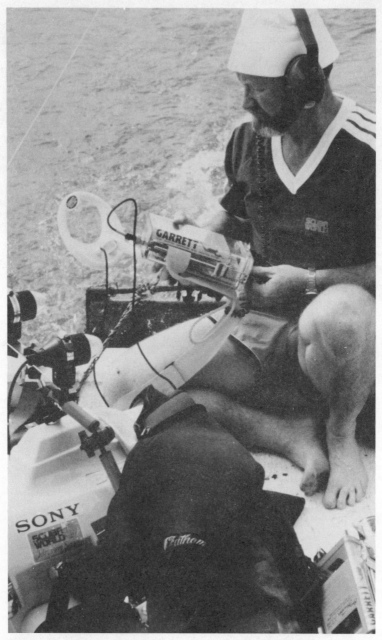

Figure 16-F: Charles Garrett checks his metal detection and other diving gear, in preparation for a dive. He and Bob Podhrasky were part of a Scuba World team who went on an expedition to Colombia. This location proved to be a perfect place for underwater exploration.

Underwater Metal Detector Short Course

There are five types of underwater metal detector circuits: BFO, TR, VLF, Automatic VLF and Pulse Induction. The first four types are primarily for fresh water operation. Pulse Induction can be used in both fresh and salt water. Certain of the VLF and Automatic VLF types may have slightly better Trash Elimination performance than Pulse Induction, but the Pulse types are the easiest to use.

To improve your understanding of underwater types, read this chapter and study the various manufacturer's literature. Basically, and very broadly, if you are planning to search mainly in fresh water, one of the first four types may be best suited. If the ground contains magnetic black sand, the VLF and Pulse types may be best. If your search leads you mainly into salt water, the Pulse may be the preferred type.

Some models have interchangeable searchcoils. The VLFs and Automatic VLFs have somewhat different trash elimination characteristics from the Pulse. To operate Pulse instruments, you need only to adjust the audio threshold to your preferred level. The other types may require an adjustment of more than one knob to achieve operation over magnetic black sand and salt water.

Some models are convertible, they can be used on land, in the surf, and submerged to two hundred feet. Some have land headphones while others come standard with submersible (consequently, totally environmentally protected) ones. Some use standard batteries, others, rechargeables.

On ocean beaches that contain no magnetic black sand, any of the five types can be used in dry sand. To operate in wetted sand or in the surf, you will have difficulty using BFO types. TRs and all VLFs must be operated in the Trash Elimination (discrimination) mode or salt water will present problems.

BFO DETECTORS

BFO detectors cannot cancel or be adjusted to ignore magnetic black sand or salt water, they are best used in fresh water situations where black sand is not present. Among quality instruments, BFOs give poorest detection depth. Their searchcoils do not have as wide a dynamic range as the other's.

TR DETECTORS

TRs are primarily fresh water detectors unless they have an adjustable Trash Elimination mode. Then, when used in salt water, the adjustment must remain at that setting. If black magnetic sand is present, the TR cannot eliminate it from detection, and some "tricks" must be used to ease the problem. (See Chapter 13).

TRs can be made to have very good detection depth. In the proper environment, only the audio control need be adjusted to achieve your preferred audio threshold level. Discriminating TRs do a very good job of eliminating trash targets and will detect coins and rings to good depths. Use only correctly calibrated TRs for prospecting and then only according to manufacturer's recommendations.

VLF DETECTORS

VLF type circuitry cannot eliminate from detection both iron mineral (black sand or magnetite) and salt water, simultaneously. The Trash Elimination mode can be adjusted to cancel wetted ocean beach sand and salt water, but not iron minerals. The VLF mode can be adjusted to cancel iron minerals but not saline solutions. This is why VLF types are recommended for fresh water use.

VLFs give excellent detection depth on coins, rings, and other metals. The Trash Elimination mode gives superior performance. In fresh water that contains no magnetic black sand, no adjustments are required for operation except to set the Trash Elimination control to your preferred level. The VLF Ground Elimination control should be set to mid-range. When beach and lake bottoms contain black magnetic sand, the VLF Ground Elimination control must be set to eliminate the magnetic material from detection. The adjustment is simple to perform.

VLF instruments that are correctly designed and have proper adjustment controls, can be used with good success in highly mineralized prospecting zones (Figure 17-1). These detectors work just the same above water as below, and can be used when searching for nuggets in dry areas in the VLF mode.

PULSE INDUCTION DETECTORS

As explained, Pulse Induction detectors simultaneously ignore both black magnetic sand and salt water. The Pulse, then, is the preferred, almost mandatory, type of detector to use where these conditions prevail, as off the coast in the New England states and on many of the beaches in California, Oregon and Washington.

Pulse detectors are easy to use. Simply turn the detector on, adjust audio for faint threshold sound and commence scanning. Quality Pulse detectors will operate with perfect stability, with the utmost precision, almost regardless of environmental conditions.

198

Figure 17-1: This photograph is a scene from the Garrett Electronics' film, TREASURES OF THE INDIAN OCEAN, starring Robert Marx. Marx examines several coins he recovered, which were part of a ship's cargo lost during a shipwreck off the coast of Madagascar hundreds of years ago. Underwater metal detectors increase the efficiency of treasure salvors by locating all types of metal objects, defining shipwreck perimeters, and identifying precious metal objects. Iron and other lower conductivity metals can be left for later salvage work. Photo Courtesy Robert Marx Archives.

If there is an adjustable sensitivity control, select the amount you want. If the detector features Trash Elimination, select the degree of rejection you desire. Coins, rings, relics and other metals can be detected to extreme depths.

Pulse detectors are not recommended for prospecting. Gold nugget detection may be poor and "hot rocks" are difficult to identify before digging.

UNDERWATER DETECTOR CONSTRUCTION

Underwater detectors are considerably more difficult to manufacture than are land models. A great amount of skill, planning, design, bench and field testing and retesting, and extremely exacting production methods must be followed in order to build quality underwater detectors (see Figure 17-2). The housing must be water tight and able to withstand great pressure. Salt environments will quickly damage ferrous metals.

In order to turn on detector power and to control the detector's various functions, control shafts must be brought out through the housing and these must not only be sealed against water, but also against contamination that is ever-present in underwater environments. The most common method of sealing the shafts that penetrate through bulkheads is the use of single or dual O-ring seals. O-rings are extremely efficient and when properly constructed will provide perfect seals.

199

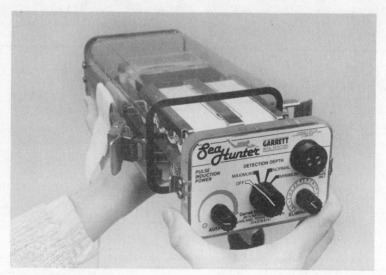

Figure 17-2: A great amount of planning, design, bench and field testing, and exacting production methods must be followed in order to build quality underwater detectors. Underwater environments, especially salt water environments, are extremely hostile to electronic components. Consequently, the housing must be totally submersible. Great sea depth pressures must be withstood by underwater detector housings. Photo by Melvin Climer.

Since salt is very corrosive and will ruin electronic components, moisture-absorbing desiccant should be installed in the control housing.

UNDERWATER DETECTOR TRASH ELIMINATION

Elimination of trash metals can be achieved in all types of underwater detectors. Pulse detectors were the last ones in which the problems of rejecting trash metals were solved. They do an excellent job of rejecting foil, iron bottlecaps and small "junk" metals, including aluminum pulltabs. Some rings and nickels may not be detected at the pulltab setting, and depending upon the amount of rust present, nails may not be rejected.

SELECTABLE DEPTH DETECTION

A selectable detection depth control (Figure 17-3) expands the versatility of an underwater detector. Objects that have just recently been lost in water can be found more readily when the control is set to minimum depth detection. Deeper metal objects are ignored while only surface or shallow objects are detected. In a situation where an extreme amount of junk is present, lower settings will eliminate most erratic responses. Individual metal targets are more readily detected at the lower depth setting.

Detection depth selection gives the operator a marked degree of ability to determine object depth. For example, when the opera-

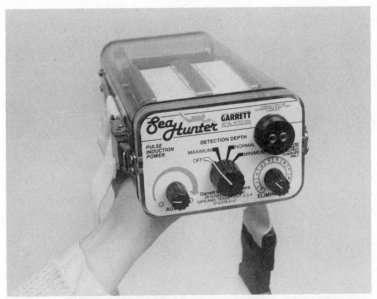

Figure 17-3: Selectable detection depth controls expand versatility. There are many reasons, as explained in the text, why detection depth controls add to the versatility and capability of underwater detectors. Photo by Melvin Climer.

tor is operating with full detection depth and detects a target, a quick switch to a lower setting will allow the operator to compare detection signal levels which, when interpreted, gives target depth.

MECHANICAL CONFIGURATIONS

Mechanical configurations are mainly of two types. One, built primarily for underwater searching (Figure 17-1) is usually constructed compactly with a short stem and suitable gripping handle and armrest. The operator scans with the searchcoil and whenever a metal object is encountered, needs only to extend his free hand to the point of detection to recover the object. Long stem detectors are not practical for underwater scanning.

The second type of construction is sometimes called the universal or convertible type (Figure 17-4) and can be used either on land or underwater. This instrument is usually built with a control housing that is mounted on a person's body with a suitable quick-release belt strap. A cable connects the control housing to the searchcoil. The searchcoil is mounted on a long, adjustable-length stem suitable for land searching. The operator simply walks along scanning the searchcoil over the ground the same as when using conventional land detectors. If wished, the operator can walk right out into the surf and continue scanning for surf treasure.

A suitable means of underwater scanning with the convertible

Figure 17-4: Not only are ocean environments hostile to metal detectors, they are hostile to metal detector operators! Consequently, during winter months, detector operators must go well equipped to withstand the elements. Here, Jack Lowry is well equipped to search for and recover coins from this Galveston beach. The Pulse instrument he is using is convertible, in that it can be used on land, as well as submerged 200 feet. Photo by Monty Moncrief.

type is with a short stem or handle about one foot in length. The searchcoil is attached to one end (Figure 17-5). The connecting cable connects the searchcoil to the control housing, which is mounted on the operator's waist, arm or leg. The operator then swims in a horizontal position, grasping the handle grip, scanning the searchcoil along the bottom. To recover detected targets, the operator merely extends his free hand forward to the point of detection. It is not efficient for a diver to use a long stem because it is a waste of time and energy to have to extend the free hand so far forward to retrieve detected targets.

SEARCHCOIL SELECTION

The selection of underwater detector searchcoils (Figure 17-6) follows the same rules as given for selection of land detector searchcoils. The smaller the searchcoil, the smaller the object that can be detected. The larger the searchcoil, the greater the distance an object can be detected from the searchcoil, but the larger the object must be.

Small three-inch to four-inch diameter searchcoils scan a more narrow path than larger ones and can pinpoint targets easier, detect

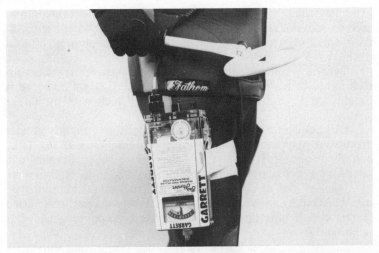

Figure 17-5: Because scuba divers are already loaded down with a multitude of diving gear, including heavy weight belts, divers can be ingenius when it comes to mounting underwater detectors. Housings can be attached to the diver's waist, arm or leg. Many divers attach the control housing to the air tank. In this photograph, the diver is preparing to dive with the housing attached to the upper part of his leg. Caution must be exercised, when attaching the housing to a person's limb, to insure blood circulation is not restricted. This diver has sewn Velcro to his wetsuit and to the detector beltstrap. This allows the detector belt to be attached loosely to the leg, preventing the detector from sliding down the leg when worn underwater.

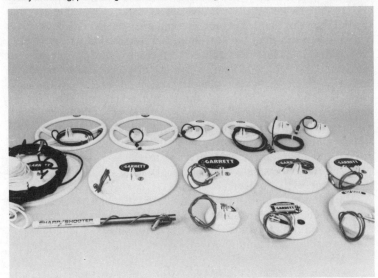

Figure 17-6: Divers, as well as surfers, need a large selection of submersible searchcoils, in order to be prepared for every metal detecting task. This photograph shows many different sizes and types of underwater searchcoils. Several are for land/beach use only, while others can be submerged to 200 feet. If you are in doubt as to the type searchcoil you need, discuss the matter with your dealer and/or the factory. Photo by Melvin Climer.

203

extremely small metal targets, and can be used in confined areas such as between large rocks, boulders, coral and bottom growth. Also, small searchcoils are well suited for operation in high metal trash areas.

General purpose searchcoils range in diameter from seven-inch to ten-inch. Within this searchcoil range, target response is roughly equal, but pinpointing is more difficult with the larger sizes.

Larger than ten-inch diameter searchcoils give slightly greater depth, but pinpointing is even more difficult. Of course, if the bottom is primarily loose sand, then pinpointing, digging and retrieving is not nearly the problem it would be if the bottom were hard packed clay or coral. Consider that when surf hunting, you may be standing in water up to your waist or deeper, recovering targets with a long handled scoop, precise pinpointing becomes important!

Larger searchcoils are desirable during preliminary shipwreck and other site searches. When it comes to the actual search of these sites, if Target Elimination is used, smaller searchcoils can identify individual targets more readily. Thus, items such as gold, silver and copper coins can be more readily identified even if lots of junk targets are present. As discussed under Super-Sniping (in Chapter 10) good and "trash" targets have the effect of canceling one another when trash elimination is used. Consequently, the smaller the searchcoil, the more good items you should recover. Of course, keep in mind, smaller diameter searchcoils will not penetrate as deeply as larger searchcoils. In cases where there is a lot of junk mixed in with good targets, it may be necessary for you to scan a given site with two or more searchcoil sizes. In loose sand areas, scan the area first with the largest searchcoil. This allows fast coverage of a site and deeper "good" targets will be detected. Then rework the area with smaller searchcoils. "Good" targets "lost" among the trash will now be more correctly identified. In difficult digging and recovery areas (hard-packed clay, "concrete" coral, etc.) use the smaller searchcoils first for quicker recovery of shallow, individual objects.

In shipwreck high junk areas where valuable gold coins and other objects may be present, it may be desirable to use "zero" or rusty iron elimination only. You'll dig more junk, but you may also dig more silver and gold.

BATTERIES

Some underwater detectors are equipped with standard batteries that need to be replaced periodically while others are equipped with rechargeables. Good design dictates that underwater detectors should be manufactured with rechargeable batteries, with the instrument sealed at the factory. Underwater detectors with conventional, non-rechargeable batteries which must be periodically replaced, may lead to grave problems, great expense and lost time for the operator. Unless extreme caution is used when replacing batteries, the circuitry can be destroyed. A single drop of salt water on a printed circuit board can cause an instant short circuit and destruction of electronic circuitry. Any moisture that is left inside a housing will cause rust, thus slowly deteriorating metal components. Of course, it is more expensive and difficult to produce detectors with rechargeable batteries, but in the long run is far cheaper and certainly results in better detectors.

The detector shown in Figure 17-7 has a unique system for recharging its batteries. The recharge connector is the same one to which the headphones are attached. Whenever the detector batteries are to be recharged, the operator simply unscrews the headphones and screws the battery recharger into the same connector.

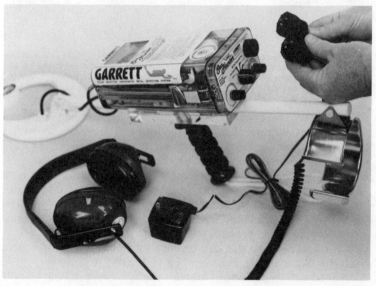

Figure 17-7: This Sea Hunter has a unique, built-in system for recharging its batteries. The recharge adapter is plugged into the connector shown on the control panel. This panel connector, however, is the same connector to which the headphones are connected. Photo by Melvin Climer.

UNDERWATER HEADPHONES VERSUS BONE CONDUCTORS

There are two types of underwater audio signalling apparatus: headphones and bone conductors (Figure 17-8). Because of underwater headphone stringent design specifications, less audio power is produced for a given power expenditure from the battery.

205

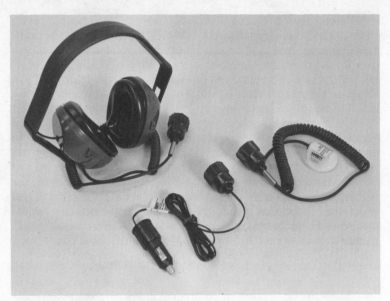

Figure 17-8: There are two underwater audio signaling apparatus: headphones (left) and bone conductors (right). Headphones are preferred because of the greater sound volume and rejection of outside noise interference. Headphones can be used underwater and on land, but bone conductors can only be used underwater. Also shown, is an automobile, 12-volt, recharge adapter. Photo by Melvin Climer.

Consequently, underwater headphones and bone conductors tend to produce less volume than land units. Properly designed underwater headphones produce more audio power than bone conductors.

Dual piece underwater headphones offer the same advantages, basically, as land detectors: the sound being channeled into both ears, and a reduction of outside noise interference. The major sources of outside noise are the scuba diver's exhaust air bubbles when the operator is submerged and surf noises when the operator is working on ocean beaches or in the surf.

There is not a lot that can be done to overcome the air bubble problem. Some divers have learned to breathe at a slower, more controlled rate with longer breath spacing. Since scuba schools warn against skip breathing, each individual must work out his own procedure if air bubbles are a bother. Some divers are not bothered by air exhaust noise and lose no detection capability.

Bone conductors are held against an ear or a temple area by the mask strap. Bone conductors, of course, are smaller and don't get in the way as much as headphones. Their convenience, however, may be offset by the outside noises that can come into the ears. Which a person uses, is a matter of preference. Obviously, bone conductors cannot be worn when ground searching above water; the audio will not be as loud outside the water as when submerged.

MAINTENANCE

Because of extremely hostile underwater environments, it is recommended that underwater detector O-rings and other seals be replaced and lubricated every other year by the manufacturer, and that the detector be cleaned, retested, and recertified. Foreign matter is present in most bodies of water. Sand and microscopic particles can filter down into the control shafts and become lodged between the O-rings and the shafts thus creating a potential problem. The cost of regular maintenance is certainly less than the cost of a complete overhaul if salt water should seep into a detector through a seal. Like your automobile, your underwater detector should be given regular maintenance.

CONCLUSION

Before purchasing an underwater detector, you should determine when and where the instrument will be used. Are you going to use the detector both underwater and on land, in fresh and/or salt water? Do you need interchangeable searchcoils? Will you be searching for gold nuggets in water where iron minerals are present? Will you be searching for gold and silver coins among iron trash?

Features like target elimination, interchangeable searchcoils, selectable depth, rechargeable batteries, land/sea conversion stems and ground elimination capability should be considered and perhaps required in the detector you purchase. There are countless millions of dollars' worth of treasure lost in the water; give thought to finding a share for yourself! (See Chapter 22 for the selection, and use of beach, surf, and underwater metal detectors).

CHAPTER 17 QUESTIONS

1. There are _____ (quantity) types of underwater metal detector circuits.
2. Which type of underwater detectors are the easiest to use?
3. BFO and TR underwater detectors cannot be adjusted to ignore magnetic _____ _____ .
4. VLF type underwater detectors can be adjusted to eliminate, from detection, both iron minerals and salt water, but not do it _____ .
5. The fact stated in Question 4 is one of the main reasons why VLF types are recommended primarily for _____ water use.
6. Pulse Induction metal detectors are so easy to use that usually all you have to do is turn the power on and adjust for faint _____ sound.

7. A selectable depth detection switch is desirable because (select best answers): (A) the ability to determine object depth is improved; (B) the need for using different sizes of searchcoils is eliminated; (C) the operator can readily determine which targets are shallow and which are deep; (D) recently lost articles can usually be found much faster.

8. Long stem underwater detector configurations are inefficient underwater because it is difficult for the operator to extend his free hand to the point of _____ to recover detected objects.

9. For underwater hunting, it is most desirable to have more than one _____ searchcoil.

10. When surf hunting precise pinpointing is extremely important because (select the most appropriate answers): (A) you might damage the object you are recovering; (B) it is more difficult to recover objects underwater than on land; (C) you'll dig too many bottlecaps; (D) precise pinpointing speeds up your recovery time and improves your efficiency.

11. Good underwater detector design dictates that rechargeable batteries be used. Why? (select best answers): (A) permanently sealed detectors eliminate salt water damage to internal circuitry; (B) operator saves money by not having to buy throw-away type batteries; (C) you get a higher voltage from rechargeables than from standard batteries; (D) standard batteries weigh a lot less than rechargeable batteries.

12. Which is the preferred type of underwater audio device to use?: (A) loud speaker; (B) bone conductor; (C) headphones; (D) a bell.

13. When headphone type audio devices are used, signals are more powerful and outside interference noises are muffled.
    True _____   False _____

14. Name four features that improve the performance of underwater metal detectors.

Each correct answer given to the multiple-answer questions 7,10,11 and 14 is worth 5 points. There is a total of 12 correct answers in these four questions for a total correct value of 60 points. Each correct answer given to the remaining ten questions are worth 4 points each. Perfect score is 100. Answers given in Appendix 2.

Figure 17-A: Here are a few rings found on a Florida beach.

Figure 17-B: Darrell Kilburn of Fairport, New York spends his spare time searching the beaches. As can be seen in this photograph, he is quite successful.

209

Figure 17-D: Bill Bosh, noted gold hunter, has turned surfer when he is not in Australia. Here are the coins, rings, and other things he found with his Sea Hunter at one swimming location. Note the camera lens.

Figure 17-E: This is a nice assortment of treasure that Bob Lieberz of Toledo, Ohio has accumulated, weekends, over an eight-month period. He mostly scans Florida beaches.

Figure 17-F: Here is a great assortment of rings and coins found by one obviously successful surf and beach hunter.

Figure 17-G: Lyle Mendicino, President of Seabred Corporation, P.O. Box 290357, Ft. Lauderdale, Florida 33329, manufactures a line of Sport Dolphins one of which is shown here. A Sport Dolphin is an efficient battery-powered underwater propulsion device, but to make it more functional, various accessories, including lights, can be installed. Here, Lyle has installed a Sea Hunter, converting the Sport Dolphin into a very compact, efficient, underwater metal detector. Photo Courtesy Seabred Corporation.

Figure 17-H: Famed underwater archaeologist and treasure salvor, Robert Marx and Charles Garrett discuss the metal detection needs of professional underwater archaeologists and treasure salvors. The author is holding one of many silver ingots that Bob has located during his lifetime of underwater salvage and recovery. Photo by Jenifer Marx.

Figure 17-I: Model Kim Acker (Miss Grand Prairie, Texas) poses with found treasure as Ric Nesbit (left) and Hal Martin photograph Kim for a Garrett Electronic's television commercial for Scuba World. Scuba World president, Perry Tong, and his crew travel the world filming their television series at exotic diving locations. Photo Courtesy Scuba World Television Series.

Figure 17-J: There is no limit to the valuable underwater recoveries that can be made. Laney Rinehart and Associate of Albany, Georgia pose beside this monstrous ship's prop they recovered using the latest underwater salvage techniques.

Figure 17-K: Charles Garrett scans in shallow water searching for crime scene evidence. The two men standing on the embankment are Dallas policemen who contacted the author requesting his assistance in this search. Photo Courtesy Dallas Police Department.

Figure 17-L: Charles Garrett, Jim Cross and Dave Loveless (camerman) survey various houses that were damaged when the town of Thistle, Utah was covered by rising water. A mudslide blocked one end of the valley causing water from a river to slowly rise to a depth of 150 feet. Cross International surveyed various submerged bridges, roads, railroad tracks, traffic signals and other structures to determine their condition. Garrett underwater equipment was brought into play to assist the divers in quickly locating the tracks, signals, and other submerged metal objects covered by mud and concealed in the darkness of the water.

Figure 17-N: A Cross International crew prepares a diver who will soon be descending to the depths of the lake created when the town of Thistle, Utah was submerged following a mudslide that blocked a river. The diver used the Sea Hunter metal detector to locate railroad tracks and other metal objects that were covered by mud.

Figure 17-P: This is another photograph taken at the site of Thistle, Utah. Note the mudslide in the back that caused the river to be blocked which resulted in the town, in the valley, to be flooded. Jim Cross, to immediate left in rubber raft, instructs his crew as they prepare to take underwater readings with a submersible searchcoil.

Figure 17-Q: Charles Garrett admires a chain of gold and silver rings found by beach hunter Wallace Chandler. Wallace, a professional hunter, has devoted most of his time during the past fifteen years searching America's beaches for lost treasure. Photo by Melvin Climer.

Figure 17-R: Robert Marx scans piles of Spanish Pieces of Eight that he recovered from a Spanish shipwreck, the Nuestra Senora de la Maravilla. Underwater salvage requires a tremendous amount of research and hardwork, but the rewards often make it all worthwhile. Read QUEST FOR TREASURE by Robert Marx, published by Ram Books. Photo Courtesy Robert Marx Archives.

Figure 17-S: Ric Nesbit, of the Scuba World crew, and Charles Garrett examine clumps of coral that contain Spanish Pieces of Eight. This shipwreck site, off the coast of South America, cannot, at this time, be revealed. Photo by Robert Podhrasky.

Figure 17-T: Each year, THE DIVING EQUIPMENT MANUFACTURERS ASSOCIATION (DEMA), sponsors the DEMA show. Underwater diving equipment manufacturers set up booths and display their products. For many years Garrett Metal Detectors has displayed its products at DEMA shows. Here, Charles Garrett talks with prospective equipment dealers. Note the "diving" mannequin "swimming" in the air above the booth. The mannequin is using a Sea Hunter to search for treasure. Photo by Monty Moncrief.

Figure 17-U: Jim Cross, President of Cross International, shouts instructions to one of his crew members. They are rigging a Garrett Sea Hunter in the nose of the submarine. A large, specially designed searchcoil, will provide the submariner with a safe means of quickly scanning the floor of lakes, to great depths, in search of metal objects. Photo by Dave Loveless.

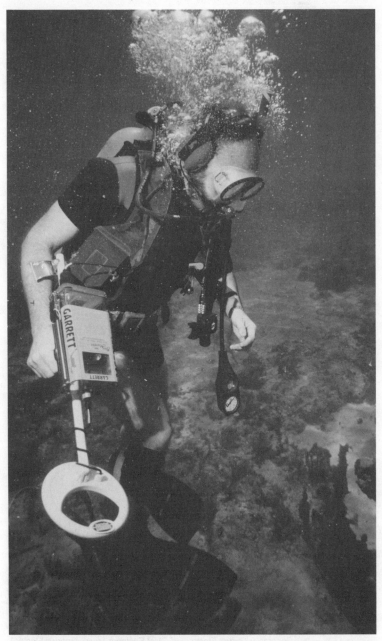

Figure 17-V: Charles Garrett descends to the bottom off the coast of South America. At this site, Spanish cannon were stacked up like cordwood—eighteen in one location. Photo by Hal Martin.

Figure 17-W: Robert Marx scans near this ancient anchor for gold escudos. Many years ago a ship ran aground and spilled its contents on the bottom. Precious cargo awaited the modern-day treasure diver equipped with efficient, underwater, treasure recovery equipment.

Figure 17-X: Robert Podhrasky, Garrett Electronics' Chief Engineer assists General Electric's engineers in encapsulating a two-box Bloodhound Depth Multiplier in a submersible ocean sled. General Electric rigged the device for bottom towing to locate sunken aircraft components. Photo Courtesy General Electric Corp.

220

Figure 17-Y: When working the surf, it is efficient to use a treasure recovery basket. When the surfer gets a metal detector reading, an underwater scoop is deployed to retrieve the detected object. Sand, mud, rock, shell and other debris also come up in the scoop. The contents is dumped into this basket but sand, rock, and other trash filters back into the water leaving the detected object exposed. This recovery basket is assembled using a thirteen-inch automobile intertube and a Garrett "Gravity Trap" Gold Pan Classifier, Model 16502.

Figure 17-CC: Gordon Culpepper (left), and George Garrett (author's brother) listen to a conversation between Jim Cross (center) and his brother John, who, at this time, is searching the lake bottom for certain sunken items. This two-way communications system is not only invaluable as for as diver safety is concerned but also improves diving efficiency.

221

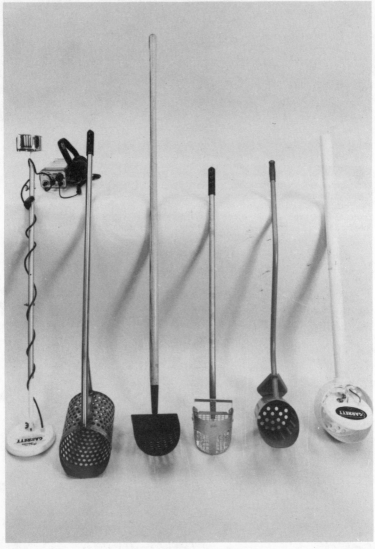

Figure 17-Z: Here are various underwater scoops. The scoop at the right, manufactured by Kenneth Wherry of Faulkton, SD is unique, in that it contains a submersible metal detector searchcoil.

Figure 17-AA: Eleanor Hube of Suffield, Connecticut is probably the most active, lady, underwater treasure hunter in the world. She regularly scans the east coast swimming areas and often travels to islands in the Caribbean where she combines her vacations with her favorite hobby . . . treasure recovery.

Figure 17-BB: Gary Lee (left), and John and Jim Cross (Cross International) assist Charles Garrett in suiting up to dive in an East Texas lake. Since this story has not come to a conclusion, its details cannot be told. Photo by Dave Loveless.

Law Enforcement and Security Metal Detector Short Course

This chapter is a complete short course on the selection, understanding, field application and operation of law enforcement and security metal detectors. The chapter consists of the following five sections:

I. Selection of metal detectors: How to select the correct type for law enforcement and security applications.
II. The metal detector: An important tool in the management of crime scene investigations.
III. General law enforcement and security applications.
IV. Metal detector search techniques.
V. Summary: The law enforcement metal detector and its deployment.

I. SELECTION OF METAL DETECTORS: HOW TO SELECT THE CORRECT TYPE FOR LAW ENFORCEMENT AND SECURITY APPLICATIONS.

The use of metal detectors in law enforcement and security is becoming increasingly important to the FBI and other governmental agencies including the Post Office department, the Internal Revenue Service, and the Bureau of Alcohol Tobacco and Firearms; various state and local agencies including prisons, correctional institutions, Fish and Wildlife departments, and local police and sheriff's departments. Garrett Electronics personnel have been working with law enforcement professionals in developing specialized metal detection equipment, assisting them in conducting metal detection training seminars, and teaching men and women one more skill to use in crime prevention and crime scene management. Law enforcement personnel have been eager to learn, and have quickly grasped metal detection concepts relating to their specialized work.

The law enforcement community has been aware of the utility of metal detection in crime scene management for many years; however, this investigative tool has been shunned or ignored, for the most part, as a credible tool for the crime scene investigator. It may be that many agencies view metal detectors as toys, used only by coin and treasure hunters, and, as such, unworthy of their consideration. Many law enforcement agencies, however, have metal detecting devices in their crime scene management equipment,

225

but unfortunately, many of these instruments are obsolete, some of World War II vintage, and others of extremely poor quality, purchased on a low-bid basis.

During the 1970s when terrorism showed a marked rise, a greater need for specialty metal detection equipment and expertise became apparent. Some agents of the FBI became specialists in this field and have developed exhaustive metal detection training seminars.

There are many areas in the field of law enforcement, such as security and crime scene management, where valuable strides are being made in the use of metal detectors. Superior equipment is being developed, and certainly the metal detector has come to the forefront as a recognized and valuable law enforcement and security investigative tool.

In the field of law enforcement, security, and crime scene investigation, the needs for metal detection are many and varied. One day an officer may need to search in a roadside snowbank to recover a pistol that was hastily discarded by a fleeing bank robber (Figure 18-1). On another occasion, the same officer may be called on to search the cold, swiftly flowing waters of a river where stolen goods or other metal evidence has been discarded (Figure 18-2). The officer may also be required to scan a bookcase (Figure 18-3) for hidden contraband, or a wooded area for a buried jewelry

Figure 18-1: Even though it was very cold, Dave Loveless (left), and Richard Graham spent two days scanning this field to locate a pistol discarded by a fleeing suspect. Near the end of the second day, Richard found the pistol beneath one foot of snow.

Figure 18-2: Richard Graham searches the cold, swiftly flowing waters of this river trying to locate metal evidence that was discarded a few months earlier. Both land and underwater detectors were brought into play. Richard searches with a submersible underwater Sea Hunter XL 500. His search proved the evidence was not there, an important fact in itself.

Figure 18-3: When metal evidence is to be located, the metal detector becomes a very important crime scene management tool. This powerful metal detector, the Inspector, Model G-100, easily penetrates all non-metallic material to locate concealed metal objects.

cache. Searching a wall for a spent .22 caliber projectile, or a lake for a stolen safe (Figure 18-4), may now be undertaken by the officer trained in metal detection.

Figure 18-4: Garland Patrol Officer, Bennelle L. Baker (left), Charles Garrett and Bob Podhrasky examine the stolen safe they recovered from a North Texas rock quarry. Two safes, two vending machine coin changers, and an automobile were located and removed from this lake in one afternoon. Photo courtesy Garland Police Department.

DESIGN FEATURES

The design features of law enforcement and security detectors must include dependability, reliability, ruggedness, and simplicity of operation. All controls must be minimized and simplified. Simplified controls are important since various officers in a department may be required to use any one given detector. A detector may sit on a shelf for an extended period of time until its services are needed. The officer should not be required to master the operation of complicated detectors. Detection instruments must be operated regularly to insure continued officer proficiency. For the above reasons, it is necessary, even mandatory, that detectors be simple to operate.

It is not necessary that every conceivable detector capability, circuit, accessory, knob, etc. be installed on law enforcement detectors. There are detection features which coin hunters and electronic prospectors employ which are of little value to law enforcement personnel.

Law enforcement detectors should be capable of detecting lead (Figure 18-5) and steel with maximum sensitivity, a detector

Figure 18-5: Former Law Enforcement Officer Jack Hube of Suffield, Connecticut, was called in by local police to assist in locating metal evidence, especially spent projectiles, at this murder site. He located the slugs and a mark on a near by fence, made by one of the bullets, which established the trajectory of the projectile. This information, establishing important aspects of the crime, led to the successful prosecution of the offender. Photo courtesy Suffield Police Department.

that does not adequately detect lead is of little use. Detectors with controls that can be adjusted to reject lead must be used by skilled operators or, a mis-adjustment could cause failure in searches.

SELECTION/APPLICATION

A discussion of the major types of law enforcement, security, and crime scene searching, and the most suitable type detector for each application is presented in the following paragraphs. Basic selection of accessories, where applicable, will be included.

LAND TYPES

The detector needed for most investigative purposes should be of the VLF type (Figure 18-6) with a wide range of available searchcoils. The VLF detector should have ground eliminating capability, maximum detection depth and stability. Searchcoils must be submersible. Protective cases and headphones are also desirable. The detector must be capable of operating under environmental extremes.

SEARCHCOILS AND ACCESSORIES

Searchcoils as small as three-and-one-half-inches in diameter and as large as twelve-inches to fourteen-inches in diameter should be available. Optional searchcoils, capable of operating in water to depths of about fifty feet, should be provided. Optional equipment such as extension handles and weighted searchcoils with a mini-

Figure 18-6: The detector needed for most investigative purposes, is the VLF type being used in this photograph, by Garland Police Officer Bill Peace. A wide range of available searchcoils are available for this universal applications instrument. Photo courtesy Garland Police Department.

mum of nine feet of cable, should be available for shallow water searching.

Deepseeking attachments with the capability of multiplying the depth of detection should be available to the investigator. For instance, officers recently located numerous automobile engines which had been buried at a depth of ten feet. The engines, considered by an auto theft ring to be ''too hot'' to sell, were removed from stolen automobiles and buried. The Bloodhound, Depth Multiplier attachment (Figure 18-7) was used to locate this important evidence.

Often, departmental budgets are tight; consequently, it is desirable that versatility include the availability of body scanning probes. This can be accomplished by employing a hipmount accessory kit. The control housing is carried on the belt (or on a waist strap) with a searchcoil attached to a short handle. The operator may use the searchcoil handle arrangement to scan parcels, mail, prisoners, suspects, etc. This arrangement is much more satisfactory than scanning a person with a standard configuration land type metal detector.

UNDERWATER TYPES

Another widely used crime scene management tool is the underwater detector. While some underwater searches will be done at shallow depths and along embankments (Figure 18-8) the detec-

Figure 18-7: One important accessory often needed by investigative officers such as this Utah Wildlife Resources Game Warden, is the two-box Depth Multiplier attachment. This metal detector configuration ignores very small metal objects, iron minerals, and subterranean water, but will locate large objects to depths of fifteen to twenty feet. Photo by Dave Loveless.

Figure 18-8: Dallas area Police Officers assist Charles Garrett as he scans this embankment for a discarded knife. Later, he scanned beneath the water with a submersible Sea Hunter XL500. Photo courtesy Dallas Police Department.

231

tor must be capable of operating to great depths. The detector should be capable of operating in extreme temperatures (Figure 18-9). Convertible detectors are available that may be used on land (Figure 18-10) and in water.

Figure 18-9: This Utah Law Enforcement Officer recovers a discarded knife from a cold lake bed. This Sea Hunter underwater detector can be submerged to depths of 200 feet. Photo courtesy Utah Wildlife Resources.

Underwater detectors must be rugged, easy to adjust and operate, and equipped with headphones. Metal diving tanks and associated gear worn by scuba divers should not interfere with the detector's operation. Rechargeable batteries are recommended; battery chargers capable of plugging into automobile 12-Volt cigarette lighter sockets and 110-Volt, 60 cycle outlets, should be available. Adaptors for recharging batteries at various other voltage and frequency levels are desirable if overseas work is anticipated.

COMPACT TYPES

The third type of commonly used detector is the small hand-held scanner used in body and wall searches, as well as in other evidence collection endeavors. A widely used scanning device is the miniature pocket detector (Figure 18-11). This detector offers simplicity of operation, stability, automatic tuning, and ruggedness. In using a metal detector for body scanning, the officer must be able to quickly scan a person for all types of metal evidence concealed in clothing, hair and body cavities.

Hand-held detectors of the type shown in Figure 18-12, are

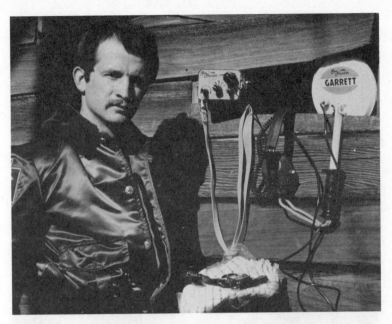

Figure 18-10: This Sea Hunter XL500 can be used as efficiently on land, as it can underwater, as proved by this Utah County Sheriff, Dennis Harris, who located a pistol concealed in the wall of this old building. Photo courtesy Utah County Sheriff's Department.

also popular. This type detector should be rugged, compact and sensitive. This equipment should be simple to operate, preferably with a single on/off and perhaps a spring-return power switch. Dozens, and perhaps hundreds of security guards may use any one given detector at an airport security check station. Consequently, the instrument must be easy to operate. This detector, with its long handle, allows a more impersonal search of a suspect; the operator's hand is kept further away from the person being scanned.

Body scanning detectors should be sensitive enough to detect the smallest weapon, such as razor blades, hat pins, knives and miniature guns. These small weapons are often concealed in the hair and body cavities.

Larger, more powerful types of portable detectors (Figure 18-13) are also needed by law enforcement. This type detector has more power; generally it has a larger searchcoil; it can cover an area much more quickly; it can scan more deeply into trees, etc., for weapons and bullets; it can scan deeper into mail sacks and large parcels to detect bombs, and can reach deeper into walls to detect weapons, hidden jewelry, etc. It can be worn on the belt, which frees one of the operator's hands. This type detector can be hand-held, if necessary, or it can simply be placed on a person's desk for convenience in checking for letter bombs and other items.

Figure 18-11: A widely used scanning device is the miniature Pocket Scanner detector, the Enforcer Model G-1. It features simplicity of operation, stability, automatic tuning, and ruggedness. It will quickly locate all types of metal evidence concealed in clothing, hair, and body cavities.

Figure 18-12: Hand-held weapons detectors like this Super Scanner, Model 11651 are very popular. With its long handle, it allows a more impersonal search of a suspect. The operator's hand is kept further away from the person being scanned.

235

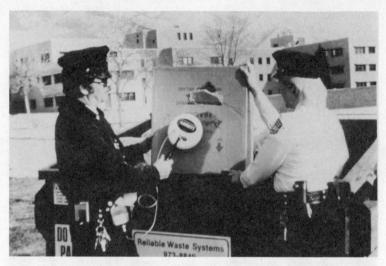

Figure 18-13: Larger, more powerful, types of portable detectors like this Inspector, Model G-100, have their place in the law enforcement field. This type detector has more power, and a larger searchcoil, giving it the ability to scan deeper into mail sacks and large parcels to detect bombs. It can reach deeper into walls to detect weapons, hidden jewelry, etc. The control housing is being worn on the officer's belt, but it can also be placed on a person's desk for convenience in checking for letter and mail bombs and other items.

SPECIALTY TYPES

There are numerous specialty types of detectors needed by law enforcement, such as the walk-through unit (Figure 18-14). Persons passing through a walk-through archway are scanned for metal objects such as a few bullets in a pocket. This type detector must be capable of detecting all-metal, and must be adjustable in order that various sizes of targets can be detected or eliminated as required. The entire walk-through area must be uniform in detection, and free of "dead spots." These detectors must be simple to assemble and operate, and must be foolproof. Advanced design walk-throughs of the type shown in Figure 18-14 can be programmed not only for various levels of sensitivity but also to "ignore" certain jewelry and other metal items. Walk-through detectors should be equipped with audible or silent detection signals, and must be capable of working properly when placed on metal floors or situated near X-ray equipment and other walk-through detectors. Special circuitry and construction to prevent tampering and detection inhibiting must be incorporated in them.

Certainly any manufacturer who produces detection equipment for law enforcement, security and crime scene personnel, should produce only the very best, most reliable instrument. Limited capability and inferior equipment has no place in law enforcement. Quality built, sensitive, rugged, environmentally

236

Figure 18-14: Persons passing through a walk-through metal detector archway are scanned for metal objects as small as a coin or bullet. This walk-through Olympian model metal detector is capable of detecting all metal objects; can be programmed for various levels of sensitivity; and can ignore certain jewelry and other metal items. This is one of sixty walk-throughs deployed at the 1984 Los Angeles Summer Olympic Games.

tested and field proven detectors are the only type equipment that should be used by law enforcement and security personnel; lives depend on it.

II. THE METAL DETECTOR: AN IMPORTANT TOOL IN THE MANAGEMENT OF CRIME SCENE INVESTIGATIONS.

Few law enforcement academies present or demonstrate the role of the metal detector as a viable tool of the crime scene and security investigator. In order for the crime scene manager to appreciate the role of the metal detector, the following review is presented to demonstrate its place in the overall crime scene program.

FACTORS WHICH INFLUENCE THE EFFECTIVENESS OF CRIME SCENE MANAGEMENT

Prior to the commencement of processing a crime scene, there are factors which significantly affect police response, and influence the effectiveness of the investigating team. These factors are broadly categorized as follows: the fixed responsibilities for a specific task at the crime scene; handling of liaison with the media; training of emergency medical personnel; involvement with the medical examiner's office; in-service training for personnel involved; involvement of the prosecutor at the crime scene; training of hospital personnel in handling of evidence relating to crime

237

scenes; development of programs to enhance the liaison between investigative, forensic, and prosecutive branches of law enforcement and police community relations.

Within the framework of the above mentioned factors, two involve metal detection. Departments need to plan and budget for the appropriation of metal detectors and other specialized equipment that will facilitate the management of the crime scene. Officers should be specifically assigned the task of metal detection, and metal detector training (Figures 18-15, 18-16 and 18-17) should be an ongoing part of in-service programs.

Figure 18-15: Charles Garrett lectures on the fundamentals of metal detectors to a group of Utah Wildlife Resources Game Wardens. Paul Woodbury, Chief of Law Enforcement Division, Utah Wildlife Resources, instigated these training programs in 1982. As a result of this ongoing training program, it is believed these dedicated men are among the Nation's most skilled metal detector operators in law enforcement.

III. GENERAL LAW ENFORCEMENT AND SECURITY APPLICATIONS

FISH AND GAME APPLICATIONS

A number of fish and game departments use metal detectors routinely during their investigations of game violations. The Utah Wildlife Resources Department (Figure 18-18) has developed perhaps the most advanced metal detection program of its kind in the world. Through the use of metal detectors, Utah game wardens have recovered metallic evidence from illegally killed animals which has resulted in numerous successful prosecutions.

Law enforcement officers historically have used creativity and innovativeness in solving complicated cases using metal detectors.

Figure 18-16: There is nothing like actual hands-on in-the-field training. Charles Garrett instructs these Utah Wildlife Resources Game Wardens in the techniques of animal scanning to locate metal projectiles. Photo courtesy Utah Wildlife Resources Department.

Figure 18-17: These Texas Game Wardens attend a metal detecting seminar in San Antonio, Texas. Up to fifty percent of instructional time is conducted in actual hands-on situations. Various size and shape targets are hidden beneath the saw dust. As part of the hands-on training, the men must be able to determine size, shape, and identity of each concealed target. Planted test targets include projectiles, guns, knives, chains, tire tools, and other metal weapons.

239

Figure 18-18: Through the use of metal detectors, Utah Wildlife Resources Game Wardens have recovered metallic evidence from illegally slain animals, which has resulted in numerous successful prosecutions. Chief Paul Woodbury stated their efficiency has greatly increased as a result of the metal detector training programs.

A case in point was related by a Texas game warden. The officer became aware of fish being poached with gill nets. Upon locating the nets, he placed his calling card inside a small metallic vial which he then forced into the stomach of one of the poached fish. He and several other game warden subsequently waited for the poacher to clear his nets and depart with his illegal catch. The violator was stopped shortly after his departure from the scene of the crime. While the official examined the suspect's fish, the poacher alledged they were caught legitimately and were not taken with gill nets.

The officer scanned the fish in question with a metal detector, immediately located the metallic vial, and retrieved his personal business card. No alibi could refute this small piece of compelling evidence.

CRIMES OF VIOLENCE

In all crimes of violence, the detector can be, and has become, an important investigation tool. Federal, state and local law enforcement departments currently employ metal detectors in their investigative work.

A retired law enforcement officer was called by a local Sheriff's department for assistance in locating spent bullets from a murder weapon. He not only located the desired slugs (Figure 18-5), but also a mark made by one of the bullets on a near by fence which

240

established the trajectory of the projectile. This information established important aspects of the crime leading to the successful prosecution of the offender.

A state Highway Patrol officer, using a metal detector, located fragments of an automobile grille which had fallen from a hit-and-run vehicle. This evidence was used to convict the subject who, subsequent to the hit-and-run, staged an automobile accident in an attempt to cover his crime.

THE MEDICAL EXAMINER

In crimes involving homicide, metal detectors should be used to scan the body (Figure 18-19) in an effort to locate valuable metallic evidence. The success which has been realized by law enforcement agencies in this area prompts me to include this section in MODERN METAL DETECTORS.

Medical examiners are discovering a new application for metal detection devices relating to examination of the body at the time of autopsy. Bodies are routinely X-rayed as part of this procedure. Metal detection instruments, however, can be used to locate metal fragments inside the body without requiring expensive X-ray equipment. Medical examiners are frequently required to assist in the processing of a body at crime scenes. A hand-held metal detector can prove to be an invaluable resource in locating and protecting metal evidence found in the body of victims.

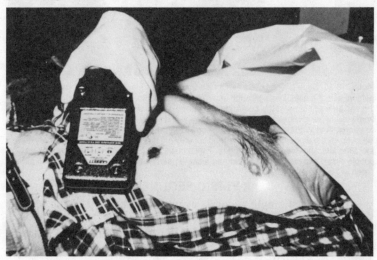

Figure 18-19: In crimes involving homicide, metal detectors should be used to scan the body in an effort to locate valuable metallic evidence. Medical examiner's have discovered the metal detector to be a new, important tool. Not only during processing of the body at a crime scene, but also at the time of an autopsy. Even though X-rays are routinely used as part of an autopsy procedure, metal detectors can be used to quickly 'locate projectiles and metal fragments inside the body.

Medical examiners will frequently examine the victim's clothing. The metal detector can also prove valuable in these searches.

AIRPORT SECURITY

Airport security (Figure 18-20) is regarded as the most visible type of security realized anywhere in the United States. More people pass through airport metal detectors than in any other type of security setting. In the 1970s, metal detectors were deployed on a vast scale in airports in an effort to curb airplane hijackings. Persons carrying concealed weapons through airport metal detection devices are readily detected and processed by law enforcement officials without undue delay or harm to other patrons.

Figure 18-20: Dave Loveless, Garrett's Law Enforcement Field Agent, instructs two security personnel in the use of walk-through and hand-held scanning devices. This security processing station was set up at the Los Angeles International Airport. Immediately, upon departing from arriving planes, foreign athletes, their luggage and equipment was meticulously scanned for weapons. Tom Wathen, President of California Plant Protection, Inc., Van Nuys, California, supplied nearly eight thousand uniformed security officers who were assigned to duty during the 1984 Los Angeles Olympic Games. These conscientious, dependable, and well-trained people did an excellent job in helping protect the nearly eight thousand athletes who participated in the Games.

OLYMPIC SECURITY

The largest single security event in the history of the United States was the 1984 Los Angeles Olympics.

Olympic Security (Figure 18-21) is discussed several times in this book, because an understanding of the complete use of metal detectors at an Olympic setting, is also an understanding of the metal detector's use in almost any other type of security event. Metal detectors were utilized in virtually every aspect of the Olympic games in an effort to provide security and safety for all participants (Figure 18-22). When it becomes necessary to scan

Figure 18-21: Bob Podhrasky, Charles Garrett and Dave Loveless (documenting discussion with camera) work with two security people to plan the deployment of nearly one-thousand security metal detectors used during the Los Angeles Summer Olympic Games.

Figure 18-22: The Garrett security vehicle became a regular feature at the Los Angeles Olympic Summer Games. Garrett teams continuously traveled throughout the one hundred square mile area, monitoring Garrett security equipment and training security people in the use of the devices.

small or large numbers of people, whether it be in a convention or industrial setting, corporate, or hospital, or any other type security, the application and operation of walk-through metal detectors is similar.

The role of metal detectors in security settings has taken on new dimensions because of their proven capabilities during the 1984 Olympics. Similar security measures were used during the 1984 Republican National Convention held in Dallas, Texas (Figure 18-23). Metal detection played a more significant role at that time than in any other political convention in history.

Figure 18-23: Eleven Garrett Olympian model walk-through metal detectors, the same used at the 1984 Summer Olympics, were deployed in the main lobby of the Dallas, Texas Convention Center during the 1984 Republican National Convention. Each day of the Convention, more than fifteen thousand persons were screened as they entered the Convention area. Garrett felt it an honor to have been selected to supply security equipment, and security personnel training, for this event. Metal detection played a more significant role at that time than at any other political convention in history.

COURT SECURITY: SECURITY FOR ELECTED AND APPOINTED OFFICIALS

In addition to the uses described above, metal detectors play an important part in the protection of our elected and appointed officials and judges, jurors, prosecutors, and defendants (Figure 18-24). We continually find the need for greater security in our nation's capitol, the White House, our embassies and other significant government installations. It is imperative that only the finest metal detectors be produced to perform with the degree of excellence which would insure the safety of all people they are deployed to protect. It's unfortunate, but a fact, that security extends into every part of our lives. Metal detectors protect us and help to insure that we have a safer existence.

Figure 18-24: Metal detectors are playing an increasingly important role in the protection of our elected and appointed officials, jurors, judges, prosecutors and defendants. All individuals were scanned for concealed weapons as they entered a courtroom in Orem, Utah. Photo by Pat Christian.

SEARCH AND RESCUE ELECTRONICS

Somewhere in the United States, Search and Rescue personnel are at work this very minute. This area of law enforcement is one of the most rewarding, yet, at times, one of the most heart breaking. I taught at the National Search and Rescue seminars in Barstow, California. I was impressed with the dedication of these men and women, as they strived to learn more about metal detection as an aid to search and rescue. I include this section in MODERN METAL DETECTORS, as a tribute to this wonderful group of people.

There has been a sudden interest in the use of metal detectors in avalanche search and rescue. Search and Rescue personnel will benefit from reading an article in the Spring 1977 issue of SEARCH AND RESCUE magazine where a research program was examined. Over fifty percent of the victims of an avalanche, are within thirty-six inches of the surface. When you consider the amount of metal items an average skier wears, the odds of finding them have significantly increased. It was demonstrated, that often avalanche victims leave a "trail" of various items including skis, poles, glasses, and other metal objects that could lead a metal detector operator to the victim.

In another type case, Search and Rescue personnel were searching for the body of a murdered lady. The victim was reported to have been buried in a certain area. The area was grided, and searched with metal detectors. A metal detector detected a ring on the victim's hand, which was six inches below the surface.

In recent years, there have been numerous mudslides in the Rocky Mountains. On one such occasion, a Volkswagen, believed to contain four small children, was swept away and buried beneath tons of mud. Search and Rescue personnel, using a Garrett Deepseeker with a Depth Multiplier attachment, located the vehicle. Fortunately, the children had escaped earlier from the vehicle. The quick response of the team in locating the vehicle, proved the value of the metal detector.

During a snowstorm, a vehicle containing two females skidded off a road and was quickly buried. A motorist who saw the accident, notified the Sheriff's department. Metal detectors were quickly brought into use. The vehicle was located within a relatively short period of time. It contained two very cold, but very much alive young ladies.

Another success story is worthy of Ripley's BELIEVE IT OR NOT. A young man was ice skating and fell through the ice. A member of a Search and Rescue team resided near the lake. According to the officer, he was getting ready for a trip to a warmer climate, where he planned to do some metal detecting. He was

246

checking his detector when an excited skater informed him of the accident. As he ran to the lake, he remembers looking in his hand to find he was still holding his metal detector. As he began a visual search, he also began scanning the ice with his detector, hoping that the skater might be wearing something metal.

Apparently, the skater had presence of mind to remain in an air space between the ice and water. He was attempting to break-through the ice with a skate, when the officer detected the skate with his metal detector...believe it or not!

IV. METAL DETECTOR SEARCH TECHNIQUES

The following methods are now presented to enable investigators to become familiar with successful search techniques which have been developed over the years. Inasmuch as crimes take place in a variety of locations, one or more of the following search methods may be employed. Innovative methods of processing crime scenes must be developed to address unusual circumstances.

SEARCH METHODS

Search methods employed by the investigator may be compared to a farmer's plowing methods. The farmer utilizes the methods best suited to his particular terrain. The crime scene investigator should do no less. Crimes may occur along a roadside, necessitating a strip type search. In an open field an investigator might conduct a grid or zone search to best address the uniqueness of the situation. A metal detection search should be conducted much as a field is plowed—attention must be paid to systematically covering every inch of the crime scene area.

The illustrations in Chapter 23, Figure 23-6, are presented to further clarify search methods recommended. The investigator may be required to expand these search techniques and develop creative new approaches in order to properly address given tasks.

LAND AND HOUSE SEARCHING (OR WHERE PEOPLE HIDE THINGS)

This book was conceived and written for all persons interested in metal detection. Most of my career as the president of Garrett Electronics has revolved around working with treasure and coin hunters, prospectors, and law enforcement personnel who spend much time during their lives attempting to locate metallic objects that have been lost or hidden. One close personal friend, L.L. "Abe" Lincoln of Rogers, Arkansas, remarked that people conceal valuables in the same locations today that they did 200 years ago. People are creatures of habit; they tend to hide their possessions where they can frequently and easily observe the hiding place. Years ago, people who did not trust banks would hide valuables in places easily seen from the bedroom window. They used a corner of the house, a well, a tree or some other landmark as reference points when burying their possessions.

So, when you are searching, set up your lines of search to correspond with prominent physical objects. The chances of finding what you are looking for will be increased a hundredfold.

Treasure hunters know that valuables have been concealed under manure piles. Recently, an arson squad in a midwestern town solicited assistance from Garrett Electronics regarding the search of a farm. The arson officers were advised to scan manure piles. They subsequently informed Garrett Electronics that they had been successful; a search of a manure pile inside a barn resulted in locating five fire bombs concealed there.

When attempting to locate hidden items try to put yourself in the position of the person doing the hiding. A person might conceal items beneath a stairway, on top of a cupboard, under a drawer bottom, or in the attic. Just use your good common sense. Make inquiries of your fellow officers and friends and determine where they might hide items of value under different conditions. "Barn storming" can lead to successful recoveries.

WATER SEARCH AND RECOVERY

Numerous cases have been solved with the recovery of evidence once thought forever lost in the murky depths of rivers, lakes and oceans. Once, a permanent depository for instruments of crime, these waterways are now giving up their secrets. Progressive law enforcement departments now include new types of sonar and modern metal detectors as part of their standard crime scene management equipment. Let's briefly discuss some of this equipment.

Submersible, underwater metal detectors and metal detector searchcoils will readily detect ferrous and non-ferrous metals. Detectors can locate metals concealed by murky water, aquatic growth, or bottom soil. Large metal masses, such as aircraft, boats, automobiles, and even safes, can be detected at surprising distances from the searchcoil. Those of you who have been involved in dark water searches know that mere inches can make a big difference in the search. (See the various underwater recovery photos in Chapter 17).

Sonar is another type of equipment which should not be overlooked by those responsible for conducting underwater search and recovery programs. Sonar sends electronic signals through the water. Upon striking a submerged object, the signal rebounds to the sonar receiver where it is analyzed and recorded on a screen or heat sensitive paper.

There are two basic types of sonar devices: sub-bottom profilers and side scan.

248

Sub-bottom profiling sonar (Figure 18-25) generally transmits electronic signals straight down from a surface-mounted transducer, thereby giving cross sectional images of targets.

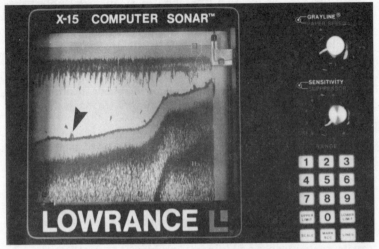

Figure 18-25: This remarkable, sub-bottom profiling sonar, the Lowrance X-15 computer sonar, is an important tool used by many law enforcement agencies. As discussed in this chapter, Jim Cross of Cross International, uses many of the X-15s in his underwater search and recovery work. This display clearly shows bottom contour, fish and an object protruding above the lake bottom as indicated by the arrow. The X-15's depth, range (upper and lower limits), and sensitivity are programmable. The height above the lake bottom, of the protruding object (indicated by the arrow,) is approximately twelve inches.

Side scan sonar, a substantially more expensive piece of equipment, emits its electronic signal from transducers mounted in a towable "fish." This "fish," or torpedo-shaped device, is submerged and slowly towed slightly above the bottom. It emits signals both to the right and left. Signals bouncing off objects protruding above the bottom are analyzed and recorded. Images recorded from side scan sonar will appear as having height and depth.

Side scan sonar is recommended for large search areas with relatively flat bottoms. Sub-bottom profilers are used in waterways with rugged bottom contours and are most effective as pinpointing devices.

Another instrument which has proved invaluable to search and recovery specialists is the electronic ranging system. The type most widely used by law enforcement personnel utilizes two primary sources of distance ranging: satellite and fixed base. As with metal detection and sonar equipment, signals are transmitted and received. Time intervals are measured, and very accurate calculations are made automatically. Positioning accuracy on the water's surface of plus or minus one meter can be maintained.

Now, let's put these systems together to organize, operate and successfully complete two kinds of underwater search and recoveries.

In the case of locating a weapon or small metal object discarded in a localized water area of one-quarter square mile or less, an organized diver search team of sufficient size should be used. A dive plan has to be established, and all divers familiarized with bottom times, signals, and search techniques. The search area is marked off at all four corners, using magnetic headings to establish marker positions. The reason for using magnetic headings is to keep search diver patterns parallel to the grid through the use of wrist compasses.

Divers are staggered, every other diver maintaining sufficient distance behind lead divers to eliminate electronic metal detector "cross talk." A six foot distance should be adequate for most detectors.

Guidelines can be used to maintain underwater sequencing. Lines must be of sufficient diameter and of a non-floating construction to eliminate hazardous entanglements with divers. Generally, a large diameter tightly-wound rope will not entangle divers and can be easily grasped and lifted off equipment. A small cord easily becomes entangled with diving gear and is difficult to remove.

A sharp knife is always recommended as part of your search diver equipment. Line anchors should be substantial so as to maintain their position, even through severe storms. A three foot diameter marker can easily move a car engine block anchor in moderate waves.

When the object of the search is located, mark the spot where it was found. Mentally record all surrounding terrain and unusual items. Photograph the entire area if possible. Remove the object, using proper techniques. Remember, a loaded gun, even underwater, can discharge, causing serious injury.

In searching large areas or in trying to locate targets such as boats, aircraft, or automobiles, a combination of metal detectors, sonar and ranging equipment must be used. A search program similar to the one used by Cross International, Orem, Utah, in locating a United States Air Force F-16 fighter which crashed into the Great Salt Lake, in Utah, shows how this equipment can be applied. (See the various photographs, in Chapter 17, of Cross International underwater recoveries).

During the wintry month of January, an F-16, flying a routine training mission, disappeared from the radar screens of Hill Air Force Base, located in Ogden, Utah some ninety miles away. Violent storms kept search aircraft out of the area for approximately thirteen hours. During this time, all traces of debris had disappeared. Cross International, a Utah based company that specializes in search and recovery electronics, was alerted and mobilized.

Heavy snow, and temperatures with wind chill factors of forty degrees below zero, made the problem of searching over seventeen hundred square miles of water more difficult. In testing equipment to be used in this particular search, it was learned that the twenty-nine percent salt content of the Great Salt Lake rendered most metal detection equipment useless. After extensive testing, the search team chose the Garrett Sea Hunter metal detection equipment because it could cancel out the heavy mineral concentration and still detect the type of metal used in the construction of the F-16.

After studying wind directions and currents during the previous twenty-four hour period, Jim Cross, president of Cross International, selected a probable area to search of approximately fifty kilometers. Fixed-base ranging stations were established at strategic points around the lake, and specialized surface craft were put on the water.

Ranging equipment and side scan sonar was installed on one barge. Diving equipment, and special helmets and suits were made ready on another. The search began.

Perimeter coordinates were established and four kilometer sweeps covering sixty meter wide paths were begun. Day after day this work proceeded until finally, on the thirteenth day, after covering almost fifty square miles, the sonar began to show what appeared to be wreckage, scattered over an area one-and-one-half kilometers long and three-quarter kilometers wide. Obviously, the high speed impact of the aircraft scattered the wrecked plane over this large area. Each sonar target was plotted and marked. Metal detection searchcoils (Figure 18-26) were lowered from the barge to verify that the targets were metal. Diving conditions were extremely hostile. To conserve the divers' energy, bogus targets such as boulders had to be identified.

During the next forty-five days, the pilot's body and ninety-five percent of the weight of the aircraft was recovered. The submersible metal detectors (Figure 18-27) greatly improved the search and recovery aspects of the work. The murky conditions sharply limited visibility but the metal detectors proved to be the best eyes the divers could have. Extremely small metal pieces, as well as gigantic ones, were readily detected. A good percentage of the aircraft pieces could not have been recovered without the metal detectors, as they were buried in mud. An extremely difficult job came to a successful ending by using the new eyes and ears of search and recovery electronics.

Figure 18-26: In the extremely cold and hostile environment of the Great Salt Lake, Jim Cross and his Cross International crew, recover hundreds of large and small metal fragments of a downed U.S. Air Force F-16 Fighter aircraft. When sonar locates targets underwater, searchcoils are lowered to identify the target as either being metal or non-metal. This identifying procedure conserves diver submerged time, and greatly improves the efficiency of the diver's recovery efforts. Cross lowers a twelve inch diameter underwater searchcoil to obtain readings which pinpoint and identify targets.

Figure 18-27: Mud and dark murky water of the Great Salt Lake reduces diver visibility almost to zero. The Cross International Search Team relies upon Sea Hunter underwater detectors to quickly locate metal parts from a downed Air Force F-16 plane. Crew Chief Roger Reynolds (with beard, facing camera) directs the raising of a tail section. The diver checks his metal detector prior to making another dive. Photo Cross International Archives.

SNOW SEARCH

Obviously, fallen snow of almost any depth can conceal weapons discarded by persons fleeing from the scene of a crime. These weapons must be located as quickly as possible (Figure 18-28). What is seemingly an impossible task, that of locating a gun in a large, snow covered field, is in reality simply one of carefully analyzing the area and conducting a systematic search, as snow does not inhibit the operation of a metal detector. Without the use of detectors in snow searches, evidence may be overlooked and suspects never brought to trial.

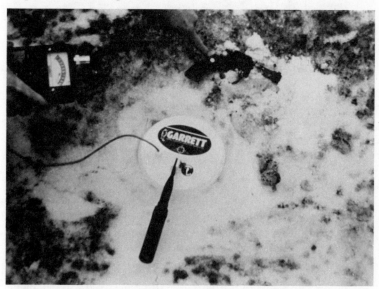

Figure 18-28: Fallen snow will conceal weapons discarded by persons fleeing from the scene of a crime. These weapons must be located as quickly as possible, making the metal detector the only tool that can do the job. Before the snow was cleared back, as shown in this photograph, the pistol was located by an investigating officer. Photo by Dave Loveless.

DISGUISED WEAPONS
(PRISON AND JAIL SEARCH)

Many times an officer will have occasion to search an individual, a room, or a jail cell (Figure 18-29) or another area in looking for contraband, weapons, or other items of evidence. The metal detector will find any metal contraband.

When a metal pen is located on a person, examine it carefully; it could be a gun or knife. A cigarette package could contain a small pistol. A large belt buckle can conceal small weapons. In fact, belt buckles are now manufactured with built-in firing mechanisms. A flare in the trunk of a car could actually be an improvised shotgun. A jewelry box may have a concealed compart-

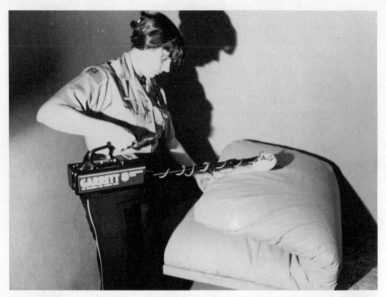

Figure 18-29: A metal detector can find metal contraband and weapons hidden and concealed on individuals in a room, jail cell, and other areas. This policewoman scans a jail mattress for hidden weapons.

ment containing a knife. Cribbage boards can easily conceal a knife (Figure 18-30). A mattress, even those in a prison storage area (Figure 18-31), can conceal a dozen weapons! Numerous times, over the years, the FBI Law Enforcement Bulletin (LEB) featured these methods of weapon concealment.

BODY SEARCHES

In law enforcement settings, it is often necessary to conduct a search incidental to an arrest. Metallic weapons may be concealed in a subject's hair (Figure 18-32), or within body cavities. Criminals often display great creativity in concealing weapons and contraband.

The search is best started at the back. The suspect should hold his or her arms straight out from the sides. The arms should not be bent. Hats must be removed and scanned with the metal detector. Make circular motions over the head and hair (Figure 18-33). Bring the detector horizontally across the neck and make several scans over the back working down to the crotch area. Pay particular attention to the small of the back and the crotch. Then scan up one side, under the armpit, and proceed along the underside of the arm to the hand. Continue along the outer arm, across the shoulders passing over the full length of the other arm, and returning by way of the inner arm to the armpit. Scan down the side following the outside of the leg to floor level. Pass the metal detector around

Figure 18-30: While on a routine inspection of a jail cell, a Utah State Prison Official scanned this homemade game box. The metal detector indicated the presence of a concealed metal object. When the official manipulated a handle lever, a trap-door dropped down, exposing the knife.

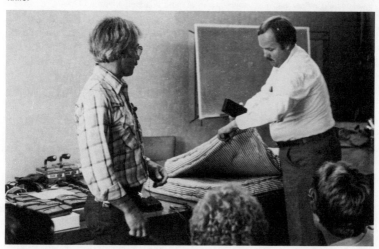

Figure 18-31: Bruce Daniels and Mike Mitchell give a demonstration on the use of metal detectors in prisons, during a Law Enforcement Seminar held in Provo, Utah. As they were leaving the prison to come to the seminar, they stopped by the prison storage area and picked up this mattress. During the classroom presentation, while scanning the mattress with a metal detector, it indicated the presence of metal. They cut a mattress seam, reached in between the stuffing, and pulled out a broad-blade putty knife. Both men were surprised, as neither had "planted" the knife in the mattress. The moral to this story is, that all mattresses in jails and prisons, both in cells and storage areas, should be thoroughly scanned with metal detectors to locate hidden and concealed metal weapons.

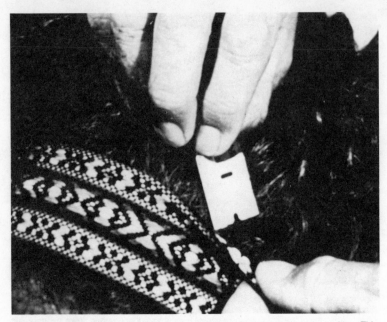

Figure 18-32: Metallic weapons may be concealed on a subject or in body cavities. This investigating officer has just located, with a hand scanner, a razor blade in this lady's headband.

the ankle and up the inside of the leg to the crotch. Proceed down the inside of the opposite leg, across the ankle, and up the outside of the leg. The person conducting the search should now move to the front of the subject and pass the detector under the chin. Several horizontal scans must be made over the torso, paying particular attention to the breast, waist and crotch areas.

The purpose of the frontal scan is to locate small metallic objects which may be concealed in the mouth (metal teeth fillings will also be detected), and items concealed in brassieres or suspended around the neck and hidden behind the belt.

It is important that the individual being searched know that the metal detector is operational. This may be accomplished by scanning the person's arm and calling attention to the signal produced by a wristwatch or ring. It is suggested that in body scanning, two additional techniques be employed. The first is to occasionally touch the body in areas such as the shoulders, arms, legs, below the knees and the back with the metal detector to make the subject more aware of the progress of the search. The second technique is for the person conducting the search to use his hands in connection with the metal detection scanning process. Prison officers agree that all of the senses should be used in body searches. The searcher's hands should be used whenever possible. For example, as the

INDIVIDUAL BODY SCANNING PROCEDURE FOR LOCATING HIDDEN & CONCEALED WEAPONS

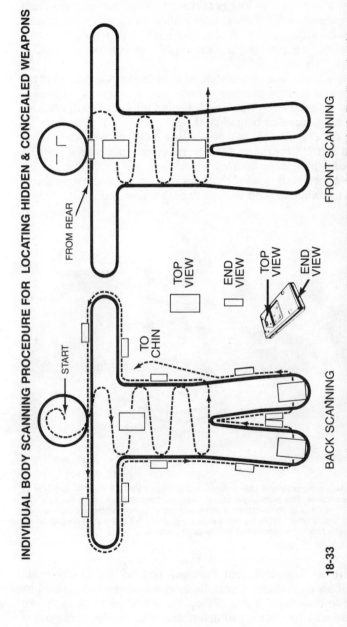

FRONT SCANNING

BACK SCANNING

18-33

Figure 18-33: INDIVIDUAL BODY SCANNING PROCEDURE FOR LOCATING HIDDEN AND CONCEALED WEAPONS. This illustration shows recommended procedures for scanning a suspect to locate metal weapons hidden on the person and concealed in body cavities. Scanning speed should be from one to two feet per second. The scanner should be held very close to the body. Inspect every item that causes an alarm. Never take the suspect's word as to the identity of detected objects.

257

search proceeds along a sleeved arm, the hand should be passed over the area indicating to the subject that a thorough review of his person is being conducted. The hands may detect items attached to the body, as well as confirm metal detection signals resulting from the presence of metal. This creates additional stress on the person and improves the search. It should be noted that certain search situations may not permit a "pat down" in conjunction with a metal detection scan.

During the course of a search, always request the person to tilt out large belt buckles enabling the searcher to determine if hidden weapons are present. A light touch behind the buckle will disclose if items are concealed behind clothing. There are belt buckles on the market (Figure 18-34) possessing built-in weapons. Also included in the illustration are several small guns which may be concealed behind large buckles.

The above body scan techniques require approximately thirty seconds to complete if no suspect items are detected.

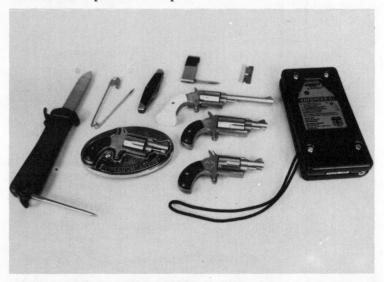

Figure 18-34: As Security and Law Enforcement officials know, the number and type of weapons is endless. This photograph shows a few weapons that are easily concealed on individuals. The Freedom Arms miniature pistols are easily concealed on many places of the body and in body cavities. While the belt buckle pistol (which is a real gun) is obvious, many belt buckles that contain weapons that are not as easily seen.

NOTE

There are many different situations that call for an electronic search of an individual. A patrolman may scan an individual just arrested to determine if that person has a concealed weapon. An employee may be scanned to determine if he or she is removing

258

company property from the premises. An individual may be scanned in an airport security checkpoint setting. A party goer may be scanned prior to gaining entrance to a night club.

WALK-THROUGH SCANNING

Walk-through metal detectors (sometimes called magnetometers) are important in law enforcement and security settings, and have proved to be an efficient method of processing large numbers of individuals. Metal objects as small as a single coin, carried by a person through the detector archway, can be detected. No metal can be concealed from the invisible electromagnetic field of the latest, state-of-the-art designs of walk-through detectors. Some people hold the belief that they can "fool" a walk-through unit by covering a large belt buckle with their hands. This is a misconception; it has no effect on the operation or detection properties of the unit. When a quality metal detector's sensitivity level is appropriately set, all metal items, regardless of orientation, will be detected.

Walk-through detectors offer various operating settings. A maximum sensitivity mode will detect all metals, regardless of their mass. A less sensitive setting (or a "discrimination" setting) allows the detection of guns and knives, etc. while ignoring certain jewelry items such as a wristwatch. The mode selection and sensitivity setting of walk-throughs should be made based upon the requirements of the person responsible for security.

The illustration in Figure 18-35 shows a typical walk-through station designed to process a large volume of people.

For optimum detection only one person should be allowed to pass through the archway at a time (Figure 18-36). The person being scanned should proceed through the center of the archway without turning his body in any direction. The arms should be held at the sides in a normal walking posture. Walk-through speed should be a normal pace, free of stopping, skipping or running. In the event the walk-through sounds an alarm the person may be processed with a hand-held weapons detector (Figure 18-37). The person may also be requested to pass through the detector a second time, following removal of all metal objects from his person and clothing.

Any items detected by the hand-held scanners, such as pocket items and cigarette packages, should be visually checked.

Some persons who have metal surgical devices implanted in their bodies will trigger a response from the walk-through detector. Most implants may be verified with hand scanners.

All detector signals must be resolved prior to the subject being allowed to pass into secure areas.

This discussion on metal detector scanning is by no means

TOP VIEW WALK-THROUGH
PERSONNEL DEPLOYMENT (HIGH TRAFFIC FLOW)

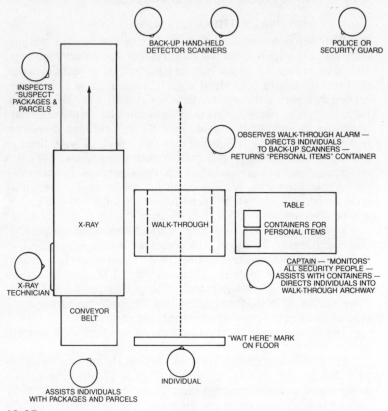

18-35

Figure 18-35: TOP VIEW WALK-THROUGH PERSONNEL DEPLOYMENT (HIGH TRAFFIC FLOW). This illustration shows the deployment of security people at a typical walk-through station designed to process a large volume of people. This is the approximate deployment pattern used at the 1984 Republican National Convention held in Dallas, Texas, where approximately fifteen-thousand people per hour were scanned by eleven walk-through metal detectors.

exhaustive. Basic techniques of scanning have been presented and discussed in general terms. Persons using metal detectors in law enforcement and security settings must learn the full capabilities and limitations of this equipment, as well as the legal aspects relating to their application (Figure 18-38).

POACHING INVESTIGATIONS

All types and sizes of projectiles, including metal arrow points, can be located in animals. The scanning process is complicated by the fact that salt, present in animal tissue, becomes conductive as

Figure 18-36: This is one of the walk-throughs that was in use during the 1984 Republican National Convention. Because traffic flow was extremely high during peak periods, several members of the Garrett Team worked various stations. Because the United States Secret Service required the instruments be set very sensitive, many backup hand-scanning personnel were required to scan the large number of people detectd by the walk-throughs.

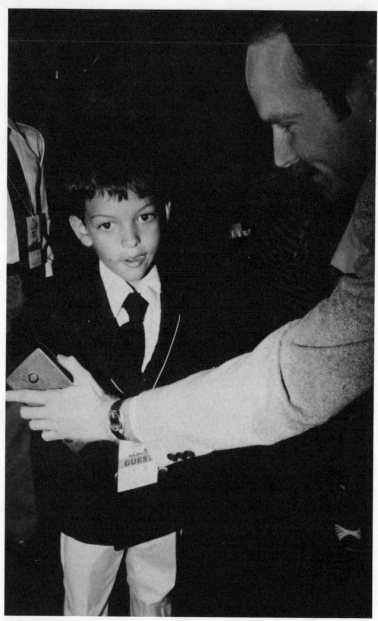

Figure 18-37: This young gentleman, who attended the 1984 Republican National Convention with his family, seems to enjoy all the excitement of convention security. His metal coat buttons, belt buckle and a metal campaign button caused the walk-through to alarm, thus, necessitating the hand scan. The man doing the scanning is one of the hundreds of Texas volunteers who freely gave of their time to act in a security capacity at the Convention.

Figure 18-38: California Plant Protection Inc., manned the largest single corps of uniformed security officers at the 1984 Olympics. Bob Podhrasky (left) instructs this CPP Security Service guard in the proper use of a Super Scanner weapons detector. During the entire two weeks, Garrett teams traveled throughout a one hundred square mile area, inspecting equipment and training security people in the use of security metal detectors.

the carcass decomposes. Body fluids, combined with salt, produce saline solutions which most metal detectors will detect, thus, masking, somewhat, the detection of projectiles. This masking process begins on about the second day following death and continues until most of the animal's fluids have dried or the meaty tissues have decomposed.

Another factor to consider, is if the ground upon which the animal is laying, contains high concentrations of iron minerals, the detector, as it penetrates completely through the carcass, will react to the iron minerals, thus, further adding to the masking effect as described.

The correct choices of metal detectors are the VLF/TR Trash Eliminator (Discriminator), the Pulse Induction, and the Pocket Scanner. All these types have been discussed many times in this book.

The VLF mode can be used with, more or less success, depending upon the degree of salinity of body fluids. These fluids will be detected, but many Game Warden have learned to "ignore" these effects, while carefully listening for projectile indications. The three and one-half inch to eight inch searchcoils are preferred. The TR mode can also be used successfully since saline solutions can be eliminated from detection in this mode. Since TR modes do

263

not have iron mineral elimination abilities, the earth's iron minerals will, more or less, affect operation.

Pulse Induction instruments, since they ignore both iron earth minerals and saline solutions simultaneously, make a good choice for the poaching investigation officer. Searchcoils that range in size from three and one-half inches to eight inches are the preferred size. Larger searchcoils do not have adequate sensitivity for the very small caliber projectiles.

The Pocket Scanner metal detector of the type shown in Figure 18-19, have become so popular with Game Warden, that many carry them either on their person or in their vehicles, at all times. These instruments are effected slightly by saline solutions, but officers are pleased with the ability of the Pocket Scanners to detect even BB caliber projectiles at good depths. The portability of the detectors make them easy to carry and their capabilities often eliminate the need for larger, more powerful, instruments. Also, these small instruments are ideal for investigation of bird, and smaller game violations.

The deer illustration shown in Figure 18-39 shows three areas where false signals often occur. In addition to the saline solutions that are present in most all the parts of these animals, these three areas contain high concentrations of detectable minerals that can fool the inexperienced Game Warden. These mineral deposits cause a metal detector to react exactly as though metal targets have been detected. The two areas at the upper leg joints are the most predominate, and false signals will be detected from both sides of the body. The area in the head produces a less pronounced signal. The head area produces a single signal regardless of whether the head is scanned from the side or top. The other two areas sometimes will produce a single signal from the sides, but when the detector is scanned across the belly and lower part of the chest, two signals, one on each side of the body will be produced. Officers who gain experience in scanning animals soon learn about these two false signals and can identify them as such.

PSYCHOLOGICAL ASPECTS OF METAL DETECTORS AND SEARCHES

There are psychological factors relating to the search of an individual with a hand-held and/or walk-through metal detector, which are appropriate to mention at this time. The officer involved in this type of search can use these factors to his advantage. Few individuals who permit themselves to be searched with a metal detector are free from some form of apprehension. This is particularly true with a criminal who would intentionally hide a weapon on his person with the thought of injuring someone. The psychological effect builds when the criminal is faced with unknown elec-

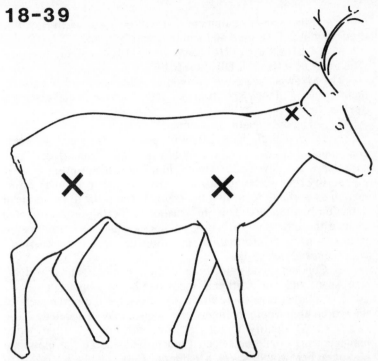

ANIMAL "FALSE" SIGNAL AREAS

Figure 18-39: ANIMAL "FALSE" SIGNAL AREAS. When the decay process begins in animal carcasses, saline solutions cause metal detector reactions over almost all parts of the body. At three areas, mineral concentrations may cause "false" detector signals that sound exactly as though metal has been detected. The two body areas, as marked by the large "X"s, are the most pronounced. The smaller "X" area is not as pronounced. Refer to the text for a discussion of these "false" signal detection areas, and a scanning method that may help you to distinguish these "false" signals from genuine projectile signals.

tronic equipment that have different sizes, shapes and colors.

During the 1984 Olympics, Garrett Electronics established an unprecedented trend by using five different types of searchcoils to scan individuals, mail, food and supplies.

And, during the 1984 Republican Convention, this same equipment was introduced. Some prisons throughout the United States are currently following this trend. The different searchcoils have kept the criminal element off guard. Whether the criminal is about to board an airplane or is in jail, he is left to wonder WHEN he will be searched, WHAT type of equipment will be used, WHERE he will be searched and HOW he will be searched.

I am reminded of a sign I saw on a fencepost of some private property, "No Trespassing—trigger-happy gunman, and a man-eating dog, patrol these premises four days a week, YOU—guess the days." I do not feel we owe the criminal any consideration. Let him guess the type of equipment that will be used, when it will be used, how it will be used and where it will be used.

V. SUMMARY: THE LAW ENFORCEMENT METAL DETECTOR AND ITS DEPLOYMENT

The following procedures should be adhered to by law enforcement agencies in their selection and deployment of metal detection devices:

1. Select only quality equipment.

2. Insist that all metal detector operators use metal detection equipment in off-duty hours, in hobby pursuits, in an effort to gain experience and develop techniques in metal detector use.

3. In crime scene applications, always gather as much information as possible regarding the crime scene prior to using metal detection instruments. This information gathering process should include the interview of primary witnesses and cooperative subjects for detailed information regarding the area to be searched with the metal detectors.

4. Conduct metal detector tests on objects of similar weight, size, shape and composition as the object being sought.

5. Conduct tests in an effort to determine the parameters of the search area where the items of evidence may be located.

(1) A quality metal detector, for use in crime scene management, should be selected much the same as a crime scene photographer would select a camera. Care should be taken to purchase only state-of-the-art, field-proven equipment.

(2) Even though a number of law enforcement agencies are in possession of quality metal detection devices, in many cases the instruments are abandoned because of a lack of trained operators. Proficiency in the use of metal detectors can be easily obtained through a minimum of instruction accompanied by many hours of practical field use. It is recommended that metal detectors not be kept in an equipment locker to be used only in crisis situations. Officers assigned to the duties of metal detector operation should be encouraged to use the police agencies' metal detecting devices in a hobby capacity which includes off-duty hours coin and treasure hunting. An officer who is able to locate coins in the earth can just as easily find small items of evidence such as shell casings and lead slugs. The value of metal detection in crime scene management is directly proportional to the experience and understanding of the operator.

(3) Prior to conducting a metal detection search, the investigator must exhaust all of his resources in an effort to narrow and limit the area to be searched. Information indicating that a weapon was thrown from a moving vehicle between locations several miles apart, is far too general to make a metal detection search practical. Likewise, information regarding a weapon reportedly thrown into

266

a river or other type of waterway, provides little detail of value to the investigator. The following procedures, therefore, should be adhered to wherever possible.

The investigator should personally interview primary witnesses and cooperative subjects for detailed information prior to conducting the search. The metal detection expert should never rely on information obtained by a third party. This information is often non-specific and fails to provide details of extreme importance to the person conducting the metal detection search.

As an example of a detailed interview, let's consider a case where a weapon was thrown from a moving vehicle. The interviewer must determine a number of facts, including the speed and lane of traffic of the vehicle at the time of the disposal of the weapon; the location in the vehicle of the person discarding the evidence; whether the person is right-handed or left-handed and which hand was used in throwing the weapon; was the weapon thrown over the top of the car or from the passenger window; was it thrown overhand or sideways; what force was used in the throw; and, of course, the size and shape of the object. Identifying markers and points of reference along the highway will help to narrow the search area.

Where practical, the cooperating witnesses or subjects should be returned to the search area and should be requested to give their best opinion as to the location where the evidence was discarded. These procedures can greatly limit the primary search area and may save the investigator countless hours of fruitless search.

It should be remembered that no matter how advanced the investigator's search techniques may be, and regardless of the quality of the detection instrument, if the item of evidence being sought is not in the area of his search, it will not be recovered.

(4) Certain tests should be conducted prior to every search. Tests to determine the sensitivity (response) of the detector to the item being sought must be conducted. A similar weapon or object, of the general size, weight and composition of the item of evidence, should be tested on the metal detector to determine the characteristics of detector response. The item being sought should be compared with other metal items buried in the general area of the crime scene. These items might include cans, pulltabs, and possibly larger pieces of ferrous metal. These tests will perhaps allow the investigator to use trash elimination circuitry which may speed up target detection and recovery.

(5) Additional tests should be conducted to determine, as precisely as possible, the parameters of the search. This series of tests, in the case of a weapon thrown from a moving vehicle, require the investigator to obtain an object of similar size, shape

and weight as the object of the search. The investigator should simulate all conditions at the time the actual weapon or other evidence was thrown from the vehicle, and conduct tests to determine the distance these items can be thrown under similar conditions. The investigator must pay strict attention to every detail obtained at the time of his interview of primary witnesses. That is to say, the test vehicle should be traveling in the same lane of traffic, at the same rate of speed, and the weapon should be thrown using the identical methods employed by the subject in the original case. This test should be conducted a minimum of three times to determine flight parameters of the object being sought. In cases involving disposal of evidence in waterways, a lightweight, strong cord should be attached to the test object so that it can be readily recovered from the water.

Adherence to the above evidence recovery rules will greatly increase the investigator's likelihood of locating evidence with a metal detector.

Many times it has been proven that important items of evidence can be located by the deployment of state-of-the-art metal detection devices. It is hoped that all law enforcement agencies will recognize that the metal detector is, indeed, a dependable and invaluable investigative tool.

Garrett Electronics has video instructional tapes available to law enforcement and security groups. These tapes cover various aspects of metal detectors, their capabilities, how they are used in law enforcement and security applications. See THE GARRETT FILM, VIDEO AND SLIDE LIBRARY section at the end of this book.

CHAPTER 18 QUESTIONS

A study of this chapter alone, will not provide the answers to all the following questions. Numerous of these questions were taken from material covered in other chapters. An understanding of all the material covered in these questions is important, and should be thoroughly covered in all Law Enforcement and Security Metal Detector training courses.

1. Metal detectors can detect metal objects through mud, water, snow, wood, concrete, and, in fact, through practically every known material except metal.

    True _____ False _____

2. VLF Ground Elimination (Canceling) detectors will: (A) dowse for precious metals; (B) ignore all trash items; (C) ignore most iron earth minerals and perform most detecting tasks quite well; (D) detect only shallow buried items.

3. The use of earphones is essential for the most efficient operation of a metal detector.

True _____ False _____

4. For maximum sensitivity, you should always set the audio tuning level at the minimum speaker or earphone sound you can hear.

True _____ False _____

5. Using larger searchcoils will: (A) provide greater discrimination; (B) make tuning easier; (C) give better performance in grass; (D) give greater detection depth especially on larger objects.

6. Using smaller searchcoils will: (A) give a sharper, more pronounced signal on individual targets; (B) find deeper objects; (C) give better battery life; (D) increase mineralization effects.

7. What is the best, "general purpose," searchcoil size range? (A) seven-inch to eight-inch diameter; (B) three-quarter-inch to three-and-one-half-inch diameter; (C) eight-inch to twelve-inch diameter; (D) the large "two-box" Depth Multiplier size.

8. Large searchcoils, such as a twelve-inch diameter size, is best used in: (A) bullet hunting; (B) underwater detecting; (C) searching for rings; (D) looking for large, deeply buried targets.

9. A three-quarter-inch search probe is used for: (A) finding .22 caliber cartridge casings; (B) finding buried firearms; (C) searching crevices and other locations that will not accommodate a larger searchcoil.

10. Some metal detectors are perfectly capable of locating metallic objects when the searchcoil is immersed in water down to thirty-inches.

True _____ False _____

11. One of the most important facts about the two-box Depth Multiplier attachments is that: (A) increased battery drain greatly reduces battery life; (B) they are more impressive to onlookers; (C) they detect large objects while mostly ignoring small objects.

12. A general rule of metal detection is: (A) "the deeper the object you are seeking, the larger the searchcoil that should be used; the smaller the object you are seeking, the smaller the searchcoil that should be used."

True _____ False _____

13. Using trash elimination (discrimination) may: (A) reduce ground mineralization; (B) give much greater depth; (C) cause some desirable objects to be rejected; (D) drain batteries rapidly.

14. Detectors set to reject aluminum pulltabs will not: (A) detect ground minerals; (B) detect bottlecap, nails, and lead projectiles; (C) detect silver quarters; (D) detect large aluminum cans.

15. Using no trash elimination (discrimination) on a correctly designed detector will: (A) cause the detector to sense all metals; (B) eliminate ground mineralization; (C) make the detector easier

to tune; (D) make the detector much less sensitive.

16. Push button (or toggle switch) retuning results in: (A) increased depth of detection; (B) elimination of ground minerals; (C) longer battery life; (D) instant detector retuning to preset audio threshold.

17. Metal detectors are manufactured that can be used as easily in a plowed field as they can to depths of 200 feet underwater.
    True _____   False _____

18. The best underwater metal detector is the _____ _____ type. This type metal detector can also be used on land, with excellent results in most detecting situations.

19. Using the VLF type detector over wet ocean salt and animal carcasses may: (A) get the searchcoil dirty; (B) provide a smoother tuning sound; (C) require special tuning procedures; (D) give more depth of detection.

20. A buried gun will produce what type of a detection signal compared to that from a .38 caliber cartridge case, if both are located at the same depth? (A) smaller; (B) the same; (C) larger and louder.

21. The hand-held Pocket Scanner, often referred to as the "Enforcer," is used primarily: (A) by Clint Eastwood as a weapon in his San Francisco law enforcement movies; (B) to locate buried guns; (C) to conduct body searches of suspects; (D) in shallow water searches.

22. In searching a person for a concealed weapon, it is necessary that the metal detector actually touch the body to detect the weapons.
    True _____   False _____

23. Some of the Pocket Scanner type metal detectors are so sensitive, they can readily detect even a single .22 caliber bullet, in fact, even a single BB shot.
    True _____   False _____

24. Since the human body contains water, salt, and other minerals, weapons like small guns and knives cannot be detected in body cavities.
    True _____   False _____

25. Walk-through type metal detectors, especially of the latest high-technology type designs, can detect even a few bullets in a person's pocket.
    True _____   False _____

26. Even though quality built VLF detectors will do just about every detecting task you require of them, perhaps the most important thing to remember is: (A) when the ground is dry, you should wait for rain so that you will get better depth detection; (B) occasionally you will, in your searching, find buried treasure and valuables; (C) keep fully charged batteries in your detector at all times; (D) success is dependent upon detector how-to-use knowledge coupled with perseverance.

27. The most popular form of metal detecting is: (A) Coin hunting; (B) Prospecting; (C) Bottle digging; (D) Relic hunting; (E) Body scanning.

28. A post hole bank is: (A) A fly-by-night banking operation; (B) A bank in the town of Post Hole, Nevada; (C) A post outside a bank where people deposited money; (D) Money hidden in a post hole of a fence.

29. Tuning your detector to operate without any sound will: (A) Give greater depth of detection; (B) Reduce detector sensitivity and detection depth; (C) Extend the life of your detector's speaker; (D) Eliminate ground minerals.

30. Reading good metal detector books will: (A) Wean you away from the TV set; (B) Improve your vocabulary; (C) Improve your metal detecting skills; (D) Make you the hit of the party.

31. The basic purpose of metal detecting clubs is: (A) To find all the treasure they can in a given area; (B) To teach members how to use a metal detector; (C) To foster and promote the hobby of metal detecting; (D) To assist community organizations and law enforcement.

32. It may be necessary, to adjust the audio/tuning control each time the metal detector is switched from one operating mode to another, if the detector does not feature automatic retuning.
    True _____   False _____

Each of the questions 1 through 32 is worth 3 points if answered correctly. Give yourself an extra 4 points if you answered question number 3 correctly. Perfect score is 100.

Figure 18-A: Ed Best, former Director of Security for the XXIII Olympiad, and Charles Garrett discuss new, innovative approaches to security in an Olympic setting. Prior to the Olympics, Best distinguished himself as Special Agent in Charge of the Los Angeles Office of the FBI. The Olympic security program (which may be the most important security team effort of this century,) as overseen by Best and his team, was such a successful accomplishment that these dedicated people, themselves, deserve a gold medal.

Figure 18-B: Stanley Kephart (left) Olympic Security, Dave Loveless, and Charles Garrett view one of the many Olympic planning and work areas. Just to view these operations was overwhelming in itself. Men like Mr. Kephart, John Underwood, and, of course, Ed Best, former Director of Security for the XXIII Olympiad, are to be commended for the tremendous job they did in maintaining absolute security for the Olympic athletes and participants.

273

Figure 18-C: Olympic Security rules were absolute. No one was allowed to bypass the walk-throughs. Even Sam the Eagle had to be checked, but, alas, he couldn't get through (top photo). Nevertheless, he was scanned, with the hand scanner as shown in the lower photograph. From the smile on his face it is obvious he is enjoying the personal attention. Photo by Dave Loveless.

Figure 18-E: Richard Graham and Charles Garrett are given a tour of the Utah State Prison. The men worked with prison officials to learn, first-hand, the type scanning equipment needed.

Figure 18-F: Bob Podhrasky and Ed McCrary (Assistant Director of Garland Police Department) examine a coin changer found in a North Texas lake.

Figure 18-G: Jack Hube and Charles Garrett train members of Canada's Royal Canadian Mounted Police in the use of underwater Sea Hunter metal detectors.

Figure 18-H: Richard Graham scans a shallow West Texas river for metallic evidence. He walks a grid pattern, scanning with a two-box Depth Multiplier attached to a Master Hunter 7 A.D.S.

Figure 18-I: Charles Garrett (left), Dave Loveless, Bob Elswood, and Jack Topham of Utah Wildlife Resources, investigate a deer carcass for metallic projectiles. Bob and Jack have become masters in the use of metal detection equipment. Because of the success they and other Utah Game Warden have had, metal detectors are now carried in many Utah Wildlife Resources vehicles. These men relate that the number of convictions, since they started using metal detectors to investigate poaching cases, has greatly increased. In 1982, Bob attended a Law Enforcement Seminar in Provo, Utah. During the seminar he and Charles had a discussion regarding the use of metal detectors to scan animals. As a result of this discussion, various seminars and numerous successful field applications, the metal detector has become accepted as an important law enforcement tool.

Figure 18-K: At this San Antonio, Texas, FBI metal detector seminar, Richard Graham, Dave Loveless and Charles Garrett assist Texas Game Warden in the use of metal detectors. (See also Figure 18-17)

277

Figure 18-L: Mail and letter bombs, as shown here, can be detected with highly sensitive metal detectors. Clock mechanisms, batteries, wiring, photo electric cells, dynamite caps, and other components of mail and letter bombs, are readily detectable by the Pocket Scanner, Enforcer Model G-1.

Figure 18-M; 18-N: Ken Schaffer of H&S Detector Center, Virginia Beach, Virginia was out surfing with his metal detector and located this unique, spy ring, microfilm container. The ring, when closed, looks like an ordinary ring. By pressing on a part of the buckle, and pulling the band a certain way, the ring opens up as shown in the bottom photograph. Ken loaned the ring to the United States Secret Service for examination. They told Ken, "The ring was certainly one of the tools of the trade, not necessarily one of ours." The ring is one of those once-in-a-lifetime discoveries.

279

Figure 18-O: Lee Pavel of LP Enterprises, Sprague, Nebraska, located this stolen coin collection for the Nebraska State Police. Because of Lee's metal detector expertise and proved track record in helping local and state police on various cases, he is often called in on cases that require the use of metal detectors. He recently helped the FBI search for a one-million dollar stolen coin collection.

Figure 18-P: If it's metal, a metal detector will probably find it.

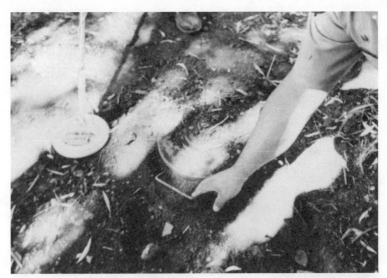

Figure 18-Q: This land mine made a gigantic target for the investigating officer's metal detector. Extensive testing has been done to determine if a metal detector's electromagnetic field will set off explosive charges. There are no known cases where this has happened. Even blasting caps have been tested with negative results. It is believed, however, that there are certain military mines that will be set off, if a metal detector is scanned over them.

Figure 18-R: This Postal Inspector prepares to scan a parcel that is suspected of being a letter bomb.

281

Figure 18-S: Charles Garrett presents a Pocket Scanner to the Assistant Chief of Police of Cartagena, Colombia. The Cartagena police were very receptive to Charles' suggestion that he return to Colombia to teach the entire Colombian police and law enforcement departments in the use of land and underwater metal detector instrumentation.

Figure 18-T: The finding of this broken screwdriver tip led to the indictment and conviction of a suspect. This is just one more case proving the value of the modern metal detector.

Figure 18-U: Even though narcotics are not detectable, they were nevertheless readily located in this can that was stashed in the wall of an old house.

CHAPTER 19

Industrial Metal LOCATOR/TRACER Short Course

There are two major types of instruments used in industry to find metallic objects: the metal LOCATOR and the pipe/cable TRACER. LOCATING means the locating or detecting of metal objects in the conventional metal detection manner. For instance, a manhole cover (with its large, flat surface area) buried several feet deep must be located using conventional deep seeking type metal detectors. But, since conventional metal detectors are surface area detectors, and are not efficient in locating rounded objects, deep pipe, cable, conduit and other elongated metal objects must be TRACED with suitable type tracing instruments.

MODERN EQUIPMENT AVAILABLE

Figure 19-1 shows the three main configurations of a twin-circuit metal locator/pipe and cable tracing instrument (Figure 19-2). Depending upon the searchcoil attached, the instrument can; LOCATE manhole covers, valve boxes, sprinkler heads, and other buried and concealed metal objects; TRACE pipe, cable and

Figure 19-1: This photograph shows the three main configurations of the LT-2000 tracer/locator. The optional accessory two-box Depth Multiplier (left); tracing probe (center); twelve-inch diameter locator searchcoil (right).

284

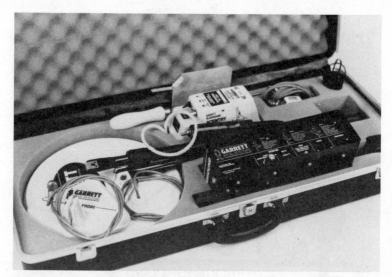

Figure 19-2: This is the compact suitcased assembly of the LT-2000 tracer/locator. All components as shown in Figure 19-1 are carried within this suitcase except the two-box Depth Multiplier optional accessory.

conduit; and MEASURE DEPTH and LOCATE BREAKS in objects being traced.

LOCATOR CONFIGURATIONS

To use this instrument as a LOCATOR, attach the twelve-inch diameter searchcoil (Figure 19-1, instrument on right) which is supplied as standard equipment. The circuits automatically switch to the LOCATOR mode, and the detector is then used in the same manner as a conventional metal detector. Large objects such as manhole covers can be located to depths of six feet plus.

The Bloodhound Depth Multiplier, an optional accessory (Figure 19-1, instrument on left) can be quickly attached to the control housing to locate large mass objects to depths of about fifteen to twenty feet.

TRACING CONFIGURATIONS

To use as a TRACING instrument (Figure 19-1, instrument in center) attach the probe, the circuits automatically switch to the tracing mode. Pipe, cable, and conduit can be traced, depth measured, and break locations determined. In the tracing mode, an energizing signal must be coupled into the pipe, cable, or conduit. This can be accomplished with either conductive or inductive coupling, Figure 19-3. An electromagnetic source (Figure 19-4) is supplied to generate the energizing signal.

To make a DIRECT connection (Figure 19-5) wire leads with alligator clips are provided. One clip is attached to the pipe, cable

PIPE, CABLE AND CONDUIT TRACING METHODS

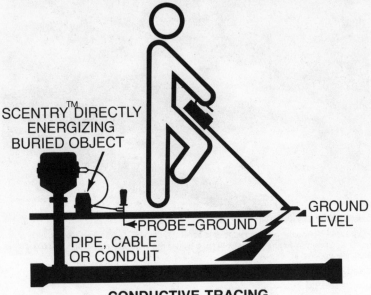

SCENTRY™ DIRECTLY
ENERGIZING
BURIED OBJECT

PROBE-GROUND

PIPE, CABLE
OR CONDUIT

GROUND
LEVEL

CONDUCTIVE TRACING

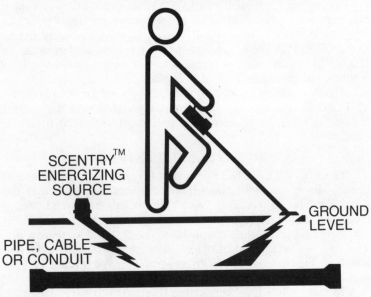

SCENTRY™
ENERGIZING
SOURCE

PIPE, CABLE
OR CONDUIT

GROUND
LEVEL

INDUCTIVE TRACING

Figure 19-3:

286

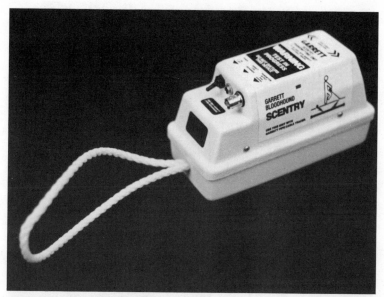

Figure 19-4: This is the LT-2000 pipe tracer/metal locator energizing source, the Scentry. This energizing signal source can be connected directly to objects to be traced, or it radiates an electromagnetic field that couples inductively into objects.

Figure 19-5: The Scentry is shown connected to a gas pipe. This type operation is called DIRECT (conductive) tracing. Note, the second alligator clip is attached to a grounding probe.

or conduit, the other is clipped to a rod, or plate that is in electrical contact with the soil. A grounding plate (standard equipment) may be used if direct contact with the soil is impossible. When the grounding plate is used, a rock or other heavy metal object should be placed on it so better ground connection will be made. DIRECT connection provides the best means of tracing because the signals in the object to be traced are generally stronger than in the induction method.

To trace INDUCTIVELY, the energizing source is placed at a point on the ground directly above where the pipe (cable or conduit) is believed to be buried (Figure 19-6). A powerful electromagnetic field penetrates the ground. Electromagnetic energy is INDUCED into the object to be traced.

Figure 19-6: To trace INDUCTIVELY, the Scentry is placed directly above where the pipe (cable or conduit) is believed to be buried. A powerful electromagnetic field penetrates the ground inducing a signal into the object.

The electromagnetic energy travels along the object, creating a re-radiated or secondary signal which radiates upward through the ground and into the air. With the tracer probe connected to the instrument, the operator simply walks along scanning side-to-side as in normal detection. The tracer probe detects the secondary or re-radiated field, alerting the operator to the presence of the pipe. The pipe location and underground route is determined as the operator marks the locations where the strongest signals are detected.

LOCATING BREAKS AND CHANGES IN DIRECTION OF CONCEALED PIPE, CABLE AND CONDUIT.

When the electromagnetic energy flowing along a conductor reaches a break, a junction, or a direction change, the characteristics of the energy field are altered which the tracing probe senses. Operating instructions are included with pipe and cable tracers explaining the various discontinuity situations so that they may be easily analyzed.

MEASUREMENT OF PIPE, CABLE AND CONDUIT DEPTH

To measure the depth of underground pipe, cable and conduit the tracer probe must be attached to the tracing instrument. The operator must determine the point (strongest signal) on the ground which is directly above the buried pipe, etc., and there, rotate the probe ninety degrees. The operator stands at right angles to the pipe. The depth measuring EDGE of the probe is placed flat (squarely) upon the ground. The instrument is then pushed away from the pipe with the measuring edge of the probe sliding along parallel with the ground (Figure 19-7). The signal will begin to decrease in loudness. At the point where a null (minimum sound) is reached, a marker should be placed. The distance between the marker and the point directly above where the pipe is buried, is equal to the depth of the pipe. Depth accuracy, which can be

Figure 19-7: Bob Podhrasky (left) and Larry Johnson measure the depth of a gas pipe. Larry demonstrates the manner in which the probe is held. As he slides the probe forward, a null in the signal will be heard. The distance between null and the location of the pipe will be the exact pipe depth.

extremely accurate, is determined by how carefully the operator holds the edge of the probe parallel to the ground and how carefully he locates the pipe and the null point. With only a small amount of experience, an operator can become quite efficient measuring depth.

TIME AND MONEY SAVERS

Industrial locators and tracers are invaluable tools for utility and construction companies who must probe, drill or excavate. These instruments are great time and money savers (Figure 19-8). Construction crews ripped through underground artery telephone lines that supplied telephone service to two large communities just north of Dallas, Texas. For more than twenty-four hours, a half-million people were without telephone service. When the cost and inconvenience caused by those severed cables is analyzed, the true value of an industrial locator/tracer employed ahead of earth moving equipment can be quickly determined.

BUILDING WIRING AND PLUMBING

Building wiring and metal plumbing can be traced using these same techniques. Plastic pipe that contains a metal tracing wire can also be traced.

Figure 19-8: Industrial locators and tracers are invaluable tools for utility and construction companies who must probe, drill, or excavate. These instruments are great time and money savers.

290

Miniature pocket detectors of the type shown in Figure 19-9 can aid the plumber, electrician, telephone repairman and others who must locate any type of metal object concealed in building walls, ceilings and floors.

Figure 19-9: Miniature pocket detectors of this type (the Pocket Scanner Model 11770) aid the plumber, electrician, telephone repairmen, and others who must locate metal objects concealed in building walls, ceilings and floors.

CHAPTER 19 QUESTIONS

1. There are two main types of instruments used in industry to find metallic objects. The metal _____ and the pipe/cable _____ .

2. In industrial jargon, _____ metal means the same thing as detecting metal.

3. Generally, standard metal locators (detectors) do not make good pipe, cable, and conduit locators because there is very little flat metal surface for eddy current generation.

   True _____   False _____

4. The main difference between the operation of metal locators and pipe tracers is that metal locators transmit their own electromagnetic field, whereas, pipe tracers generally use a separate means of electromagnetic field generation.

   True _____   False _____

291

5. A metal locator is of much more value to utility and construction crews if various sizes of_____ are available for the locator.

6. There are two tracing configurations or methods by which the electromagnetic field signal is coupled to buried pipes, cables, and conduits. These two methods of coupling are _____ and _____ .

7. _____ tracing (direct connection) provides the best means of tracing because the signals to be traced are generally stronger than in the _____ method.

8. When using versatile tracing instruments, pipes can be traced and the following things can be done: (A) junctions can be found; (B) a change in pipe direction can be determined; (C) treasure can be found; (D) breaks can be located.

9. Pipe depth measuring accuracy is determined by how carefully the operator holds the edge of the probe parallel to the _____ , and how carefully he locates the _____ and the _____ point.

10. Pipe, cable, and conduit depth measuring is so accurate that it can be done within inches or even fractions of an inch.

    True _____   False _____

11. The locating of extremely deep manhole covers, valve boxes, and other large metallic objects require the use of large searchcoils and/or the Depth Multiplier type attachment.

    True _____   False _____

12. Building, wiring, and metal plumbing cannot be traced as easily in wooden buildings as in the ground, because building construction nails tend to interfere with the process.

    True _____   False _____

13. Rebar and other metal reinforcing rods in concrete necessitate extra careful tracing procedures.

    True _____   False _____

Each correct answer given in questions 1,6,7,8 and 9 is worth 3 points. Total value of these 12 correct answers is 36 points. Each correct answer given to the remaining 8 questions is 8 points. Perfect score is 100. Answers given in Appendix 2.

CHAPTER 20

Metal Detectors Worldwide

Metal detectors of all types are in use throughout the world. In the United States, the majority of metal detector operators search for lost coins, jewelry, and money caches. In most other countries, this also holds true, although in some countries specialized forms of hunting take predominance.

In the United States, every conceivable use to which metal detectors can be applied takes place on a regular basis. Coin hunting is the most popular metal detecting activity, relic hunting, electronic prospecting and beach hunting follow next. Law enforcement applications are numerous; crime scene investigations with metal detectors occur regularly. Since terrorism and hijackings are constantly taking place, walk-throughs and hand-held weapons detector applications are increasing. The use of metal detectors, pipe and cable tracers, is common throughout the utility and construction industries.

In Australia, where it seems the ground is literally paved with gold, gold seekers make up the majority of metal detector owners and operators. It is not known how much gold has been taken out of Australian gold fields, but the amount is in the multiple tens of millions of dollars. Peter Bridge of Perth, Australia, who is President of Hesperian Detectors and is the "Father" of Australia's modern-day electronic "Gold Rush," (Figure 20-1) reports that one gold nugget found with a metal detector brought one million dollars to its finder (Figure 20-2). There are numerous reports of finders receiving fifty thousand, one hundred thousand, and even a quarter-million dollars for single gold nuggets. There seems to be no end to the Australian gold supply. While Australians make up the majority, a surprising number of gold-seekers, scanning the outback, are from other countries. Australian gold tours often originate in the United States.

There are many professional treasure hunters who make regular trips to Australia where they stay up to three months (Figure 20-3). Since these prospectors make regular return visits, it's a sure thing they are finding enough gold to make it worthwhile.

Even Royalty gets into the act, when crown Prince Charles, heir to the British throne, made a state visit to Western Australia in 1979, a highlight of his visit was a metal-detecting, gold-hunting safari to the rich Murchison gold fields located approximately four hundred miles north of Perth. This is one of the areas where gold

Figure 20-1: Peter Bridge, President of Hesperian Detectors, Victoria Park 6100, Western Australia, the "father" of Australia's modern-day electronic gold rush, holds a replica of a nugget that was found one hundred years ago. Because of Peter's investigative work, Australia's twentieth century gold rush began in the 1970s. Tens of millions of dollars in gold have been located with modern metal detectors.

Figure 20-2: These two Australians hold the Hand of Faith, the largest nugget found with a metal detector. It weighs sixty-two pounds (twenty-eight kilograms) and was purchased by the Las Vegas, Nevada (U.S.A.) Golden Nugget Casino for a reported one million dollars. Photo by Bob Grant.

Figure 20-3: Peter Bridge and Charles Garrett survey mining property near Australia's Kalgoorlie Mining District. Earlier this century, United States President Theodore Roosevelt was president of a large mining concern that operated at this site. Photo by Frank Mellish.

nuggets are continually found. The quantity of gold that Prince Charles found is not known, since no reporters were allowed on the trip. The secrecy was probably due to security factors and the possibility that the landowners did not wish to publicize the location of their gold field.

One reason gold hunting is so lucrative and interesting in Australia, is the lack of government taxation of gold finds. Electronic prospectors who find gold in Australia pay no tax to the Australian government.

Beach hunting is on the rise. For well over a hundred years sunbathers enjoyed the beautiful Australian beaches, and it was not until the early 1980s that metal detectors were used to search these lucrative areas. On a trip to Australia in 1979, several American and English treasure hunters spent some time scanning a popular Sydney beach. We were amazed at the large quantity of coins and jewelry that we uncovered in a very short time.

There is a considerable number of shipwrecks that lie in shallow waters all around Australia. Since all treasure belongs to the Crown, apparently very little activity with underwater metal detectors is taking place.

The Australian government has been using deepseeking VLF detectors for years, to clean practice bombing ranges of unexploded bombs.

In Central and South America, metal detectors are used primarily in the gold and silver fields and in areas where known caches are buried in the ground or concealed in building structures. It seems everyone in Mexico knows a story about a rich treasure cache that was secreted away and never recovered by its owners (Figure 20-5). Countless ruins dot practically every area of Mexico. A one hundred and fifteen pound coin cache was discovered during one treasure hunt in Mexico. Gold and silver coinage and caches are often reported. Sales of deepseeking equipment take the lead in Mexico, with cache hunting detectors being sold at a much swifter pace than coin hunting models.

Figure 20-5: It seems everyone in Mexico knows a story about a rich treasure cache that was secreted away and never recovered by its owners. Countless ruins dot practically every area of Mexico. Charles Garrett pauses for a few minutes from other treasure hunting activities to scan for lost coins near this ancient ruin. Not far from here a one-hundred and fifteen pound silver cache was located. Photo by Monty Moncrief.

There is often brisk electronic prospecting activity in the gold and silver regions of Central and South America (Figure 20-7). The quantity of silver being recovered far outweighs that of gold, but that is primarily because there is an abundance of silver that can be found with metal detectors.

Since the government controls mineral resources in Central and South America, and metal detecting is restricted, it is questionable whether successes to equal Australian gold finds will take place. Of course, coin hunting on thousands of beaches (Figure 20-8) can be very good as most have never been scanned with a detector.

In Canada, coin hunting is quite popular; electronic prospect-

297

Figure 20-7: Brisk electronic prospecting often takes place in the gold and silver regions of Central and South America. Left to right are American prospectors Roy Lagal, Don Garrett (author's brother), Charles Garrett, Curley Jones, Victor Moreland, Monty Moncrief, David Medrano, and kneeling, is Art Griffith. Photo by George Mroczkowski.

Figure 20-8: Charles Garrett scans for coins on this Cartagena, Colombia South American beach. There are hundreds of miles of popular beaches in Central and South America that have never had a metal detector scanned over them. Photo by Bob Podhrasky.

ing comes in a close second. Coin hunting is most popular near the populated areas, and beachcombing is on a sharp increase. Ghost town hunting is popular as there are numerous ghost towns dotted all across Canada.

Electronic prospecting is an extremely active metal detecting hobby. For instance, in the Cobalt, Ontario region, a steady stream of electronic prospectors (Figure 20-9) scan their searchcoils back and forth searching for, and finding, native silver. During the early part of the twentieth century, countless miles of underground tunnels were dug in this region. The majority of this ore can still be found lying about in road beds and monstrous rock piles throughout this region. Electronic prospectors are having success in finding silver that early-day miners missed. Large quantities of silver float are found all around the mining areas. Silver chunks weighing hundreds of pounds are often found. One such piece was sold to a smelter for ten thousand dollars. I have found silver in Canada, the largest piece weighed fifty pounds and is worth five thousand dollars. (See photo, Chapter 25.)

Here's a little secret that could lead you to a fortune in silver; should you decide to go electronic prospecting in Cobalt, Ontario, take along and use one of the Bloodhound Depth Multipliers described in other chapters in this book. Attach it to an A.D.S. detector and search for the many, many large chunks of silver ore

Figure 20-9: Electronic prospectors Jim Paul and Jack Hube retrieve a large chunk of silver ore that Jack just located with his detector. This multiple pound rock was nearly pure silver. The mining districts around Cobalt, Ontario have proven to be fruitful locations for today's modern electronic prospector.

that are waiting to be found in the Cobalt outlying regions. My fifty pound chunk and the other mentioned one hundred and fifty pound pieces (see Chapter 25) were found with smaller searchcoils that also found many very tiny, and not very valuable, pieces. With the Depth Multiplier, you won't waste time digging the smaller material (and for moisture and water pockets) as it will detect only very large, multiple-pound pieces of metal that are worth a fortune. Just walk the outback regions and find the big stuff!

The "father" of electronic prospecting, Roy Lagal, came to the same conclusion I did when we both searched the Cobalt region for several days. So, don't take this tip lightly. When you make a strike with the Bloodhound Depth Multiplier, it'll be a big one! The largest "chunk" of silver found in the Cobalt region was named the Silver Sidewalk. It was a solid vein of silver that was waiting just a couple of feet below ground surface when found. It measured approximately thirty feet long by fifteen feet wide by fifty feet deep! Refer to Figure 20-10, and see the crevice that was left when the silver was removed.

In the United Kingdom, the majority of hunting takes place on private land areas. Some underwater work is being done. A good situation exists in England between individuals and the government. The Crown requests that all finds

Figure 20-10: A vein of nearly pure silver was removed from this crevice located in the Cobalt, Ontario, Canada silver mining district. The vein measured approximately thirty feet long by fifteen-feet wide by fifty-feet deep. It was nicknamed the Silver Sidewalk because, for many years following its discovery, the owners allowed miners to walk on the silver. Near the end of the silver boom, the silver was removed.

Figure 20-11: Treasure hunts are held almost every day, it seems, somewhere in countries where metal detectors are popular. This was a hunt that was held in Canada on a weekend during a treasure hunting and metal detector seminar sponsored by Keith and Mary Edwards of Canadian Metal Locators, Inc., Waterford, Ontario.

be turned into the British museum. All artifacts are evaluated, and if the Crown so decides, the relics will be purchased from the finder at fair market value. Those finds the Crown does not wish to purchase, are returned to the finder. Occasionally, large hoards of Roman coins are found. A fifty-thousand-coin hoard was found in the early 1980s.

Even though the private possession of hand guns is prohibited in the United Kingdom, guns and other weapons are smuggled into the country. The famed Scotland Yard has purchased hundreds of miniature Pocket Scanners (Figure 20-12) to use in their investigative work.

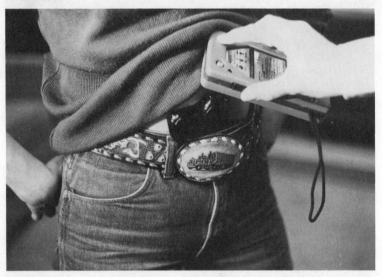

Figure 20-12: Not only have Pocket Scanner metal detectors become popular treasure hunting tools, they have also become very popular with law enforcement and security agencies in many countries of the world. These scanners will readily locate the smallest of metal objects. This instrument, the Pocket Scanner, Model 11616, quickly located this concealed weapon.

It is reported that metal detectors are being smuggled into Russia and other Iron Curtain countries. Russian tourists come over to England and various Western Europe countries to purchase metal detectors and smuggle them back into their home country.

Our West Germany distributors W. A. Albrecht and H. G. Scholz, owners of A&S Handelsgesselschaft mbH & Co. KG in Dusseldorf, relate that laws relating to metal detecting are reasonably liberal. Searching, by means of locators, is permitted, excavation is permitted on private ground only. Many areas have been declared "cultural-historic areas," and as such, are off limits to metal detecting. It appears that regulations there are similar to those in the United States.

The ground all over World War I and II European countries is a true treasure chest. Countless individual, family, and even government treasures were buried for safe keeping during the wars. Countless tons of treasure is still in the ground. Often, reports of extremely valuable treasure finds come to my attention. Several of these finds (Figure 20-13) have been written about in SEARCHER magazine and in various other treasure publications. Coin and cache hunting is very popular in Western Europe but since the government controls the use of metal detectors possibly no more than one percent of the potential lost wealth in Western Europe will ever be discovered. Certainly, millions of war relics, (Figure 20-14) can be found. However, relic hunting on World War II battlefield sites is considered highly dangerous because of the vast quantity of unexploded munitions.

Plebe Ciro (Figure 20-15) of Livorno, Italy, has worked out a unique arrangement with his government. The government sanctions his land and underwater metal detector searches (Figure 20-16), and all finds are turned over to them. Plebe is awarded a small, yet agreeable, percentage of his finds. Good finds have been reported (Figures 20-17 and 20-18).

Throughout Western Europe, historians and research teams are using metal detectors to scan historical sites, battlefields, ancient cities, etc. It will require several lifetimes to examine all

Figure 20-13: Alfred Wucherpfennig digs for buried treasure. He recovered this gold coin cache (inset) in the Netherlands.

303

Figure 20-14: Vaughan Garrett (wearing wool cap), Jonathan Patterson (wearing lanyard around neck), Charles Garrett and three West Germans display an assortment from hundreds of pounds of World War II relics they uncovered during two hours scanning at a Siegfried battle-line bunker site. Mortars, bullets, hand grenades, weapons, coins and personal items of all descriptions were located. Photo by Bob Grant.

the battlefields mentioned in the Bible, alone. Researchers are using detectors at these sites to locate relics that will establish dates, define perimeters, and ascertain other details of these battles.

Because oceans and lakes have been used extensively for thousands of years, tens of thousands of shipwreck sites, many sunken harbors and cities, and much lost treasure, await the underwater explorer. It is estimated that ten times more treasure is "lost" in water than in the ground. Metal detectors are being used underwater in the same manner as on land: to locate sites, define perimeters, locate treasure, establish dating, determine ship and cargo types, etc.

Sales of equipment to South Africa have been steadily increasing for several years. Mr. E. G. Beaton, owner of DECO, in Durban, South Africa, reports that the hobbyist and electronic prospectors are about equal in number. Coin and cache hunting is very popular in the more urban areas.

Throughout the world, the use of metal detection equipment shows continual signs of increasing. Terrorists attacks, bombings, hijackings, and other lawlessness, necessitate the use of walkthroughs and portable hand-held body scanning detectors. Letter and mail bombs are increasing at an alarming rate, which causes an increase in the use of instruments to detect such devices.

Industrial applications of all types of metal locating and trac-

Figure 20-15: Garrett's Italian Distributor, Plebe Ciro, via Ernesto Rossi No. 31, 57100, Livorno, Italia, scans this ancient Roman road. The general use of metal detectors in Italy is not allowed except through government grants. Plebe has worked with the Italian government at several sites and has reported many valuable discoveries.

Figure 20-16: Plebe Ciro's work with metal detectors extends into the underwater realm. Here it appears they are combining business with pleasure as they prepare to scan with submersible searchcoils and Sea Hunter detectors. This craft was specially designed and manufactured by the Italian Pirelli manufacturer.

ing equipment are increasing. Industrial metal detection equipment tends to be specialized, with each application being different.

The use of underwater equipment continues to be in demand in most countries as ten times more wealth is believed lost in the earth's bodies of water than is lost and buried in the ground. Of course, searching for underwater treasure is at least ten times more complicated and costly than land hunting; nevertheless, the rewards are much greater. The cost and extra effort do not hinder many of those who are determined to strike it rich.

Three factors prevent rapid growth in world-wide detector usage: one is stiff governmental restrictions and high import duties and taxes, the second is the complexities of reaching those who have need for metal detection devices, and the third is the failure of the majority of the world's population to understand the value of the metal detector. Most people do not know what metal detectors are, and a good percentage of those who do, don't believe that they work, and do not understand the simple metal detector procedure one uses to locate concealed metal objects.

Nevertheless, the demand for metal detection equipment throughout the world is growing, and will continue to grow. The producers of quality detectors, who spend the time and effort to develop world markets, are the ones who are supplying, and will continue to supply these markets.

Figure 20-17, 20-18: In the upper photograph, Plebe Ciro explains to the author the various markings on some of the coins he discovered in Italy. The lower photograph is a close up of these coins. Photo by Melvin Climer.

307

CHAPTER 20 QUESTIONS

1. In the United States most metal detectors are used in the search for treasure. The same holds true in all other countries of the world.
   True _____ False _____

2. Of course, in all countries there are numerous other metal detector applications. The two most predominant are _____ _____ and _____ applications. (Each correct answer is worth 5 points)

3. It is estimated that about two million dollars worth of gold has been found throughout the world, with metal detectors.
   True _____ False _____

4. In Australia, as well as in most other countries, swimming _____ hunting is popular.

5. In the countries where gold, silver, platinum, copper, and other conductive metals can be found, _____ prospecting is becoming increasingly popular.

6. The largest known dollar amount paid for a gold nugget, found with a detector in Australia, sold for the staggering sum of one _____ American dollars.

7. In Canada, large chunks of silver are being found. One such piece that weighed over one-hundred pounds sold for $_____ American dollars.

8. Large nuggets are commonly found in the United States. You don't hear much about these large nuggets because finders usually keep it quiet. Wouldn't it be nice if all countries, like Australia, declared precious metal finds to be tax free?
   ☐ Yes   ☐ No

9. During World War I and World War II, countless thousands of money and treasure caches were buried in the ground and in various water sources. Since there are so many metal detectors in use in Western Europe, probably most of these treasures have been found.
   True _____ False _____

10. One good way for the hobbyist to combat anti-metal detecting legislation, is for local detector clubs to offer free assistance to law enforcement departments when these departments need to locate metal crime scene evidence.
    True _____ False _____

Each correct answer is worth 10 points. Perfect score is 100. Correct answers given in Appendix 2.

Figure 20-A: Garrett's Greek distributors, Lela Harisi, Alexandras Ave., 29, Athens, Greece and Kostas Karathanasis, Egnatia St., 6, Thessaloniki, Greece, demonstrate Garrett instruments to booth visitors. At this yearly trade show, thousands of Greeks and visitors from other countries express their interest in metal detectors.

Figure 20-B: A Tarahumara Indian guide shows the author the probable location of buried treasure. Somewhere in this location, there is a cave filled with gold and silver artifacts from the eighteenth century. This location is in the southern tip of Mexico's state of Chihuahua. This photograph was taken during a month long excursion that Garrett and several other Americans made into this region. Photo by Javier Castellanos.

Figure 20-C: It was at this Southern European site that Charles Garrett and several Americans located relics and coins of the (Circa) 400 B.C. period. It is believed that these coins are the oldest ever found with a metal detector. Photo by Vaughan Garrett.

Figure 20-D: Peter Bridge, Charles Garrett and Bob Wieland of Associated Press discuss gold hunting in Australia. Photo by Melvin Climer.

Figure 20-E, Charles and Vaughan Garrett, Bob Grant and a treasure hunter from Holland scan an 1815 Waterloo battlefield site. Coins, buttons and numerous projectiles were located.

Figure 20-F: The author's friend, Javier Castellanos, demonstrates a discriminating metal detector to Mrs. Pancho Villa. Charles Garrett and A. M. VanFossen (right) observe. Mrs. Villa was skeptical until she placed her gold medallion on the ground and asked Javier to scan it. When the metal locator indicated the medallion to be precious metal, a smile came across her face. She asked the men to go with her to two locations, one in Texas and one in Mexico, where her husband, Pancho Villa, the famous Mexican revolutionary had buried treasure in the early part of this century. Photo by L.L. "Abe" Lincoln.

Figure 20-G: Richard Ray and Charles Garrett examine one of several vaults, where in times past, Yucatan Mayas buried their valuables. Several treasures hidden centuries ago in similar storage vaults have been found by modern-day fortune seekers.

313

Figure 20-H: United States Ambassador James W. Hargrove, Charles Garrett and Peter Bridge discuss gold hunting in Australia. Garrett electronics was invited by the United States Department of Commerce to display electronic prospecting products at Australia's First International Mining Conference and Exhibition which was held in Sydney, Australia, in 1979. An Australian mining publication selected the Garrett booth as one of the two most interesting at the show. The Ambassador holds a twenty-two ounce gold nugget that was on display in the booth. The next day the Ambassador returned with his wife who was interested in seeing the gold nuggets displayed there.

CHAPTER 21

Attachments and Accessories

There are many different kinds of attachments manufacturers make available for users of their equipment. Not everyone will use all the attachments that are available; some will perhaps use only one or two, others as many as a dozen. The most popular attachments are described so you will have an understanding of them and can select those you can put to good use.

HIPMOUNT KIT. This is a popular accessory (see Figure 21-1). A typical hipmount kit includes brackets, screws, and other hardware for converting a standard configuration detector to the hipmount (Figure 21-2) and sling mount (Figure 21-3) configurations. The hipmount configuration allows the majority of the control housing weight to be attached to the operator's belt. The searchcoil is attached to the handle, and its cable provides a flexible link between the control housing and the searchcoil. It reduces operator fatigue, especially if larger than seven-inch to eight-inch searchcoils are used. Larger searchcoils are heavier, consequently, the more difficult and tiring they are to scan for

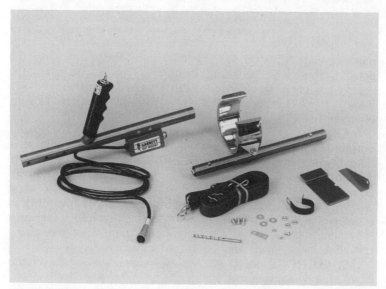

Figure 21-1: This is a popular hipmount kit accessory. It includes brackets, screws, and other hardware for converting standard configuration detectors to hipmount and sling-mount configurations.

Figure 21-2: Eleanor Hube of Suffield, Connecticut generally uses her detector in the hipmount configuration. This accessory allows the control housing to be carried on a belt, thus, removing weight from the searchcoil-stem arrangement. It allows an operator to scan for hours with little or no fatigue.

hours on end. When the sling mount is used, the person slings the detector around his neck and shoulders. One belt suspends the control housing while another securely fastens it around the person's waist so it does not swing about, especially when the person kneels or stoops to dig.

ARMREST. Since this type armrest (Figure 21-4) is usually not needed for balance with small, lightweight searchcoils, it is normally used only with larger ones. This accessory attaches to the detector handle. The balance and ease of operation achieved with an armrest makes the cost a worthwhile expenditure. The latest types of detector configurations (Figure 21-5) feature an armrest as an integral part of the detector design. This built-on feature improves the balance and ease of operation, providing much less tiring operation, even during long periods of scanning.

SEARCHCOIL SKID PLATE. Searchcoil skid plates (Figure 21-6) are popular items, available for most size searchcoils. They are simply a round, plastic disk-shaped cover that fits over the bottom of the searchcoil. They are held in place by friction, and generally contain no mounting brackets or screws. Skid plates

Figure 21-3: The sling-mount configuration is also very popular. Henry Tellez demonstrates the ease and convenience of carrying the control housing on a sling. A second strap can be placed around the waist which keeps the control housing snug against the body. Note the ease with which he can operate the handle-mounted Master Control switch and panel controls.

Figure 21-4: When very large searchcoils are used, hipmount kits and armrests (shown here) reduce operator fatigue. The balance and ease of operation achieved with an armrest makes the cost a worthwhile expenditure.

Figure 21-5: The Freedom 2 Coin Commander features a built-in armrest support. It gives good balance and control, improving operation during long periods of scanning. It is called a natural arm-extension design.

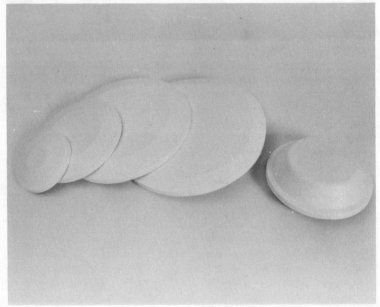

Figure 21-6: Searchcoil skid plates, available for most size searchcoils, are popular accessories. They protect against scraping, bumping, and gouging when slid over ground and rocky areas. They keep searchcoils in good condition which increases value at detector resale time.

318

provide protection to the searchcoil against scraping, bumping, and gouging when it is slid over the ground or scanned over rocky areas. They prevent holes from being worn in the searchcoil. Skid plates, in addition to providing protection, keep searchcoils in very good condition, adding to their resale value.

HEADPHONES. Headphones are so important that every owner and user of the detector should have one or more sets. Headphones are perhaps one of the most misunderstood and least used, yet important, accessories available. Headphones have many advantages. They allow the operator to hear deep and very small targets that produce faint whispers of detector signals that could not be heard otherwise. Most types of headphones sold by manufacturers provide ear covers that prevent outside noise from entering the ears. Noises caused by wind blowing through trees, surf noises, automobile traffic, etc., will mask weak detector signals, causing the operator to miss targets. Headphones allow private listening and will help keep your ears warm in the cold weather. In hot weather, headphones can become extremely bothersome and hot, but, regardless, should be used whenever possible.

Headphones (Figure 21-8) with individual earpiece controls, allow each side to be adjusted to suit the ear. And, what is very important, headphones with controls allow metal detector volume to be set to maximum, while the headphone volume controls can be set to a comfortable listening level.

Try this test and you'll quickly convince yourself of the value of headphones. Without using them, bury a coin in the ground at a depth that causes the speaker to just barely make a sound. Connect your headphones and readjust the detector audio level to a faint threshold sound. Recheck the coin. You will be amazed at how much better you can hear the signal.

The recommended type of headphones are those that have an extra-heavy-duty coiled cord, because the cord is the source of most wear. They should have adequate mufflers or cushions to mask most of the outside noises. And, as stated, headphones should have individual earpiece adjustable volume controls to set sound levels to suit the operator's own hearing requirements. I recommend that you purchase one or more sets of headphones and use them; you'll soon see that headphones pay for themselves many times over.

SPEAKER COVER. When it comes to operating in the rain, the most vulnerable component may be the speaker. Some speakers use waterproof mylar cones, others use paper. Should the paper cone in your detector become wet, the sound will become muffled; you will be unable to hear high sounds or the whispers of sound so vitally important to detection. When your speaker cone dries, it may or may not recover its full sound reproduction characteristics.

To protect your speaker, some manufacturers offer optional speaker covers as shown in Figure 21-7. Speaker covers prevent water damage but will reduce speaker volume.

Figure 21-7: Inexpensive, worthwhile speaker covers keep out moisture, dust and other contaminates. Even though speaker covers prevent damage, they reduce detector volume.

AUDIO CASSETTE INSTRUCTIONS. There are some manufacturers who provide audio cassette instructions (Figure 21-8). Most instruction tapes cover the basics of detector operation. Cassettes are inexpensive and even if they do nothing more than teach you to correctly tune your detector, are easily worth many times their cost.

CARRYING BAGS AND SUITCASES. Carrying bags and suitcases (Figure 21-9) are optional pieces of equipment that a person may wish to buy. There are many different types and styles on the market; some are made of flexible vinyl plastic and others are made rigid like a suitcase. The latter provides maximum protection for your detector regardless of whether it is stored or transported.

Flexible bags come in several kinds: some have a single long pocket the detector can be slipped into; others have draw strings, zippers, and snaps; and some have pockets for carrying various things like headphones, shovels, finds, and spare batteries. Suitcases are of several types, but mostly look like enlarged briefcases or equipment cases. Locks may be desirable.

COIN APRON. A coin apron (Figure 21-10) is certainly a must in any kind of coin hunting and other light detector hunting

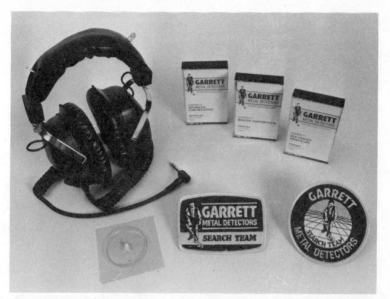

Figure 21-8: Shown here are various available accessories, including headphones (with individual earpiece adjustments,) audio cassette instruction tapes, a speaker cover and clothing patches. Good quality headphones are many times worth their cost.

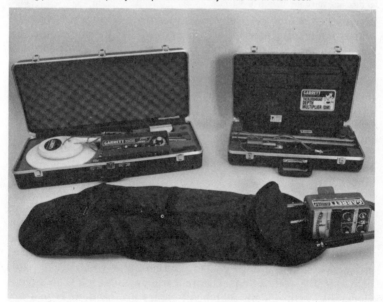

Figure 21-9: There are various suitcases and carrying bags available for metal detectors. The suitcase on the left contains a complete detector, including seven-and-one-half-inch and twelve-inch diameter searchcoils. The suitcase on the right contains a two-box Depth Multiplier attachment. The flexible bag allows the metal detector to be inserted without dismantling.

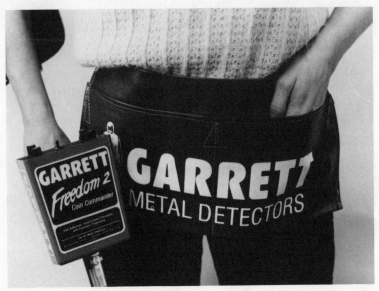

Figure 21-10: A coin apron is a must. This waterproof model has two pockets, one for treasure, one for trash. Always carry off and discard all trash you locate or dig. This helps keep parks and playgrounds clean, and should you or another treasure hunter come along later to search for treasure, you don't have to re-dig trash.

activity. They are generally constructed of waterproof material with two pockets, one for good finds, the other for junk items. All found junk, of course, should be collected for later discarding. Never leave junk trash lying about!

COIN PROBE. Coin probes are certainly a must! They are inexpensive and provide an accurate means for pinpointing your finds. Be sure the one you make or buy has a rounded, smooth point and by using it, it will stay that way. A coin recovery slide presentation, illustrating the correct use of coin probes, is available on a loan basis to clubs. (See the information, THE GARRETT FILM, VIDEO AND SLIDE LIBRARY following the Appendixes.)

EXTENSION ARM. There are various extension arm designs which, true to their name, extend the reach of your arm. These generally extend your searchcoil reach to about six to eight feet. They allow searching in deep water, up in trees, across overhead ceilings, and in other, hard to reach inaccessible places. The use of an extension arm allows you to scan an extra wide sweep path; consequently, you can cover more territory with each scan sweep. Generally, extra-length searchcoil cables are needed. If you are planning to search in water, you may wish to purchase submersible searchcoils designed specifically for that job.

HELPER HANDLE. Helper handles provide a greater ease in

swinging the searchcoil. Most people who have hand or wrist injuries, tennis elbow or other various muscle or joint problems, will find the speed handle a joy to use; you simply guide and direct the searchcoil along with your left hand. Maneuverability is precise, and many people find they actually enjoy using speed handles. There are minor inconveniences; you have a slight additional weight added to the detector, and each time you lay it down you have to do something with the speed handle. In other words, it must be moved out of the way in order to dig, etc., but it is considered an asset by many people.

RECHARGEABLE BATTERIES. Rechargeable batteries are now reasonably reliable and long lasting. The user can save money, especially if the detector is used often.

Follow the manufacturer's recommendations on keeping batteries in a fully recharged condition. Ni-cads are notoriously bad to take a "set," or in other words, to internally adapt to a use to which they are subjected. If the rechargeable battery is discharged one hour, recharged, discharged one hour, and recharged again, the battery will soon take a set, and you will only be able to get one hour's life from what otherwise might be a ten hour battery. So, vary the time which you use your detector. Recharge the batteries promptly, and do not charge longer than manufacturer's recommended length. Battery manufacturers recommend that ni-cads be completely discharged and then fully recharged once every three months or more often; this extends their life. To discharge ni-cads, simply operate the device in which they are installed until the batteries are fully discharged, then recharge them. Additional ni-cad battery discussions will be found in Chapters 9 and 29.

NI-CAD RECHARGE ADAPTORS. There are various kinds of recharge adaptors available for ni-cad batteries. Two United States models are the 110V, 60 Hz and 12V cigar lighter rechargers. In foreign and overseas countries, voltages are generally higher, with the frequency slightly lower than United States ratings. Adaptor kits are available which let United States rechargers operate on other voltages. If you are planning to travel abroad, make sure you have the correct recharge adaptor kit. It's usually much cheaper to buy them in the United States than to wait until you get to your destination. In fact, you may be unable to find the correct adaptor kits abroad; so, plan ahead.

CORDLESS HEADPHONES. There are numerous types of cordless headphones on the market. Some of them are modifications of existing AM/FM radio headsets. Generally, there is a great amount of static generated. If you are near a radio station transmitter, you may have difficulty in keeping the radio station from serenading you while you work. There may be snaps, and pops in your headset. You may find that the detector threshold signal changes as you swing the searchcoil from side to side. Swing the searchcoil to the left and the audio threshold will be at one level; swing the searchcoil to the right and it will change to yet, another. That can be annoying! Before you buy, try to get a moneyback guarantee. When you receive the headphones, if you do not like them, return them immediately, in new condition, for a refund. If you use and abuse them and get them dirty, don't expect a refund.

MISCELLANEOUS ACCESSORIES. There are various other miscellaneous accessories such as battery trays (Figure 21-11), touch-up paint, extra battery doors, foreign language instruction manuals, etc. There is one miscellaneous accessory: an extra lower stem that attaches to the searchcoil. Normally, to change searchcoils, you have to loosen the wing nut, remove the screw, remove the searchcoil, place another searchcoil on the lower stem, realign the holes, insert the screw, mount all the hardware, and tighten the wing nut, wrap the cord around, etc. You can purchase from some manufacturers extra lower stems, screws, and wing nut hardware. This will allow you to keep a lower stem attached to each searchcoil; and then, when you wish to change searchcoils, it's a lot easier and faster.

MISCELLANEOUS CLOTHING, HATS, CAPS, ETC. Many manufacturers offer caps, coats, patches, bumper stickers and different kinds of paraphernalia. There's nothing wrong in using

Figure 21-11: It is a good idea to carry spare batteries along on all metal detecting excursions. Some detector operators prefer to carry complete battery slide tray assemblies such as the one shown here. These can be purchased from your metal detector dealer. Rechargeable batteries are available which can be recharged with the battery tray inserted in the housing or pulled out.

any of these. In fact, many people like the sense of belonging. They are proud of their hobby and the equipment they use. So, if you see a jacket, T-shirt or cap that you like, buy it! Caps and T-shirts designed in good taste can do a great deal towards promoting the use of metal detectors.

CHAPTER 21 QUESTIONS

1. To greatly reduce operator fatigue during long hours of searching, especially with larger searchcoils, you should use either a _____ kit or an _____ . (Each correct answer is worth 10 points)

2. Searchcoil skid plates do the following (select correct answers): (A) protect searchcoil against scraping, bumping and gouging; (B) prevent hole from being worn in searchcoil; (C) keep searchcoils in very good condition; (D) probably keep value of metal detector higher; (E) allow searchcoil to slide easier over the ground. (Each correct answer is worth 5 points)

3. Headphones have numerous very important advantages. One of the most important is that headphones with individual earpiece volume controls allow metal detector volume to be kept at maximum, while headphone volume can be set to a comfortable listening level.

    True _____ False _____

4. Rechargeable batteries are recommended. However, they are prone to take a "set" if not used correctly. A "set" means: (A) you should take along a spare set just in case; (B) when you set them on the shelf, they can last a long time; (C) they can take on a reduced usable life of fixed length; (D) you can set them at any voltage output you require.

5. Battery manufacturers recommend that ni-cads be completely discharged and then fully recharged once a year. This extends ni-cad battery life.

    True _____ False _____

Each correct answer is worth 20 points. Perfect score is 100. Answers given in Appendix 2.

How To Choose and Use The Correct Metal Detector

PART I: HOW TO FIND QUALITY

The selection of a metal detector is more involved than finding the one that costs the most or the one that the treasure hunter in the magazine article said found fifty thousand coins. Quality can be found, and the more diligent you are, the more attuned you will become to recognize it when you find it. Metal detectors are easy to learn to evaluate and successfully use. That's the whole purpose of this book to make all these things easy for you.

A metal detector selection should be based upon at least four of a detector's features: ability, versatility, capability, and quality. Quality is not an accident. The more you study detectors, the better will be your ability to find quality. You should study all manufacturer's literature. Make a chart, and list the various brands and types of detectors, their capabilities, the various available searchcoils and accessories, and what you like, and don't like, about them and their cost.

If a manufacturer says a detector will do a particular job, study his literature to determine if he gives you in-depth information regarding that detector and it's capabilities, and has not simply made a quick competitive statement that his detector can be used for this or that. Visit or contact several detector dealers. Talk to them about the various kinds of detectors.

Which instruments do full-time professionals use? Read the various magazines and books published. Notice which detectors people are using.

TEST THE INSTRUMENT YOURSELF. Turn the detector on and tune it, and if you are not able to do this, ask the dealer for assistance. See how easily he tunes the detector. Does he seem to know what he is doing? If he cannot tune the instrument and show you easy steps to operating it, perhaps you should doubt his ability to correctly advise you.

When the dealer hands you a detector, turn all the controls several times and then hand it back to him and ask him to retune it. If he can accomplish this quickly, perhaps it is safe to consider his recommendation.

Don't believe such statements as "Oh, that particular detector is junk," "No good," and "You don't want it." When you hear those kinds of statements, ask the person making them why he said that; listen to what he tells you. Ask him for specifics and not generalities such as "All other brands of detectors are no good!" Try to judge for yourself the accuracy of such statements. Talk to detector owners and dealers about metal detectors and then try to average out what they say. Don't take the word of just one person as to which detector is the best or which is the worst; talk to a lot of people. Oftentimes a detector owner will experience a problem with a detector. It may be serious, or only minor, or, in fact, the owner may not have correctly learned how to use the detector, but that person may forever be against that particular brand and will tell everyone he meets. That type of information may not be the most desirable upon which to base your decision.

You are advised to select a detector built by a progressive company that has a continuing program of detector improvement. Does the manufacturer test his own instruments? Does he get out into the field and use them under all kinds of situations? Does he travel to various locations to test varying soil conditions to insure his detectors work regardless of conditions? Are company engineers active in the field?

Pay no attention to magical, fanciful, and mysterious descriptions. If a person calls a detector a "super-duper triple snooper" or says that this detector has "unparalleled performance," or that detector is "raring to go with amazing performance," or that "this detector is not a BFO but a genuine VLF detector with a patented trash reflector circuit," pay no attention to that malarky. Those are simply "sell" statements and do nothing to increase your knowledge of detectors. The manufacturer who says his detectors are the best, above all others, should be asked to prove it. After all, HE made the statement, its not up to YOU to prove it! And, while he is trying to do the impossible, go buy the best detector for you.

There is no one particular brand or type of detector that is perfect and that will do every job perfectly with total capabilities. There are, however, many types of detectors that will perform admirably in many situations and under extreme environmental conditions, and a few detectors that will do most jobs quite satisfactorily.

If possible, rent a detector of the type you wish to buy. Spend as many hours as possible using that detector to learn its characteristics and capabilities. There is no better way to find out for yourself if a detector is suited for you, than to use one. Many dealers do have rental programs; the few dollars that you spend renting the detector may come back many times over. Some rental contracts specify that a portion of, or all, rental fees can be used toward the purchase of a new detector.

Don't make the very common mistake of thinking that if you look around and choose the highest priced detector you will be getting the best detector. This is not true, and probably you will go wrong by selecting your detector based upon this criteria. Manufacturers aren't required to set their prices at any given level, but should be permitted to make a fair profit. It takes profit to pay for engineering design on next year's detector that you may purchase.

It has happened many times that the detector with one square foot of printed circuit board was out-performed by a detector with a playing card size board. And, think of what it may cost you to have that one square foot of printed circuit board repaired! Don't fall for the gimmick that "this detector has the equivalent of ten thousand transistors or has thousands of transistors more than a competitive instrument." Someone may be trying to dump an engineering nightmare on you that wears out batteries every thirty minutes. KNOWLEDGEABLE AND CONSCIENTIOUS ENGINEERS CONTINUALLY STRIVE TO DESIGN CIRCUITRY WITH MINIMUM COMPONENTS. The more components there are, the less reliable the product.

Be sure to take a look at the detector. Does it look like quality? Does it have jagged edges or unfinished parts? Is it ruggedly built or does the control housing flop on its handle? Pick up the detector and feel it. Does it feel like quality? Grasp the control housing and rock it back and forth. Is it solid or loose? Turn on the detector and put it through its paces by tuning the detector and adjusting all the controls. Are they smooth to operate? When you put the detector through its tuning and adjustment paces does it respond smoothly or are there sudden changes and squawks and squeals in the audio? COMPARE SEVERAL BRANDS OF DETECTORS.

The searchcoil should be extremely well made and the components mated together properly. If there is a visible bonding seam, it should be a uniform bead properly applied. The stem mounting brackets on the searchcoil should be correctly aligned, and there should be two upright brackets, not just one. The method used for mounting the stem to the searchcoil should be simple, yet strong and functional, with only a reasonable twist of the wing nut or locking nut to securely hold the searchcoil in position, even when the searchcoil is bumped against the ground, stumps and bushes. Quality construction should be demanded! If you find less than the best construction in any of a detector's components, it may pay you to doublecheck everything else.

Is the detector reasonably stable, or does the audio and meter indicator change (drift) so that you have to continually make tuning adjustments? Check the sensitivity of the detector in air, using various small and large targets. Check detection distance with a small coin like a penny. Don't use a silver dollar! The smaller coin is a better test target. If it will detect a penny to a good distance it will surely detect a silver dollar to an even greater one. While the air test is not one hundred percent accurate, it does indicate, at least somewhat, the sensitivity and depth you can expect to achieve in the ground.

SELECTION CHECKPOINTS

When selecting a metal detector, here are a few specific points to consider:

I. Portability.

A. When not in use, the equipment may be quickly and easily disassembled, without tools, for storage in a protective case.

II. Ease of Operation.

A. The equipment should be lightweight and engineered for comfortable use over extended periods of time. Remember, the lightest equipment may not be sufficiently durable.

B. The equipment should have only the controls and functions necessary to do the job intended.

1. Extra controls and functions require extra circuitry which can degrade reliability.

2. Extra controls and functions can confuse an operator, especially one who uses the equipment only occasionally. Misadjustment or improper use can decrease the effectiveness of a search.

C. The equipment must have certain controls and functions to be effective.

1. A circuit or means to check the batteries.

2. A push button or automatic retuning system.

3. A circuit or control to eliminate the effects of iron minerals in the soil and/or ocean beach salt if you are a beachcomber.

D. Access to batteries (if not rechargeable) should be easy. Are the batteries readily available and reasonably priced?

III. Capability.

A. The detector should be capable of performing, with good efficiency, all the tasks you intend for it to perform.

B. Necessary searchcoils and accessories should be standard equipment or available for optional purchase.

IV. Depth Detection.

A. When evaluating a metal detector, depth detection, which is the ability to detect an object at a given distance, is sometimes the only point a purchaser considers. A well-built detector should also have excellent sensitivity, mechanical and electrical stability, AND THE ABILITY TO OPERATE OVER HEAVILY MINERALIZED GROUND. Without all these characteristics, you may have an inadequate metal detector.

B. When evaluating sensitivity, evaluate different types of objects. Some instruments are more sensitive to iron, some are

329

less sensitive to coins. Can the detector with trash elimination (discrimination) reject bottlecaps and perhaps pull tabs? TRY IT! Detection depth on coins, however, can be greatly reduced when operated in the trash elimination mode. So, make sure that not much detection depth is lost when target rejection is dialed in.

V. Stability.

A. No detector, regardless of features, is worthy unless it is stable.

1. Electrical stability is the ability of the detector to produce no erroneous signals due to limitations of the electrical circuitry. Some items that can cause problems in improperly designed or manufactured equipment are:

a. Changes in battery voltage.

b. Minor temperature changes in circuit components.

c. Current leakage on the printed circuit boards due to moisture.

d. Poor quality components.

e. Poorly designed searchcoils.

2. Mechanical stability is the ability of the detector to produce no erroneous signals or tuning changes due to normal scanning movement of the detector. Some things that can cause problems are:

a. Movement of the searchcoil connector.

b. Movement of improperly secured internal wiring and connectors.

c. Movement of improperly secured batteries.

d. Movement of the printed circuit board due to the flexing of the detector housing when the detector is lifted or moved by the handle.

e. Flexing of the searchcoil as it is moved back and forth over the ground.

f. Movement of internal searchcoil components when the searchcoil is bumped against an object, such as a large rock or tree trunk.

REMEMBER: The most sensitive equipment may not have the stability to be effective.

VI. Durability.

A. A metal detector will often be used many hours in rugged environments. Electrically, detector circuits are expected to be functional for many years, so a strong mechanical package is important. Some points to consider are:

1. Metal structural components should be of sufficient strength to prevent excessive flexing. This flexing can cause metal fatigue and breakage and also can be a source of mechanical instability.

330

2. Rivets, screws, and other fastening devices should be of sufficient quality to prevent loosening of the mechanical package due to use.

3. Plastic parts should be properly designed and manufactured from the proper material, to prevent breakage, warpage, melting, and cracking from heat and cold.

4. Carrying cases should be available to protect the equipment during transportation and storage, if required.

VII. Environmental.

A. Environmental considerations are important in selecting a detector. Some examples of problems due to environment are:

1. For operation at temperatures below freezing, alkaline or nickel cadmium (NiCad) batteries should be used.

2. Moisture protection is important, as the equipment may be used in the rain or among wet vegetation.

3. Submersible searchcoils allow searches in shallow water.

4. If the equipment is to be used under water or is to be used extensively in shallow water, a guaranteed sealed underwater detector is necessary.

5. If the equipment is to be used in a salt beach environment, a sealed underwater detector may be necessary to eliminate the effects of sand, moisture, and the corrosive atmosphere on the circuitry, controls, and metal surfaces. (Some protection is achieved by placing plastic bags over control housings when you use a land detector on salt water beaches.)

EVALUATION SUMMATION

When evaluating a specific detector, here is a summary of things to look for:

A. Are the instrument and its components well protected for storage, transportation and use?

B. Is the detector easily assembled and are the batteries and all controls readily accessible and properly located?

C. Does the equipment have good weight (mechanical) balance?

D. Was the equipment constructed with strength and durability in mind? Look for areas that are mechanically weak and flex easily. Look for controls, meters, or other items that protrude which could be broken off. Are there sufficient fastening devices, locking nuts, etc., to keep the handle and stems from working loose?

E. Is plastic used properly in the equipment? Are the searchcoils made of heavy gauge ABS for long wear and abrasion resistance? Are the searchcoils solid filled with urethene foam for mechanical stability and long life? Is the plastic stem or stem extension made of materials such as Lexan to prevent breakage?

F. Does the equipment have the desired operational features such

331

as a battery check, detection depth control, ground elimination, and earphone jack?

G. Are desired accessory searchcoils available? Can all searchcoils be submerged?

H. Are the controls marked to make the operation of the equipment clear? Is the instruction manual easy to understand?

I. Is the equipment designed to do the jobs intended? Is it suitable for the operating environments in which it will be used?

J. Bench test the equipment indoors. Be sure the searchcoil is not on a metal table or near metal table supports.

    1. Turn the equipment on, set the audio, and listen for a smooth sound with no jitter.

    2. Listen to the sound and watch the meter. If the detector has an automatic tuning switch feature, it should be switched off. The sound and meter should remain reasonably constant. If the detector is not already at room temperature, a small change can be expected due to the temperature stabilization of the circuit components and the searchcoil.

    3. Check the detection depth (distance) and sensitivity to a representative group of targets, for example coins, guns, knives, etc. If the detector has more than one operating mode, check them all.

    4. Check the sound for loudness and tone quality.

K. Take the equipment outside, away from metal in walls, floors, furniture, etc., and test for mechanical stability. Turn the detector on and set the audio threshold before making the following tests.

    1. Grasp the searchcoil with one hand and squeeze and flex the coil. Normally the sound will change, the less the better, but it must return to the starting point when the coil is released. No pops or crackles should be heard. (Be sure the wire is wrapped lightly around the stem and you do not change the angle of the coil on the stem during the test. Either of these can cause a faulty test). Also, be sure to remove your rings and watch before making the test.

    2. Take the detector and bump it from all sides with your hand. No pops or crackles should be heard. The batteries should not jar loose.

    3. While holding the detector by the handle, lightly bump the searchcoil against a large rock or wall; the tuning should not change.

    4. While holding the detector by the handle, raise the searchcoil above your head and lower to two feet off the ground. The sound should not change significantly.

    5. In an area with grass or vegetation more than three inches high, moisten the vegetation with a hose. Now test the Faraday-shielding of the coil. Movement of the searchcoil through the

vegetation should produce no, or very minor, audio response. L. While outside, use the detector by checking balance, ease of operation, sound level, detection depth (you may wish to bury some representative targets), mechanical and electrical stability.

PART II: HOW TO CHOOSE AND USE THE CORRECT LAND AND UNDERWATER METAL DETECTOR

This is a basic selection guide to help you choose the correct, or optimum detector, for the type of searching you will be doing. It is divided into three categories: Treasure Hunting for coin, cache and relics (see also Chapter 24); Underwater Hunting (see also Chapter 17); and Electronic Prospecting (see also Chapter 25). Various detector characteristics, including ground elimination, tuning and scanning, are discussed.

There are numerous books written which describe the various facets of metal detecting in much greater detail than space allows in this book. The DETECTOR OWNER'S FIELD MANUAL, THE VLF/TR METAL DETECTOR HANDBOOK, ELECTRONIC PROSPECTING, and SUCCESSFUL COIN HUNTING, all published by Ram Publishing Company, are recommended. To further your detector how-to knowledge, and to learn how to become more efficient in all phases of detector use, you should read all of these books and acquire their valuable knowledge.

The table (Figure 22-1) lists the most popular metal detectors and how they are suited to perform various functions. The higher the number, the better suited is the detector to perform that given function. Number "10" is the highest rating, "NR" means not recommended, and "NS" means not suited. Do not try to correlate these number ratings with number ratings of other selection/recommendation tables in this book.

Your selection and purchase of a metal detector ought to have the same careful consideration that goes with anything you buy. Shopping has become very much a part of life, and as you have probably learned, you must depend upon yourself to make the right choice. The more clearly you understand what you want, the more likely you are to be correct in your choice. Choosing a metal detector should take no less time and consideration than buying any other valuable and expensive item. Buying the correct instrument depends heavily upon whether you understand all the important facts about the different types and what your requirements really are.

In this chapter, I list most of the facets of metal detector usage; and I recommend the type instrument or instruments and searchcoils to use. I describe tuning and operational aspects so that you can compare the features and capabilities of the various brands and

METAL DETECTOR APPLICATIONS VS METAL DETECTOR TYPES	LAND MODELS						UNDERWATER MODELS			
	BFO	TR	VLF/TR	VLF/VLF	AUTO VLF	TRACER	TR	VLF	AUTO VLF	PULSE
COIN HUNTING	5	6	7	10	9	NS				
CACHE HUNTING	5	NR	10	10	NR	NS				
RELIC/BATTLEFIELD HUNTING	5	6	9	10	8	NS				
GHOST-TOWNING: BUILDING	10	9	10	10	10	NS				
GHOST-TOWNING: LAND	5	5	7	10	9	NS				
ELECTRONIC PROSPECTING	5	NR	10	10	NR	NS				
NUGGET HUNTING	5	NR	10	10	NR	NS				
VEIN LOCATING	5	NS	10	10	NR	NS				
ORE SAMPLING (A)	9	NS	10	10	NR	NS				
BLACK SAND SEARCH	10	NS	10	10	NR	NS				
POCKETS & FLOAT	5	NS	10	10	NR	NS				
LAW ENFORCEMENT: LAND	5	6	9	10	NR	NS				
LAW ENFORCEMENT: UNDERWATER	NS	NR	8	9	NR	NS				
TRACING: INDUSTRIAL/UTILITY	NS	NS	NS	NS	NS	10				
GENERAL SEARCHING	5	6	8	10	8	NS	6	8	8	8
BEACH HUNTING	5	7	9	9	9	NS	8	9	9	10
SURF: FRESH WATER	5	7	9	10	10	NS	9	10	10	10
SURF: SALT WATER	NR	NR	7	9	8	NS	NR	8	8	10
UNDERWATER: FRESH (B)	5	7	9	10	NS	NS	9	10	10	10
UNDERWATER: SALT (B)	NS	NS	8	9	NS	NS	NR	8	8	10

CODES: (A) WITH CALIBRATED (HIGH GRADE) CIRCUIT; (B) WITH 50-FOOT CABLE SUBMERSIBLE COIL; NS–NOT SUITABLE; NR–NOT RECOMMENDED.

Figure 22-1: This table will help you select the best detector for any given application. The recommendations are determined from the capabilities and performance characteristics of the various types of detectors.

types. This information will help you decide if the metal detector you are thinking of buying will, indeed, do the job you intend for it to do.

CACHE OR MONEY HUNTING

You should choose a MANUAL-ADJUST Ground Eliminating VLF type detector with large searchcoil and/or Depth Multiplier capabilities. The Bloodhound Depth Multiplier should be used whenever possible, as it detects deeply and ignores small objects like nails, etc. You are not looking for small objects, so forget small coils. A ten-inch size would be good, but a twelve-inch size might be better. When using large searchcoils, an armrest or hipmount configuration is recommended. (See Chapter 21 for discussion of the hipmount accessory). Do not use trash rejection; cache hunters have learned that success often follows lots of dug trash.

COIN HUNTING

The best instruments to use when coin hunting, are the Manual-Adjust VLFs or the Automatic VLF Ground Elimination types. To locate the maximum number and deepest targets, the all-metal VLF mode is recommended. If you do not want to dig junk targets, use the VLF trash elimination or TR discrimination mode. Remember that some good targets may be rejected as described in Chapter 10. Of the two target elimination modes (VLF & TR), the VLF elimination mode, (Figure 22-2), is the easiest to use and the one most recommended.

TR discrimination (if your detector is so equipped) can be used best when mineralization is non-existant or is present only in very moderate amounts. Over heavily mineralized ground, the TR discrimination mode can be used to reverse discriminate to identify targets. (See Chapter 10.)

A seven-inch to eight-inch diameter searchcoil is preferred for coin hunting. This size is lightweight and has good depth detection and scanning width. For deeper penetration, use the ten-inch to twelve-inch sizes. Pinpointing will be a little more difficult with larger searchcoils, but you can expect to get the deeper coins. For operation in tight places adjacent to sidewalks, metal buildings and fences, and for Super-Sniping, use a three-inch to four-inch diameter searchcoil.

To achieve maximum depth with Manual-Adjust VLF's, adjust the Ground Elimination control for zero or minimal ground pickup. Always use headphones and tune the audio to achieve a faint

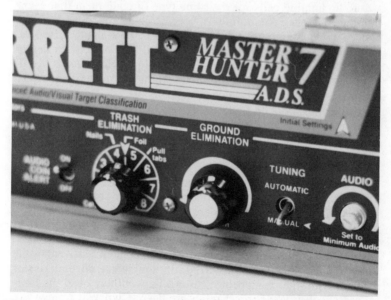

Figure 22-2: The VLF target elimination mode is superior to the TR target elmination mode because the VLF detects deeper and ignores iron earth minerals. The TR coin hunting mode is acceptable on non-mineralized dry sand beaches.

335

threshold. If you operate the adjustable VLF "silent", you may lose some depth. Automatic VLF Ground Elimination detectors automatically adjust out iron minerals, and may be operated "silent."

COIN HUNTING IN HIGH JUNK AREAS

Some of the most troublesome places over which to search are high junk areas. It doesn't matter what type detector you have, you'll have some erratic operational problems due to the presence of a lot of metal. In effect, the detector just cannot decide what's down there. Consequently, when scanning high junk areas you may find it necessary to reduce detection depth. You will actually gain efficiency. You'll find the detector will be easier to operate and you'll be able to dig more good targets. The reduced detection depth allows the detector to more easily isolate and identify individual targets. Another excellent method to use when searching high junk areas is the Super-Sniper method which you'll find explained in Chapter 10. Also, certain VLF's that have classifier meters and audio systems that continue to classify detected targets even when the trash elimination control is set to "zero," will prevent "loss" of good targets even in trashy areas.

RELIC HUNTING

Relic hunting calls for the same type of equipment that cache hunting requires. You definitely need large searchcoils. You will need a good hipmount configuration, and headphones. Be prepared to dig Minie balls (thumb size Civil War bullets) to depths greater than two feet, and if you use the Bloodhound Depth Multiplier be prepared to dig two, four, six, eight feet, and perhaps even deeper, for larger objects such as cannons.

Projectiles will be found at depths of four, five and six feet. Most relic hunters do not use any form of Target Elimination, they don't want to take the chance of missing valuable iron relics. Some use a small amount of Target Elimination if they are searching only for brass and lead objects.

When searching for relics in water, you can submerge submersible searchcoils about two and one half feet. For deeper operation, searchcoils with longer cables are recommended.

If you are a scuba diver, select a quality submersible underwater detector; either the VLF or the Pulse Induction type is recommended. If you are searching in salt water areas that contain black sand, the Pulse Induction type is preferred. If you select an underwater detector with interchangeable searchcoils, you may need the largest searchcoil if you suspect relics are deep. Civil War relics were often discarded in water and relic hunters who have learned this have made many valuable finds.

336

GHOST TOWN SEARCHING IN THE GROUND

If you are looking for coins, rings and jewelry, a VLF type will give the best results. Most ghost towns are high junk areas; therefore, you need light Target Elimination. A great amount of junk may necessitate your reducing the detection depth of your detector.

If you are searching for ghost-town relics and money caches, use a Manual-Adjust VLF in the all-metal detection mode. It would be best to use the largest searchcoil you have available. Guns, weapons and large caches can be detected to good depths. Large money caches may be quite deep, so you should consider using the Bloodhound Depth Multiplier attachment. This multiplies the depth capability of VLF detectors, producing great depth on objects larger than quart size while almost completely ignoring nails and other small metal trash. The Depth Multiplier is not affected by ground minerals, tree roots, voids, water, etc.; consequently, you won't dig false holes. Keep the Depth Multiplier "nose" close to the ground (Figure 22-3), and walk straight ahead. When you reach the end of your search path, turn around, move over one or two feet and walk a return parallel path. The use of headphones, of course, is recommended. No ground tuning or adjustments of any kind are necessary. It is not wise to use automatic tuning.

Figure 22-3: To achieve the deepest, large object detection depth, the Depth Multiplier attachment should be used. It can double detection depth; ignore minerals, moisture and small metal objects; and pinpoint precisely. No adjustments are required: simply select the VLF Manual mode, set audio to threshold, and start scanning. You achieve the greatest depth when the "nose" of the Depth Multiplier is held close to the ground.

GHOST TOWNING IN BUILDINGS

Almost all types of detectors are suitable for searching buildings, except Pulse Induction types. One of the greatest problems you'll encounter is the detection of nails. Most detectors, however, can be adjusted to eliminate the majority of them. Some buildings, especially stucco buildings, contain reinforcement screen. It is very difficult to search walls with this type construction. It is best to reduce sensitivity and dial in a certain amount of target elimination. Also, try holding the searchcoil several inches away from the wall surface. This will lessen the detection of the wire, permitting large solid masses to be detected. It has been done!

Underwater Hunting
BEACHCOMBING

One of the best instruments to use when ocean beach hunting is Pulse Induction with target elimination. Adjustable discriminating TRs can be used on salt water beaches that are mostly void of magnetic black sand. To search fresh water beaches, all types of detectors are more or less suitable.

Manual-Adjust VLF detectors cannot ignore both salt water and black magnetic sand simultaneously, but Pulse Induction detectors can. Automatic VLF Ground Elimination types can be adjusted to ignore salt water and magnetic sand simultaneously.

There is a phenomenon that causes Pulse Induction detectors to detect coins and rings extremely deep in salt water. Consequently, immediately after they were first placed on the market, they became a favorite among beach coin hunters, especially those who search ocean beaches.

The operation of the Pulse Induction detector is extremely simple. Turn the instrument on and adjust the audio threshold to the lowest sound level you can hear; then, start scanning. All minerals are ignored. If you wish to detect only coins, rings, and jewelry, adjust the elimination control to your desired rejection level. It is best to scan with the searchcoil held close to the ground. Don't forget to use your headphones! Scan slightly slower than when using one of the VLF or TR types. When you get a signal, stop, scan slowly back over the target and mentally draw an imaginary "X" by hovering over the target. Pinpointing takes a little getting used to but after a few dug targets you'll become fast and efficient. Be prepared to dig many deep holes!

Other excellent beach hunting instruments are the Automatic VLF Ground/Elimination and VLF/TR types. Be sure to wear headphones for maximum depth detection and elimination of surf noise. Walk out to the edge of the waterline and hold the searchcoil about four feet above the water. Activate the trash elimination mode and retune to slight audio threshold sound. Adjust the trash elimination control to the bottlecap elimination setting. Lower the searchcoil to the surface of the salt water. If the audio threshold does not change, the detector is properly set. If the sound increases, adjust the trash elimination knob to a higher number. If the sound decreases, adjust to a lower number. Raise the searchcoil back up in the air, press the retune button and again lower the searchcoil back down to the surface of the water while listening for a change in audio. Continue this procedure until the audio remains steady or changes slightly, as the searchcoil is lowered to the water.

Now, you can scan the beach at the water's edge, over the water, or submerged in water. If the bottom contains excessive amounts of conductive minerals, a slight readjustment of the elimination control may be necessary.

UNDERWATER RECOVERY

There are two basic mechanical configurations. One is designed primarily for underwater searching. This type has the searchcoil, handle, and stem, all permanently attached to a short stem. The stem is too short to use above water. Convertible model accessories are available (Figure 22-4) that convert long-stem land units to the short stem arrangement for underwater use.

Headphones should be used for maximum sensitivity and depth. Some underwater detectors use meters and lights. Indicator lights are not as sensitive as meter indicators, which are very sensitive but are difficult to watch at all times and, in all but clear water, become difficult to see.

If you are using headphones underwater, follow the manufacturer's recommendations. Some manufacturers place a plug in each headphone piece that must be removed for underwater diving so water pressure can equalize. When using headphones above water, the plugs need to be inserted to reduce outside interference noise.

TR underwater detectors should be used only in fresh water, unless the manufacturer states that salt water can be nullified. Even then, specific operating instructions must be observed.

Most underwater detectors are designed to work to depths of two hundred feet. This depth should not be exceeded. Leakage may result at depths greater than manufacturer's specifications and there is a real risk of the housing being crushed by water pressure (implosion).

Tune your underwater detector as you would a detector on land, with faint threshold sound. This will give you maximum performance.

Rechargeable battery types are recommended, even though they present some limitations. If you forget to recharge the detector overnight, the next day you may have to allow charging time before entering the water. One advantage of rechargeables is you

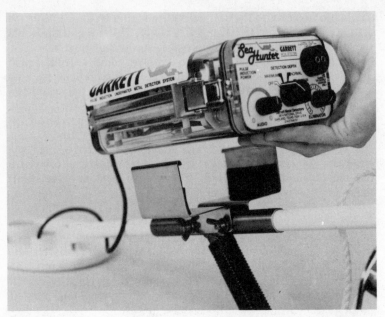

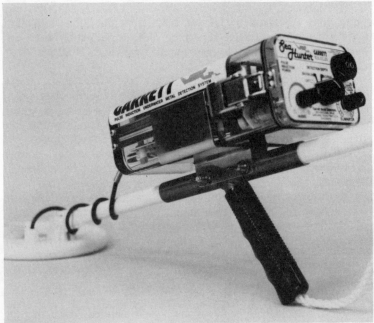

Figure 22-4: If you plan to search underwater, you should consider this Sea Hunter accessory, Model 16084. It converts Sea Hunter XL500 detectors to a one-piece hand-held unit as shown.

340

never have to open the detector. If the detector has to be opened often for battery replacement, sooner or later you may have severe printed circuit board damage from water, especially salt water, getting into the control housing.

ELECTRONIC PROSPECTING

The recommended type detector for prospecting is a Manual-Adjust VLF Ground Elimination detector that has been proven in the field. Not all VLF's are the same. Some are more versatile and sensitive than others and some are more capable of operating over highly mineralized ground. You should select a model that has a wide range of searchcoils from which to choose.

NUGGET HUNTING

Depending upon the location where you search and the size nuggets you want to find, the size searchcoil you need can be anywhere from a three-quarter-inch probe to a fourteen-inch searchcoil. Extremely small, fractional-gram-size nuggets have been found in ore dumps in Canada with a three-quarter inch probe. Monstrous ten, twenty, thirty ounce, and larger nuggets have been found with larger searchcoils in the United States and Australia. So, the size nuggets that you are looking for and their depth will dictate the size searchcoil you need. A good, general purpose, all-around searchcoil size is from a seven-inch to about a ten-inch diameter. During your scanning, if you are detecting extremely tiny nuggets, a smaller size searchcoil may find even smaller ones. If you are detecting large ones in the fringe area (Figure 22-5) a larger searchcoil may help you find large nuggets at deeper depths. However, larger searchcoils are sometimes more difficult to use in prospecting areas over jumbled ore matrixes.

Selection of the right searchcoil depends, to a great extent, upon you. How well you have mastered your detector and how well you apply your experiences and observations, will in large measure determine your success.

ORE SAMPLING

Three-inch to eight-inch diameter VLF searchcoils are recommended. The smaller searchcoils will identify more of the marginal samples (those that contain very small amounts of conductive metals).

For best ore sampling (high grading) results, your detector should be factory calibrated. If it is not pre-calibrated, you will have to follow the manufacturer's instructions, if available, for adjusting the detector each time you test an ore sample.

A quality BFO with a three-inch to five-inch diameter searchcoil is highly recommended for ore sampling, but either a factory calibrated VLF or TR, or a BFO will get the job done.

Figure 22-5: The measure of the quality of the detector is not determined by how large an object it will detect, but how deeply it will detect that object, and also be capable of detecting small objects to good depths. Jack Lowry joyfully eyes a gold nugget he found at a depth of several inches. Several nuggets he found were considerably smaller than this one. It is possible for quality electronic prospecting detectors to find fractional gram-sized nuggets to several inches depth. Photo by Melvin Climer.

The Pocket Scanner (Figure 22-6) is calibrated to check ore samples. It is easily carried in the lucrative field of ore sampling.

VEIN LOCATING

The Manual-Adjust VLF Ground Elimination type with a large twelve-inch or fourteen-inch searchcoil is recommended. Operate in the VLF all-metal mode and adjust the Ground Elimination control until the ground, mine wall, or ceiling is nulled out. Scan slowly and methodically.

The Bloodhound Depth Multiplier attachment will give you multiplied depth on large ore veins, even those containing iron ore. Iron ore, when in association with gold and silver, can enhance the detection characteristics of veins.

FLOAT AND POCKETS

When searching for float, ore pockets, and chimneys, a Manual-Adjust VLF Ground Elimination detector is necessary. Large searchcoils and the Depth Multiplier attachment will give the greatest depth.

SCANNING MINE DUMPS AND DREDGE PILES

Use the same detector, searchcoil and scanning techniques as recommended in the nugget hunting section. For best results (Figure 22-7) carry along a plastic Gravity Trap gold pan. When you get a signal, use a shovel or other tool to dig down into the rocks. Then,

342

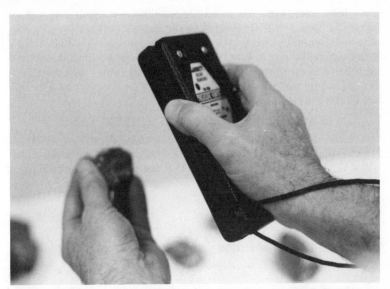

Figure 22-6: For the most efficient ore sampling (high grading) results, the detector must be factory calibrated. Otherwise, you will discard valuable ore specimens. The Pocket Scanner, Model 11770, is calibrated to check ore samples. It is easily carried and used in the lucrative field of ore sampling.

Figure 22-7: Often, electronic prospectors find valuable ore in mine tailings and dredge piles. The nature of some ore makes it difficult to pinpoint in a jumble mass of mineralized rocks. Roy Lagal uses a Gravity Trap gold pan to speed up recovery. He places several shovelfuls of ore in the pan. He then locates the detected object by hand sorting and detector scanning. This method helps prevent detected objects from falling further down into the ore.

343

place the contents into the pan and scan them with your detector to locate the object that responded to the detector. It may be a good idea to individually check each piece of ore for signs of conductivity. Bring individual pieces toward the bottom of the searchcoil, turning each piece several times in order to check all sides. A thin section of gold can be misread by the detector if the gold is aligned with the searchcoil's axis during the test.

SEARCHING FOR BLACK MAGNETIC SAND

You should use a quality BFO or Manual-Adjust VLF with the largest searchcoil available. The operational characteristics of black sand searching are different from normal metal searching, so study the BLACK SAND LOCATING section in Chapter 25.

CHAPTER 22 QUESTIONS

1. Metal detector selection should be based upon at least four metal detector features: _____ , _____ , _____ and _____ .

2. If a magazine article says a man found, with a particular metal detector, fifty thousand coins, that should be enough to convince you that model is the best detector.
    True _____   ·False _____

3. One of the best ways to determine performance of an instrument is to test the instrument _____ .

4. There are many steps to take in determining quality, but a sure-shot shortcut is to find the highest priced detector and buy it.
    True _____   False _____

5. Another way to determine quality is to shop around and buy the detector that has the largest printed circuit board square footage.
    True _____   False _____

6. The metal detector with numerous integrated circuits that have an equivalent of five thousand transistors has got to be a lot better than the one that has fewer integrated circuits with an equivalent of only one thousand transistors.
    True _____   False _____

7. If you are shopping for a good coin hunting detector, you can best determine the sensitivity and detection depth of any given detector by using a very large coin such as a silver dollar as your test piece.
    True _____   False _____

8. If there are two different detectors, and they seem to have equivalent performance capabilities, then the one to choose is the detector that has the most knobs and switches. This statement is (select one): (A) True; (B) A lie; (C) Not necessarily true; (D) A joke.

9. The better you know what type of hunting you will be doing, the more likely you are to be correct in your choice of metal detectors.

True _____ False _____

10. A certain cache hunter uses an automatic VLF type metal detector with an eight-inch diameter searchcoil. His choice of detectors is very good.

Yes _____ No _____ If you said "No", why?

11. The Depth Multiplier (two-box) type accessory is a good choice to use when cache hunting because it detects large objects deeply and _____ small metal objects.

12. Even beginning coin hunters should use ten-inch and larger diameter searchcoils because they cover a wider sweep path and will detect coins the deepest.

True _____ False _____

13. To achieve maximum depth with Manual-Adjust VLF's, adjust the ground elimination control for minimal _____ pick up.

14. Since VLF's are super-sensitive, it is not necessary to use headphones for best results.

True _____ False _____

15. One of the most troublesome areas to search is _____ junk areas.

16. Relic hunting calls for the same type of equipment and searchcoil sizes that coin hunting requires.

True _____ False _____

17. One of the greatest problems you will have in scanning and searching buildings is the detection of nails, consequently, you will need a detector that has a ground elimination control.

True _____ False _____

18. Quality TR's with a trash elimination (discrimination) control can be used very successfully on salt water beaches and in the surf, especially, if there is no magnetic black sand present.

True _____ False _____

19. Since Pulse Induction metal detectors ignore salt water and magnetic black sand, they can probably be used in any fresh water or ocean beach surf in the world.

True _____ False _____

20. Headphones are a must when metal detecting in the ocean's surf because of (select all correct answers): (A) surf noises; (B) wind noises; (C) you need fringe area detection; (D) they can keep your ears warm in the winter.

21. Let's say, that one day, you are electronic prospecting in the mountains and you begin finding large gold nuggets in the fringe area. It is probably a good idea to switch to a smaller, highly intense searchcoil in order to find large nuggets at deeper depths.

True _____ False _____

22. A marginal ore sample is the one that probably contains a very small amount of _____ metal.

23. Iron ore, when in association with gold and silver, can enhance detection characteristics of veins.

   True _____   False _____

Each correct answer given in questions 1 and 20 is worth 2 points. Total value of these 8 correct answers is 16 points. Each correct answer given to the remaining 21 questions is worth 4 points. Perfect score is 100 points. Correct answers given in Appendix 2.

CHAPTER 23

OPERATOR: Know Your Metal Detector

This chapter contains practical methods, tips and procedures recommended to all who use a metal detector.

A poorly-built detector will produce more in the hands of a professional than will a quality-built detector in the hands of a person who does not know how to use that instrument. There are various grades of detectors being sold. Some detectors will barely detect a coin one inch deep, yet others will detect that same coin extremely deep. A most important factor, however, in successful detector operation is the expertise and ability of the operator.

Metal detector manufacturers get letters from customers who complain they cannot find anything but bottlecaps with their detector. On the other hand, letters come from people who are bubbling over with enthusiasm and joy because they are finding coins, rings, jewelry,, and other valuables. These people often send in photographs of the tremendous quantities of treasure they have found.

What is the difference? Certainly, it does not lie in the capability of the detector. One can take identical instruments and place them in the hands of two different people and the results may be entirely different.

To be successful, you must learn how to use your detector (Figure 23-1). Success obtained is in direct proportion to the amount of time and study that the operator devotes to learning how to use his instrument.

Books and hundreds of manuals have been written that instruct the operator in the correct usage of metal detectors. Often this information gives many details and operating instructions. Some manuals even go so far as to precisely detail tuning methods, searchcoil selection, scanning, and dozens of other operating characteristics. So, when all else fails...read the instruction manual!

GETTING STARTED

If you buy through the mail, or from someone who won't or can't instruct you, you will probably miss far more treasure than the dollars you save by ordering from the cheapest source you find. Your goal should be to find treasure, not a metal detector bargain!

Getting hands-on instructions from the dealer from whom you purchased your new detector is the first step. This step cannot be overstressed. Learn all you can from your dealer, then go into the

Figure 23-1: Important factors in successful detector operation are operator expertise and ability. To become proficient in the fastest possible time, you should get training from your dealer and take advantage of other specialized training when it is available. Roy Roush, lifelong treasure hunter and electronic prospector, has been teaching metal detection classes for many years at the Los Angeles City College. His classes include classroom training as well as in-the-field training. Here, he instructs students on the fine points of nugget hunting. The success you attain will be in direct proportion to the amount of time and study you devote to learning how to use your equipment.

field with a notebook and write down all questions and problems you have, return to the dealer for your answers. Don't neglect this vital first step!

Assuming that you have made a careful study of the metal detector market, and have selected an instrument you feel is the best for you, the next step is to make up your mind that you are going to learn how to correctly use your detector regardless of the time and effort it takes. Never deviate from your decision! A detector will remove the blindfold and permit you to "see" coins, treasure and other buried and concealed metal. But you have to trust your detector. You have to learn the correct methods of operating it. You have to learn its idiosyncrasies. You have to learn what makes it tick! In other words, LEARN YOUR METAL DETECTOR and don't worry at least at first, about what you are finding!

As you start putting miles behind your searchcoil, you will find yourself getting better and better with your detector. You will find you are more at ease in using it, and there are fewer and fewer "problems" that bother you. The quantity of found items will be growing at an accelerated rate.

All through your learning and training period and even on down through the years, you must develop persistence. Never give up!! Persistence, persistence, persistence! These are the words of successful operator, L.L. "Abe" Lincoln. You must stay with it and never give up.

Wnen you begin your home study, don't immediately assemble the detector and run outside to begin finding things. The first thing to do is to read your instruction manual, not once, but several times. The first time through, read it as you would a novel—from front to back without stopping. You should pay no attention to the metal detector or its controls; simply read the instruction manual. If you have a factory audio instruction tape, listen to it several times. Then, assemble your instrument according to the manufacturer's instructions; take the time to do it right.

An instruction manual should start at the very beginning, with the assembly of your instrument. Once you have done this, the next step is to become familiar with the various controls. The instruction manual should explain each switch and each control, describing to you its function and basic operation.

The next step is to begin to operate your detector in its various modes and functions. The instruction manual and tape should guide you through this learning process, starting with the various controls. When you have learned the basic operation of each control, it is time to start practicing with your detector.

Lay it on a wooden bench or table. If you use a table with metal legs and braces, the metal could interfere with your testing. Begin with the part of your instruction manual which tells you about the operation of each control. Go through the procedures! If your detector is equipped with a detection depth control, reduce it all the way. When you have adjusted each control, and understand how it works, you can begin to test the instrument with various metal targets. After you have become familiar with the sounds of your instrument, the meter functions, how the detector works and its response to various targets in various modes, it is time to go out into the field.

You will be glad you studied the controls ahead of time because when you had your instrument inside, on a table, it was probably very easy to tune, but now, outside, the situation changes. If you tune the instrument with the searchcoil held in the air, and lower the searchcoil to the ground, you may be in for a surprise. As you lower the searchcoil, the audio sound may begin to change with the meter deflecting upward or downward. These changes could be due to minerals or metal targets that are in the ground where you are doing your testing. It will be necessary for you to learn exactly what is causing any signal changes.

On many metal detector models there are "set and forget"

controls. Controls like TONE, AUDIO (TUNING) AND MAN-
UAL AND AUTOMATIC TUNING are just that; once you set
them, you rarely have to change or reset them. If you set them
when you followed your preliminary inside instructions, you don't
have to worry about them outside. So, you are now left with
Ground Elimination (if your detector has this control) and Trash
Elimination (discrimination). The beginner should initially consider the Target Elimination control as a "set and forget" control.
Set it to zero elimination (all-metal detection) and leave it there
until you have at least ten hours operating time on your detector. In
other words, dig everything!

During your learning phase, keep in mind that you should
work smarter, not harder. As you scan along, each time you receive
a signal, before you dig the target, try to guess what the target is,
what size it is, its shape and its depth. You should analyze the
audio and/or meter signals. Say to yourself, "This is a coin, or this
is a bottlecap." "It is approximately three inches deep." Then pay
careful attention when you dig the object. Learn how deep it is and
how it was lying in the ground. Did you guess right? Great! If not,
try to determine why. The more you do this, the greater your
success will be. Very quickly you will learn how to use and
actually "read" your instrument and understand everything it is
telling you.

As you scan the searchcoil over the ground, use the straight-
line sweep method recommended later in this chapter. You should
hold the searchcoil slightly above the ground and scan at a rate of
about one foot per second. Don't get in a hurry, and don't try to
cover one acre in ten minutes. Remember, what you are looking for
is buried just below the searchcoil scanning sweep you are now
making, not across the field.

After you have several hours on your detector, you can begin
using your target elimination mode. Be sure to study the instructions.
Don't use too much Target Elimination, just enough to eliminate
from detection the junk you have been digging. Do not set the
control to eliminate pulltabs, as that can come later when you know
more about your detector and when you feel it is absolutely necessary.

If you haven't started using headphones, now is the time to do
so. You'll learn how important they really are. You'll dig coins that
you couldn't detect before you started using headphones. You'll
hear sounds you didn't hear before. Headphones may get hot and
the cord may get in the way but your rewards will make it all
worthwhile.

After you have even more hours on your detector, and are
beginning to get comfortable with it, it's time to go back over the
same areas you searched before you really learned how to use your
machine. You are going to be surprised at the quantity of coins and

other things you missed. In fact, come back to these places six months and a year later and each time you'll find more coins and other things, especially at deeper depths.

Begin to learn about other forms of treasure hunting such as ghost towning, relic and cache hunting and prospecting. Learn about the various optional accessories and searchcoils that are available for your detector. Start getting prepared now, so when other treasure hunting opportunities come along, you'll be ready.

In the remainder of this chapter, you'll find a Beginner's How-To-Use Short Course on how to make your own test plot and dozens of tips that will help you to get more from your detector. Be sure to keep in mind that detectors are not complicated or difficult to learn to use. The first time you drove a car it was difficult, but now you drive without thinking about it. The same will be true with your detector. Take it easy, and don't give up if you think it is not working as it should. Just keep working with your detector, restudy your manual, contact your dealer or manufacturer, and ask for more information. Quite often, problems are cleared up with just one simple demonstration by your dealer or someone who knows how to use detectors. Remember, keep the Detection Depth control turned to minimum or to the "Initial" set point. Scan with the searchcoil about two inches above the ground and scan at a moderate speed. Even in high junk areas which are very difficult to work, the reduced detection depth and moderate scanning speed can help you to hear the individual target signals rather than just a jumbled mass of sounds.

Every day success stories are told. A lot of treasure is being found and a lot of treasure is waiting to be found where you live. Detectors are not magic wands but when used correctly they will locate buried and concealed treasure. Keep your faith in your detector, have patience and continue using your detector until you have it mastered. Success will be yours!

MAKE YOUR OWN TEST PLOT

One of the first things a new detector owner does is bury a few coins and see how deeply they can be detected. This usually results in disappointment. The longer an object has been buried, the easier it can be detected. Not only is a "barrier" to electromagnetic field penetration created when a coin is first buried, but no "halo" effect has been developed. As time passes, coins become closer associated, electrically, with surrounding earth materials and the molecules of metal begin to leave and move out into the surrounding soil. Also, it is theorized that in some cases (especially in salt water) the coin's surface becomes a better conductor. All of these phenomena result in coins being detected more easily the longer they are buried. It is estimated that coins and other buried metals can be detected at twice the depth or deeper, after sufficient burial time, as that of objects which are freshly buried.

Select an area where you can make your own test plot. First, scan the area very thoroughly in the all-metal mode and remove all metal from the ground. Select targets such as various coins, a bottlecap, a nail and a pulltab. Select also a pint jar filled with scrap metal, a long object such as a foot long pipe and a large object such as a gallon can. Bury the objects about three feet apart, in rows, and make a map showing items buried, location and depth.

Bury pennies at varying depths, beginning at one inch. Continue, with the deepest buried about six to eight inches deep. Bury one at about two inches but stand it on edge. Bury a penny at about two inches with a bottlecap about four inches off to one side. Bury the bottlecap, nail, and pulltab separately at about two inches deep. Bury the jar at twelve inches to the top of the jar (lid). Bury the pipe horizontally, three or four inches deep. Bury the gallon can with the lid two feet below the surface.

The purpose of the buried coins is to get you familiar with the sound of money. If you can't detect the deeper coins, don't worry. After a while, you will be able to detect them quickly. If you can detect them all, rebury some out of detection range. The penny buried next to the bottle cap will give you experience in Super-Sniping (as described in Chapter 10) and will help you learn to distinguish individual objects. It will also be a good test to help you understand "detuning" (see Chapter 10). The jar and gallon can will help you in learning to recognize "dull" sounds of large, deeply buried objects. The pipe will help you in learning to contour (as explained in Figure 9-2). Check the targets with and without headphones; you'll be amazed at the difference headphones make.

The test plot is important. Don't neglect it and from time to time expand it, rebury the targets and add new ones. The test plot is important because it will be a measure of how well you are progressing and how well you have learned your equipment. Remember to MAKE AN ACCURATE MAP!

MISCELLANEOUS TIPS

When searching adjacent to wire fences, metal buildings, metal parking meter posts, etc., reduce detection depth and scan the searchcoil parallel to the structure. You may also try detuning (as explained in Chapter 10) and operating in the "silent" tuning zone especially if the manufacturer recommends "silent" operation.

Learn to use a probe to locate the exact point where coins are buried. This will help you retrieve coins with minimum damage to grass.

Why not join with thousands of other individuals and organizations throughout the world who have endeavored to preserve their lands and heritage and create good will by following basic rules which have been declared as the METAL DETECTOR OPERATOR'S CODE OF ETHICS?

METAL DETECTOR OPERATOR'S CODE OF ETHICS

I will respect private and public property, all historical and archaeological sites and will do no metal detecting on these lands without proper permission.

I will keep informed on and obey all laws, regulations, and rules governing federal, state, and local public lands.

I will aid law enforcement officials whenever possible.

I will cause no willful damage to property of any kind, including fences, signs and buildings, and will always fill the holes I dig.

I will not destroy property, buildings, or the remains of ghost towns and other deserted structures.

I will not leave litter or uncovered items lying around. I will carry all trash and dug targets with me when I leave each search area.

I will observe the Golden Rule, using good outdoor manners and conducting myself at all times in a manner which will add to the stature and public image of all people engaged in the field of metal detection.

MORE TIPS

Coins lying in the ground at an angle may be missed on one searchcoil pass but detected when the searchcoil comes in from a different angle. If your detector has a volume control, keep it set at maximum. Don't confuse volume control with audio (threshold) control. You should use earphones that have individual earpiece volume adjustment and set each one to suit yourself.

Never dial in more Target Elimination than you need, as too much may reduce detector efficiency.

If you are working on the beach, set target elimination at about bottlecap rejection. A slight amount of adjusting may be necessary but you can set the detector to ignore salt water. Pulse Induction detectors, however, ignore salt water automatically.

Learn the "detuning" method of pinpointing.

Learn "Reverse Discrimination" as described in Chapter 10. You may need it some day to correctly identify some targets if your metal detector only has a TR trash elimination mode. If your detector has a ground elimination mode with trash elimination, you perhaps won't need to use the reverse discrimination method.

Use your common sense. THINK your way through perplexing situations. Remember, success comes from detector expertise, research, patience, enthusiasm and using common sense.

Don't expect to find tons of treasure every time you go out! In fact, there may be times when you don't find anything. But the fun and reward of metal detecting is never knowing what you'll dig up next!

Be sure to check your batteries before you venture out and always check them often. Carry spare batteries with you every time you go searching.

Always keep the searchcoil level as you scan (Figure 23-2) and

23-2 KEEPING SEARCHCOIL LEVEL WHILE SCANNING

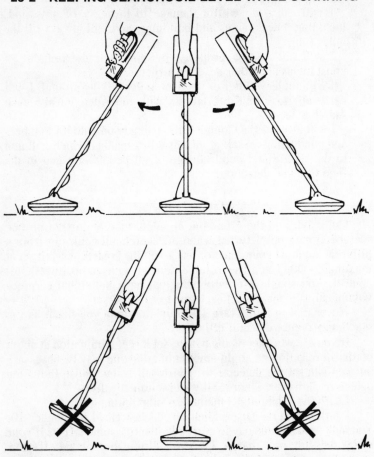

Figure 23-2: Always keep the searchcoil level as you scan. Do not let the searchcoil swing upward at the ends of the scan. Always scan slowly and methodically.

scan slowly and methodically. Be sure to scan the searchcoil from side to side in a straight line in front of you as shown in Figure 23-3. Do not scan the searchcoil in an arc unless the arc width is narrow (about two feet) or unless you are scanning extremely slow. The straight-line scan method allows you to cover more ground width in each sweep and permits you to keep the searchcoil level throughout each sweep. The straight-line scan method reduces skipping and helps you more easily maintain uniform overlapping. Overlap by advancing the searchcoil as much as fifty percent the diameter of the searchcoil at the end of each sweep path (Figures 23-3 and 23-4). Occasionally, scan an area from different angles. Do not raise the searchcoil above scanning level at the end of each sweep. When the searchcoil begins to reach the extremes of each sweep, you will find yourself rotating your upper body to stretch out for an even wider sweep. This gives the double benefit of scanning a wider sweep and gaining additional exercise. To insure that you completely scan any given area, use string or cord to mark scan paths (Figure 23-5). The path widths can be from three to six feet wide. See Figure 23-6 for various area search (scan) methods.

STRAIGHT-LINE SIDE-TO-SIDE SEARCHCOIL SCANNING

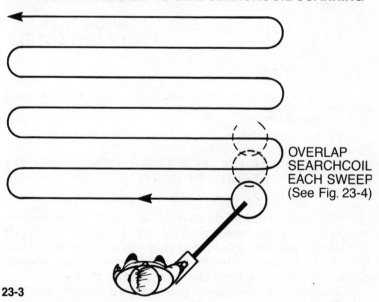

OVERLAP
SEARCHCOIL
EACH SWEEP
(See Fig. 23-4)

23-3

Figure 23-3: One excellent, efficient scanning method is to scan the searchcoil from side-to-side, in a straight-line path, in front of you as shown in this illustration. There may be times when you prefer to scan in an arc, but this should be when your sweep path is narrow and you are scanning very slowly. The straight-line scan method allows you to cover more ground width and it helps you keep the searchcoil level throughout each scan. It also reduces skipping and helps you maintain uniform overlapping.

23-4 SEARCHCOIL OVERLAPPING

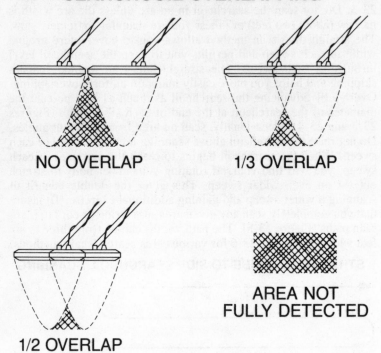

NO OVERLAP   1/3 OVERLAP

AREA NOT
FULLY DETECTED

1/2 OVERLAP

Figure 23-4: Since a searchcoil's detection pattern does not have vertical sides, but is cone-shaped, you should overlap the searchcoil each successive scan. This illustration vividly proves the value of overlapping.

When you dig a target, always scan back over the hole to make sure you recovered everything.

FILL YOUR HOLES. PICK UP AND CARRY OFF ALL TRASH. DON'T DESTROY PROPERTY!

SHORT COURSES FOR THE BEGINNER

This short course is intended solely to get you started using your detector in the easiest possible way. This method will help you learn to use your detector and gain confidence in its abilities. This short course is no substitute for study, application and practice. These instructions are for manually adjusted VLF detectors.

1. Assemble your detector according to the Manual, using the smallest diameter searchcoil (three-inch to four-inch minimum) you have.

2. Hold the detector with the searchcoil about four feet in the air.

3. Turn the detector on and reduce detection depth to minimum.

4. Adjust the AUDIO or TUNER to achieve a very low sound.

Figure 23-5: To completely scan an area without skipping, it is necessary for you to use one or more grid methods. To further insure you completely scan a given area, use string or cord to mark scan paths.

23-6   AREA SEARCH (SCAN) METHODS

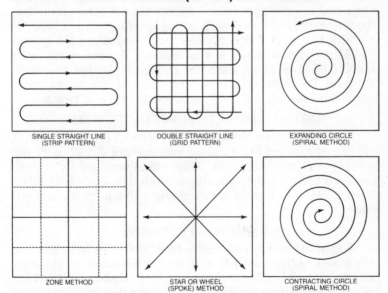

Figure 23-6: There are various area-scan methods. Select the one (or one of your own devising) that best suits the conditions.

This is your threshold level. Depending upon your type detector, you may have to hold a switch in the depressed position while you make this adjustment.

5. If your detector has a Tuning Selector, select the MANUAL mode.

6. Select the all metal detection (no trash elimination) mode.

7. Adjust the ground elimination (cancel) control knob (if your detector has one) to the "center" position.

    a. If it is a one-turn control, rotate the knob to the half-way point or the initial preset arrow.

    b. If it is a ten-turn control, rotate the knob either direction ten turns. Turn the knob five turns in the opposite direction. This will be the center point.

8. Momentarily press your retune switch. If there is no retune button or switch, rotate the tuning control, if necessary, to again locate the audio threshold point.

9. Lower the searchcoil to a height of about two inches above the ground. If you continue to hear the faint threshold sound, begin slowly scanning the searchcoil over the ground, keeping a constant height. (See NOTE.)

10. Where the audio increases, a target is buried in the ground.

NOTES

If the ground is extremely mineralized, the mid-point ground elimination adjustment (number 7 above) may not permit operation. The threshold level may change as you lower the searchcoil to the two inch height. If that is the case, you must adjust the ground elimination control. Refer to your manual. Remember that each time you make an adjustment to the ground elimination control, or whenever the threshold sound level changes due to minerals, temperature change, etc., press your retune button or switch.

INITIAL "PRESET" POINT DETECTORS

If your detector control panel has initial "preset" points, it will be easier for you to learn to use your detector. Set all knobs and switches to these preset points. These adjustments are for average soil and operating conditions. Any controls that do not have initial preset points may then be set according to the instructions given above.

HEALTH SAFEGUARDS

Within the past twenty years, metal detecting has become a very popular activity. People, of all ages, roam parks, ghost towns, beaches, and gold mining areas in search of treasure. Occasionally, but not often, persons complain of pains after they have used metal detectors for long periods of time. Most often, these complaints come from persons who are just beginning the hobby and the first day out, they spend, perhaps, ten or twelve hours swinging their detector over the ground. The next day, they wake up with a good case of sore muscles.

Of course, after a few days, the soreness has gone and off they go again. Others, and the instances are rare, suffer from tennis elbow. Tennis elbow is a perfectly real condition—an injury to the tendons of the elbow-whose medical name is epicondylitis. Epicondylitis is characterized by mild to sharp pain at the side of the elbow. It is believed to be caused by a gradual weakening of muscle tissue. Repeated muscle strain without time in-between for the muscles to repair themselves, causes the problem.

I have been using metal detectors for most of my adult life and have never had tennis elbow or any serious problem. I develop more problems from using my gym equipment. Over the years, I have developed four ways to lessen the dangers of strained muscles.
1. Select the proper equipment including accessories.
2. Strengthen the hand, arm, back and shoulder muscles through an exercise program.
3. Before beginning each day's detecting activity, spend a few minutes doing warmup exercises.
4. During your metal detector activities, use the correct scanning techniques and take intermittent break periods from scanning.
Let's expand each of these four preventive measure procedures.

Proper stem length and balance are key things to achieve. Adjust the stem to the proper, not necessarily shortest, length. If it is too long, you will have a balance problem and your swing will be awkward. If it is too short, you'll have to search stooped over. If large searchcoils do not give proper balance, use a hipmount kit or armrest.

There are many books written on the subject of muscle strengthening. You should select a program that will strengthen your fingers, hand, arm, shoulder and back muscles. You don't need much strengthening, not even bar bell and dumbell workouts. Toning up is of primary importance. As you use your metal detector you'll develop the correct muscles. It's just that at the beginning, and after periods of inactivity, you should protect against strained muscles and ligaments. And, that brings us to the third preventive measure.

Warmup exercises should be done just pior to each day's metal detecting activity. A few minutes of stretching and muscle-use activities will loosen the muscles and joints and prepare you for a day's work. Begin, by observing how the cat stretches itself and then you do likewise—a most important thing to do everyday anyway. A brisk walk, a few toe touches, a few arm and wrist curls with a one or two pound weight held in the hands, a few body twists at the waist standing erect and perhaps a minute or two running in place will get the job done. You can develop your own warmup exercises.

Now, to the proper scanning methods. First, don't try to scan while balancing on one foot. Keep a firm footing and do not scan in awkward positions. This can cause your muscles to make unnatural movements. Keep all movements as natural as possible. If you find yourself scanning on steep hills, in gullies, and other unlevel places, keep good balance, take shorter swings and don't place yourself in awkward positions.

Grasp the metal detector handle lightly. Slight wrist and arm movements are O.K. if your searchcoil swing, from side-to-side, is short. But, when you swing the detector widely from side to side, use a method that is natural and one that causes the least unnecessary wrist movement as possible. Let the entire arm "swing" with the detector. Occasionally, change hands and use the other arm to swing the detector. If you feel yourself tightening up, stop and rest. Most likely, however, each time you stop to dig a target, you will get the rest you need. Actually, you should think of your next detected target as a blessing. You'll get to stop, stoop down and dig the target. This activity gives other muscles a workout, which will help prevent sore muscles that come from long periods of continuous metal detector swinging without a break.

GOOD HUNTING!

CHAPTER 23 QUESTIONS
1. A poorly built detector will produce more in the hands of a professional, than will a quality built detector in the hands of the person who does not know how to use that instrument.

True _____   False _____

2. Success obtained in using a metal detector is in direct proportion to the amount of time and study that the operator devotes to learning how to use his or her instrument.

True _____   False _____

3. The first step after you have purchased a metal detector is to get "hands-on" _____ from the dealer or person from whom you purchased the detector.

4. In addition to training and field experience, you must develop _____ in order to be successful.

5. At least, during your training period, you should read your _____ _____ several times.

6. It is advisable that during your first ten hours of metal detector operation you should dial in _____ trash elimination.

7. The construction and regular use of a test plot is important because it will be a measure of how well you are _____ and how well you have _____ to use your equipment.

8. Every metal detector operator should learn and live by the metal detector operator's Code of Ethics.

True _____ False _____

9. Coins lying in the ground, at an angle, may be missed on one searchcoil pass, but detected when the searchcoil comes in from a different direction.

True _____ False _____

10. The more target elimination you use, the more efficient you will be, because you won't dig as much junk.

True _____ False _____

11. The fun and reward of metal detecting is that you never know what you will _____ _____ _____ .

12. The straight-line scan method reduces _____ by helping you to maintain uniform _____ .

13. The straight-line scan method improves your chances of detecting fringe area targets.

True _____ False _____

14. Initial "preset" points on a detector's control panel allows the control knob and switches to be set for average soil and operating conditions.

True _____ False _____

Each correct answer given in questions 7 and 12 is worth 7 points. Total value of these 4 correct answers is 28 points. Each correct answer given to the remaining 12 questions is worth 6 points. Perfect score is 100. Answers given in Appendix 2.

CHAPTER 24

What Treasure Hunting Is All About

Treasure hunting is the search for and recovery of anything that has value to you. Coins, jewelry, money caches and relics are all treasure just the same as gold and silver. Treasure hunting is difficult to define because it means different things to different people. Some people want to strike it rich the very first time they turn on a detector while others are content to find a few coins in the local park. Some hunt treasure for the excitement of digging a treasure out of the ground while others are fascinated by the "historical" discoveries they make. Some find joy in returning lost class rings and other valuables to their rightful owner. Other people enjoy displaying their found treasues in their homes. There are some who write magazine articles and enjoy sharing their finds and learned treasure hunting techniques with others. Yet, some simply enjoy getting out into God's great outdoors; the treasure they find is icing on the cake.

WHO HUNTS FOR TREASURE?

Treasure hunting has become a family hobby; the husband, wife and children all quickly become dedicated treasure hunters. The majority of all metal detector users search for coins and jewelry (Figure 24-1) lost at countless recreational sites located throughout the world. Sometimes only the man of the household enjoys the hobby, but often the wife will go alone if the husband won't go. Often, children become better hunters than their parents. Hunters, fishermen, campers, vacationers and backpackers are adding metal detectors to their sports gear.

TREASURE HUNTING IS HEALTHFUL

Who can deny that outdoor activities are healthful? Treasure hunting takes you out of doors into the fresh air and sunshine. Scanning a detector over the ground all day, digging hundreds of targets, hiking several miles over the desert, or climbing a mountain in order to reach a ghost town can become tiring. But, this is where an extra added benefit is realized. A "built-in" body building program is a valuable side benefit of treasure hunting. Leg muscles firm up, flab around the middle begins to diminish as excess pounds drop off, breathing improves and nights of restful sleep result. Good physical exercise is required in treasure hunting and can lead to a longer, healthier life. (Figure 24-2.)

Figure 24-1: Darrell Kilburn of Fairport, New York displays a tremendous assortment of found treasure. It is obvious that Darrell has mastered his equipment. Thank you Darrell for sharing your story with us.

Figure 24-2: Roy Lagal and the author survey a Northwest U.S. river crossing site where, in 1877, Chief Joseph and the Nez Perce Indian Tribe crossed the river with a large herd of cattle. The men were searching for a gold hoard.

TREASURE HUNTING IS PROFITABLE

Treasure hunting is profitable, simple and easy. Why not consider the hobby of coin hunting? The majority of all treasure hunters begin their new hobby by coin hunting. Countless millions of coins have been lost and await recovery by the metal detector hobbyist. More coins are being lost today than are being found. (Figures 24-3, 24-4, 24-5.)

Figure 24-3: Robert Kelly of Kelly's Metalcraft in Grant's Pass, Oregon shares with us recent finds he and his family made. Bob's entire family are active treasure hunters and prospectors.

OTHER BENEFITS ARE REALIZED

Most important to many people is the awareness and enjoyment of the treasures of nature God has placed upon the earth for all of us to find. Whether the ''big money treasure'' has been found is not always the point. It is truly gratifying to see nature in its purest form all around us, and to be a vital part of it. This alone could well be the greatest treasure ever found. (Figure 24-6.)

The educational factors related to treasure hunting are equally stimulating. Relics and artifacts of bygone eras create many questions. Who were the people that once lived and prospered where faint memories of a city or old lumber town remain? Where did they come from? Why was the area deserted? These and many more questions can usually be answered with proper research and examination of the artifacts found.

Figure 24-4: Our thanks to an unknown treasure hunter for this photograph of a few of his valuable finds. A study of this picture clearly reveals the many, varied treasures that can be found.

Figure 24-5: Our thanks to this treasure hunter for supplying this photograph of the treasure he has found with his detector. It is obvious he has mastered his equipment.

Figure 24-6: Thank you Jerry Fuller (Forest Ranch, California) for sharing with MODERN METAL DETECTOR readers some of your unique ghost town finds.

OTHER REWARDING TREASURE HUNTING HOBBIES

Treasure hunting for other valuable items is very profitable and rewarding. Many persons who begin with coin hunting quickly extend their hobby into other areas of treasure hunting. Searching ghost towns and old houses for hidden money caches, and trash dumps for relics and rare bottles can be very rewarding. One treasure hunter found $41,000 (Figure 24-7) in currency in a metal box that was cached in an old dumping ground. Another man in Idaho found a $20 gold piece estimated to be worth hundreds of thousands of dollars. Hundreds of small fruit jar and "post hole" money caches are found each year. (See Figures 24-8, 24-9, 24-10 and 24-10A)

JOIN A CLUB!

There are approximately three hundred fifty treasure hunting clubs in the United States with a total of over five hundred clubs located throughout the world. Why not join one and take an active part? (See Figure 24-11.) Clubs are an invaluable source of information. You can learn about metal detectors and treasure hunting from those who are active in the field. You will meet people, share their success stories, and perhaps gain a few hunting partners. You will be encouraged by found treasure, and you can swap some of your treasure and build up your collection.

Figure 24-7: One treasure hunter found forty-one thousand dollars of rotted currency in a metal container in a trash dump.

Figure 24-8: Thank you Frankie Angona for sharing this treasure find with us. Frankie found this coin purse in an abandoned house in North Texas.

Figure 24-9: This is how silver dollars can look after they have been buried many years. Occasionally, coins remain bright and new looking even after years of burial. The container and burial conditions determine the condition of recovered coins.

RESEARCH IS IMPORTANT

Research is a key to successful treasure hunting. Without proper and adequate research, you are shooting in the dark. Your efficiency and likelihood of successful recovery increase as the amount of research you do increases. Without research, you may not be as successful as you should or could be. Ninety-five percent of a successful recovery is due to research. You must go where the treasure is located. Most of the time, in order to find where it is, you must do a certain amount of research. You won't find treasure where it is not! You will find treasure where it is! In order to find it, it will be necessary to study, read, and follow up leads. It's wise to talk to people. In short, do your research.

It seems true that the successful treasure hunter appears to expend no energy at all, while the mediocre treasure hunter runs about constantly in a helter-skelter fashion, looking for the will-o-the-wisp and never really being satisfied or successful.

A metal detector must be used correctly and in the right places before it will pay off. Most successful finds result from research. (See Figure 24-12.) Of course, a lot of treasure is found by accident, and all of us dream of finding the "big one" simply by stumbling over it, but that is hardly the way to go about professional treasure hunting.

It is sad, but true, that most treasure hunters do not educate

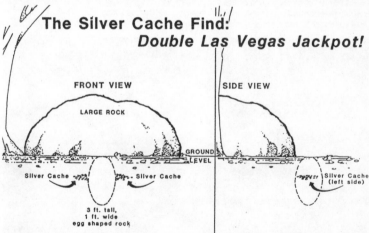

The Silver Cache Find:
Double Las Vegas Jackpot!

FRONT VIEW

SIDE VIEW

LARGE ROCK

GROUND LEVEL

Silver Cache — Silver Cache

Silver Cache (left side)

3 ft. tall,
1 ft. wide
egg shaped rock

Figure 24-10: The author displays leaf silver that he discovered near Cobalt, Ontario, Canada. This is the contents of two silver caches he located at one spot. These caches were probably buried sixty to seventy years ago by a miner who had high graded the silver from a mine. This illustration shows how they were buried, one on each side of a large rock. Photo by Melvin Climer.

themselves on the correct usage of metal detectors. They do not go to the trouble to get correct data on treasure sites. They just don't go where the treasure is located. Usually, however, these people are the first to give up, perhaps blaming their instrument for their failure.

Figure 24-11: This is a portion of the contestants who attended Search International's First International Competition Treasure Hunt which was held in the Dallas-Fort Worth, Texas area. More contestants and visitors attended this hunt than any other treasure hunting event.

Figure 24-12: Treasure hunters searching for outlaw bank loot in Oklahoma made this discovery. It was found in a collapsed cellar near a farm in southern Oklahoma.

Figure 24-13: Famed treasure hunter, George Mroczkowski, shows us this beautiful hand-carved statue he found at a desert site. Obviously, it was an ancient altar long since abandoned. It was concealed in a rock pile. A large quantity of melted wax on the rocks attested to the fact that it was used many years, as a place of worship. There were no other signs of habitation for miles around.

The greatest difficulty facing the professional treasure hunter is deciding which of the dozens or hundreds of leads to follow. He tries to avoid bum steers. He uses his brain and he thinks; common sense is a big factor in successful treasure hunting. The professional treasure hunter doesn't search for one treasure; he keeps many leads on the back burner. He is always looking for new leads to follow. Often in researching one story, he will run across information that applies to another. The professional will select several treasure leads to follow and gather all the information he can about each of them. He will follow each one as far as he can and then will let it lie dormant for a while, letting his subconscious work on it while waiting for new leads to come along. Maybe the professional only hits once a year but often that is more than enough to repay the effort. (See Figure 24-13.)

Whether you are a coin hunter, cache or relic hunter, or a prospector, research is vitally important. It is a tool you cannot neglect to use.

Many books are written on the subject. Karl von Mueller's two books, TREASURE HUNTER'S MANUAL #6 and #7 published by Ram Publishing Company, are the two primary research-related books available to you. Both of these books should be on your bookshelf and should be read often.

The successful treasure hunter lives and breathes his hobby. It is always on his mind. Consequently, everything he reads and everyone he talks with are potential sources of fresh treasure leads or data he needs to help him in his work.

If you are a coin hunter, for instance, you can find recent date coins all day long at the park, playground, and along the parking meter grassy strips. If you really want to start finding old, rare date, valuable coins, you must do your research. You must learn where the old settler's campgrounds, carnival and fairground sites are located. These are the really valuable hot spots; here you will find treasure that makes hunting worthwhile. (See Figures 24-14 and 24-15.) The same applies to any other facet of treasure hunting. If you are a prospector, you know you have to go where the gold is located. Gold and silver have been found in many locations throughout the world, and to have the greatest chances of success, you must find the best places to prospect. If you are a relic hunter or a cache hunter, the same thing applies. Do your research, find the hot spots, then put your expert detector knowledge to work. It will pay off!

PATIENCE

If you have been hunting treasure for almost any length of time, you have probably run across mention of the word ''patience''. Absolutely, positively, unless you possess a great amount of patience

Figure 24-14, 24-15: These photographs show the front and reverse side of this beautiful gold medallion found in Europe.

and put it into practice, you won't be as successful as you could be.

Experienced cache hunters have learned that success comes as infrequently as one in ten tries. Consequently, a person without patience to spare will surely give up long before success rolls around.

Four professional treasure hunters, who you perhaps already know about, Roy Lagal, L.L. "Abe" Lincoln, George Mroczkowski and Karl von Mueller, possess an overabundance of patience. They know that you don't find treasure every time you run out and turn on a detector. They know and have preached on many occasions, that to be successful, patience must be in your tool kit.

These men have been successful many times. They keep perhaps a dozen or more leads going at the same time. Many of Roy's successes are described in two of his books published by Ram Publishing Company, DETECTOR OWNER'S FIELD MANUAL and VLF/TR METAL DETECTOR HANDBOOK. Roy has kept one project going for about fifteen years. "It's there someplace," said Roy, "they put 'er down good!" But he's determined to find it and hasn't given up in all these years, nor has his enthusiasm waned. Someday he'll find it!

These men have been written about in books and magazines many times. An article about "Abe" Lincoln explained that his successes were due in part to his patience. "Abe," (Figure 24-16) stated that patience is a true key to making finds and that if you are going to be successful, you better gather plenty of it in store for yourself and put it to use.

If you have read George Mroczkowski's book, PROFESSIONAL TREASURE HUNTER, published by Ram Publishing Company, you know that George possesses an abundance of patience. Just read through several of his treasure adventures that span decades and you will see that George has learned the value of

Figure 24-16: Famed treasure hunter, Abe Lincoln, of Rogers, Arkansas, displays some of his treasure finds. Since Abe's retirement as a Commander in the United States Navy, he and his wife Betty have spent much of their time treasure hunting in the great northwest. Abe has been very successful and owes much of his success to patience. He will quickly tell you that one of the virtues of successful treasure hunting is patience.

patience. Patience and hard work are two of George's greatest virtues and reasons for success.(Figure 24-17).

HARD WORK

Von Mueller once wrote, "You can put on your cap of patience and it'll serve you well, but you better also pick up the shovel of hard work if you want to experience the joys and rewards of finding treasure!"

Treasure hunting is hard work. In fact, it's one of the hardest jobs a person could undertake. You could sit on a rock all day long with patience to spare, but all you would accomplish is keeping the rock warm; that rock will never hatch; you must get out into the field, swinging that detector from dawn to dusk and dig every signal, regardless of how weak or how strong.

Many people enjoy going to a park and scanning a searchcoil back and forth over the ground for a while with discrimination set to its maximum and just occasionally digging a coin or two. There is nothing wrong with that, if it is what a person wants. But there is a greater reward in hard work, sweat and the sound of money jingling in the pocket (Figure 24-19).

VARIOUS FACETS OF TREASURE HUNTING

To round out this chapter, the various facets of treasure hunt-

Figure 24-17: Here is another of George Mroczkowski's desert finds.

Figure 24-19: Bill Kasselman (and Jim Alexander) of Houston recovered several such fruit jars at a location in Houston, Texas. Photo courtesy Alexander Enterprises Archives.

ing are discussed below. Remember, in Chapter 22, HOW TO CHOOSE AND USE THE CORRECT METAL DETECTOR, metal detector selection recommendations are given to help you select the best detector for every task you undertake.

LET'S GO COIN HUNTING!

Coin hunting is the searching for and retrieving of lost coins. Countless millions of coins have been lost and await recovery by the metal detector hobbyist. Thousands of Indianhead and Wheat pennies, Buffalo nickels, Barber dimes, Liberty and Washington quarters, Liberty Walking half-dollars, silver dollars, early colonial coins, gold coins and many other types of coins are being recovered every day. People are losing more coins today than the coin hunter is finding! Coins are lost everywhere people go, and coins are being found everywhere people have been. Coin hunting is one of the most active family hobbies in America.

The person not familiar with this hobby finds it difficult to believe that coins can be found. "Who loses coins?", they say. "Surely, there are not enough lost coins to make it worthwhile to buy a metal detector or spend time looking for them!" I have said many times..."any active and experienced coin hunter can find five thousand coins each year." This is only an average of one-hundred coins found each weekend for fifty weeks...a reasonable and obtainable goal. If you'll apply the principles set forth in my book, SUCCESSFUL COIN HUNTING, you'll easily find five thousand coins each year and more! (See Figures 24-20, 24-21, 24-22 and 24-23.)

Don't make the mistake of believing there are no coins to be found where you live. If you don't have the experience now, you soon will gain the knowledge to convince yourself that coins are truly found everywhere. The first place every person should start searching is right in his own backyard; branch out from there. Many people erroneously believe there is nothing in their areas worth searching for. The truth is, all the good coin hunting sites will never be cleaned out.

EXPLORE A GHOST TOWN

A popular and rewarding hobby is "ghost-towning" which includes a number of activities. In ghost towns you may discover old coins, perhaps a buried treasure cache, relics or antiques dating back to the Pilgrims, or lost items from only yesterday. Any place people have gathered will produce relics and coins. There are thousands of abandoned town sites, old forts, homesteads and farmhouse locations. The list is endless. Finding a place to search will never be your problem! Finding the time needed to pursue and enjoy your hobby is often more of a challenge. You will need a

Figure 24-20: Here are a few ancient coins the author found at a site in southern Europe.

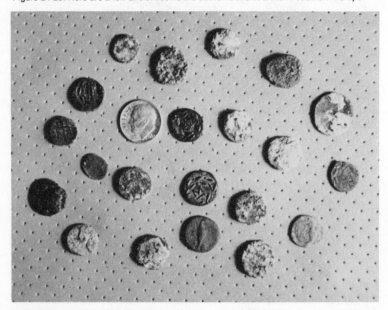

Figure 24-21: Here are additional coins the author found in southern Europe. Some have been cleaned, some are exactly as they were found. A few of these coins are among those the author found that date (Circa) 400 B.C.

378

Figure 24-22: T. R. Edds of Merritt Island, Florida is a noted, successful beachcomber. He is among the top ten successful treasure hunters who search the beaches. He and his partner, Walter Stark, can write the "book!" Thank you Tom for showing us a few of your finds.

Figure 24-23: Here are a few more finds that Jerry Fuller made while searching ghost towns in the great northwest. You can dig a lot of trash at ghost town sites, but finds like these make it all worthwhile.

good metal detector since most surface items have already been picked up and those remaining will lie below the surface. (See Figures 24-24, 24-25, 24-26, 24-27 and 24-28.)

Figure 24-24: Hardrock Hendricks and the author found several hundred of these nineteenth century tokens where they had been dumped along a side road near the town of Cripple Creek, Colorado.

A one hundred year old rifle was found in Athens, Texas, by a treasure hunter who was curious enough to search the attic of an old house. Karl von Mueller, in one of his TREASURE HUNTERS MANUALS, tells of a straw-encased bottle filled with 773 dimes which was found with a metal detector near Maitland, Florida, over the doorway of an old shack. All the coins were dated prior to 1918. There were forty-six of the rare 1916-D's, worth more than one hundred dollars each; two 1895-O's, worth more than fifty dollars, and ten 1904-S's, worth more than ten dollars apiece. The numismatic value of the other coins brought the total value of the cache to over five thousand dollars, with today's value many times more than that amount. The most significant aspect of the find, however, is that when the coins were hidden they were probably worth little more than their face value of $77.30. In other words, they were probably not hidden by a wealthy person but rather, as the modest shack would indicate, by someone relatively poor. This bears out the old cliche that, "treasure is where you find it."

380

Figure 24-25: Tommie T. Long of Outdoor Hobby Supply in the Clarkston/Lewiston (Washington/Idaho) area, discovered this filled mercury flask in a mining area in Idaho.

Figure 24-26: An unknown treasure hunter shares his finds with us.

381

Figure 24-27: The author has had this photograph in his files for nearly twenty years. It was sent to him by an unknown treasure hunter. The joy of treasure hunting, not knowing what you will dig up next. This is a unique treasure find.

Figure 24-28: Thanks to another treasure hunter for sharing his finds with us.

TRY CACHE HUNTING TOO!

Cache hunting is seeking money or valuables that have been put away or cached by someone, the little old lady's "hard times" coins she buried in a jar in the garden fifty or one hundred years ago, the old man's bank jar he kept hidden in the bottom of a fence post hole or, the washtub filled with gold coins. These are all "caches"! There are many, many thousands of these treasures waiting for the detector operator who seeks them out. (See Figures 24-30 and 24-10.) They are buried from only a few inches to arm's length below ground surface. If they are not dug up by the treasure hunter, they will stay buried forever. These treasures can be found anywhere: in the chicken coop, halfway between the well and a tree, between two trees, in the ground under the horse stall, in the walls of houses and barns, etc. (See Figure 24-31.)

Figure 24-30: Roy Lagal, Tommie T. Long and Charles Garrett search for a treasure cache somewhere in the great northwest. The author uses the Depth Multiplier attachment.

BATTLEFIELD RELICS CAN BE FOUND

Many thousands of people have found an interesting pastime in the collecting and studying artifacts and other items from the great home war. The values placed on most War Between The States items are often astronomical. Simple buttons from Union and Confederate uniforms have been sold at open and private auctions for as much as one thousand dollars. Buckles, (Figure 24-32) a favorite item with most collectors, are highly sought and

Figure 24-31: Thank you Tommie T. Long for sharing with us yet another of your unique treasure finds.

Figure 24-32: Thanks to this relic hunter for sharing this photograph of some of his found battlefield treasures. These U.S. Civil War belt buckles command a premium.

often demand prices beginning as low as twenty-five dollars for common buckles in poor condition to more than two thousand dollars for the more rare or ornate ones. The finding of battlefield relics brings history so close that one can visualize it in the making. (See Figure 24-33.)

384

Figure 24-33: This unique and very valuable Bronze Age ax head was found near Bristol, England.

The numerous battle and skirmish sites of the eastern and western campaigns and naval operations abound in relics and artifacts valued by the States War buff and professional collector. All types of weapons or instruments of the war are being located by the persistent metal detector operator. (See Figures 24-34, 24-35 and 24-37.) There are many "known" battle areas in the country, however, protected by state and federal governments. There areas, rightfully so, are protected and strictly "off limits" to all metal detector operators.

THERE IS MUCH LOST TREASURE ON THE BEACH!

On some beaches there are roped-off areas designed for swimming. Search these places first! Strike up a conversation with the lifeguard or concession stand operators. It may be that the swimming areas of bygone days were located elsewhere on the beach. You would certainly want to search those sites. Also, lifeguards may know where rings and valuables are reported to have been lost. Try working along the water's edge at both low and high tides as both could be profitable. You will encounter much less trash near the water, but remember, some very valuable coins and jewelry have been found back away from the beach in the heavy traffic areas. There are thousands of swimming beaches no longer used. Visit your library and do a little research to locate

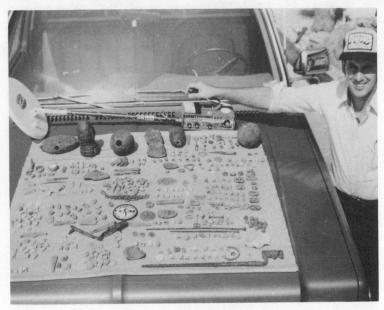

Figure 24-34: Thanks to Dorian Cook, noted battlefield searcher, for giving us a glimpse of a few of his valuable battlefield finds. See also Figure 24-35.

Figure 24-35: Again, thank you Dorian Cook for giving us a glimpse of a few more of your valuable battlefield relics. The shell, with its intact sabot is a unique find. Often, battlefield searchers find single Minie balls to depths of two feet.

Figure 24-36: Eleanor Hube obviously wins top prizes at most of the competition field trials she enters. She and her husband, Jack, travel throughout the United States attending competition treasure meets.

Figure 24-37: Thank you Carl Perham for sharing this story with MODERN METAL DETECTOR readers. Carl found this buried World War I German field cannon at a New Zealand park. Working from leads, Carl continued his search (after others had failed) until he zeroed in on this great find. The cannon has been restored and is now on display in the New Zealand town where it was buried immediately following World War II. The joy of treasure hunting, is not knowing what you'll dig up next. Photo courtesy Carl Perham.

these resort and health spa swimming areas where much treasure awaits discovery. (See Figure 24-36.)

ROCKS, GEMS AND MINERALS

The most important and useful tool of the rockhound (besides his rock hammer and patience) can be the metal detector. If it is properly understood and operated, its use can be very rewarding and interesting, but it should not be used as the ultimate answer to the positive identification of all detectable specimens. The metal detector should be used as an accessory to the rockhound's field equipment, to aid in locating conductive metallic specimens that the human eye cannot distinguish or identify. Check known samples and become acquainted with the metal detector. You cannot see inside an ore specimen but a good quality VLF or BFO detector can.

For our purposes, "metal" is defined as any metallic substance of a conductive nature in sufficient quantity to disturb the electromagnetic field of the searchcoil. If your detector responds to a target as "metallic," bring it in; it contains conductive metal in some form. (See Figure 24-38.) If the detector responds as "mineral," it means only that the specimen contains more iron mineral than it does metal in a detectable form. As a result of a few minutes work, you might find some high grade metallic sample that has been passed over for years by fellow rockhounds.

Figure 24-38: Treasure hunting extends into many fields, one of which is meteorite locating. These iron meteorites were found with metal detectors. At certain meteorite sites, there seems to be an unlimited supply of meteorite fragments that can be found. The large meteorite is worth several thousand dollars. Thank you, Jack Lowry, for supplying several of these for the picture.

When searching for high grade specimens of metallic ore, pay close attention to old mine tailings. You may find that a "worked out" area isn't so barren after all. Certain gems, such as the thunder-egg, have a covering of outside magnetic iron. Some forms of jade and even garnet respond to a good detector.

NOTE: Ore sampling can only be accomplished with a detector that is designed for prospecting and is correctly calibrated to give exacting ore sample identification. To learn about, select, and correctly use calibrated instruments, read the books Roy Lagal and I wrote, ELECTRONIC PROSPECTING and THE COMPLETE VLF-TR METAL DETECTOR HANDBOOK, both published by Ram Publishing Company.

The Little Treasure Hunter metal detector is the rockhound's perfect field companion. (See Figure 22-6.)

LAWS ABOUT TREASURE HUNTING

While this book does not attempt to give legal advice, you need to become aware that there are laws applicable to various treasure hunting situations. Each state has its own laws concerning where you can hunt for treasure and whether you may keep treasure when it is found. You should learn these laws.

All states have laws against trespassing. If a sign says, "Keep Out," do just that. It is always best to seek permission. With the proper attitude and a true explanation of your purpose, you will be surprised at the cooperation you will receive from most landowners. The majority of them will be curious enough about your metal detector and what you hope to find, to agree to let you search. Offer to split, giving them twenty-five percent of all you find and they will be more willing. If large amounts of treasure are believed to be hidden or buried on another's property, a properly drawn, legal agreement between both you and the landowners (husband and wife, etc.) will eliminate any later disagreements which might otherwise arise.

In most cases, public property is open to you. Do not destroy the grass or leave trash or holes. Most park superintendents know that conscientious coin hunters pick up trash and leave the grounds in better shape than they found them. There are several ways to properly remove coins from the ground. You should read Chapter IX "How To Dig That Coin and Tools You'll Need," in my book, SUCCESSFUL COIN HUNTING (See Recommended Supplementary Books).

Also, you should contact Garrett Electronics Customer Service Department and order a copy of one or more slide and film shows or video tapes of various "HOW TO" metal detecting presentations. See the back sections of this book for the listing.

All treasure hunters must become aware of their responsibility

389

to protect the property of others and to keep public property fit for all. Persons who destroy property, dig large holes and leave them unfilled, or tear down buildings in search of valuables, are not to be called treasure hunters but, more properly, looters or scavengers. (See Figures 24-39 and 24-40.)

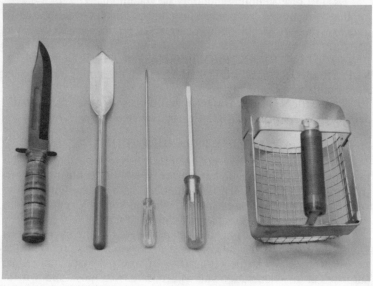

Figure 24-39: Here are a few digging and retrieval tools. A long-bladed knife for plug cutting and digging; a sharp-edged garden trowel for wet sand or cutting through thick rooted grass; two long-bladed screw drivers for pinpointing and retrieval; and a sand scoop for dry, to slightly moist sand.

UNCLE SAM'S INCOME TAX LAWS

All treasure you find must be declared as income during the year in which you receive monetary gain from that treasure. If you find one thousand dollars in coins that you spend because they have no numismatic value, then you must declare their face value in that year's income tax report. If, however, you find a valuable coin or, say, an antique pistol, you do not make a declaration until you sell the item and then only for the amount you received for it. If you decide to donate some of your finds to historical societies or museums, you may be able to deduct the fair market price of the items as charitable contributions. Simply stated, the tax laws require you to declare all income from treasure hunting.

You may be allowed to deduct some or all of your expenses but you must have expense receipts, so keep good records. You are advised to check with a tax accountant, especially if you plan on becoming a full-time treasure hunter. An accountant will advise you as to what type records you are required to keep.

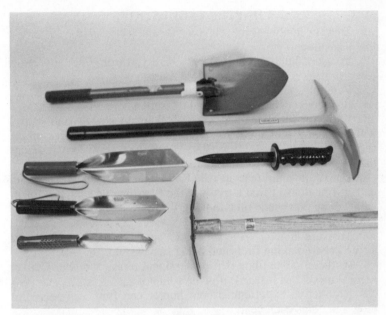

Figure 24-40: Here are a few more tools you may need. A folding shovel, and Estwing pick, several specially designed digging tools, a knife, and a pick.

The hobby and sport of metal detecting has been kept clean and dignified by people who care about their hobby, themselves, and their fellowman. Most detector owners go out of their way to protect a most rewarding and enjoyable hobby and to share their enjoyment with others. To keep the hobby clean, takes the effort and dedication of everyone, not just a few. So, as you go about enjoying your leisure, or perhaps full-time activity, be professional! Be worthy of your calling!

CHAPTER 24 QUESTIONS

1. Treasure hunting is the searching for and recovery of _____ that has value to you.

2. Treasure hunting can not only be a rewarding activity but it can also be a very _____ activity.

3. Certainly, one key to successful treasure hunting is _____ .

4. Just remember, you won't find treasure where it is _____ .

5. Karl von Mueller once wrote, "You can put on your cap of patience and it will serve you well, but you had better pick up the shovel of _____ _____ if you want to experience the joys and rewards of finding treasure!"

6. One of the main reasons why Roy Lagal has been so successful is that if he doesn't find a treasure the first time he searches for it, he never again spends time looking for that same treasure.

    True _____   False _____

7. Treasure hunter, "Abe Lincoln," stated that _____ is a true key to making finds and being successful.

8. If, there is one thing that professional treasure hunter George Mroczkowski has learned, it is the value of _____ .

9. Any active experienced coin hunter can find _____ thousand coins each year.

10. One of the best places where every beginning treasure hunter should start searching is right in his own _____ .

11. Learn to use your head and think! Treasure is where you _____ it.

12. Money caches are rarely ever buried deeper than arm's _____ .

13. You cannot see inside an ore specimen but a good quality VLF or BFO metal detector _____ .

14. All treasure you find must be declared as income during the year in which you find it.

    True _____   False _____

Question 3, answered correctly, is worth 9 points. Each of the other questions answered correctly is worth 7 points. Perfect score is 100. Answers given in Appendix 2.

Electronic Prospecting Creates Modern Gold Rushes

GOLD CAN BE FOUND!

Just as I began final editing of this chapter, I received a letter from an electronic prospector who, this past summer, found one hundred nineteen (119) ounces of gold! One nugget alone weighed in at a whopping ninety one (91) ounces! He and his partner found the gold in a well-known gold area of the United States.

Often, I receive letters, with photographs, from electronic prospectors who have found gold. The value of the gold being found with metal detectors, that I am aware of, totals in the tens of millions of dollars. The people who write are bubbling over with joy as they share their "sudden wealth" stories with me.

Gold and silver is being found with metal detectors. Sure, you don't just run out, turn on your metal detector, and start finding gold. If that's the way it worked, I would just forget about this chapter and head out with MY metal detector.

I have found gold and silver with my metal detectors; just about every time I go electronic prospecting. Sometimes, I find a small amount, sometimes several thousand dollars worth (Figure 25-1). Searching for precious metals with a metal detector is profitable but it takes time, energy and patience. You can find your share of gold, silver, platinum and copper if you will put forth the effort. Precious metals can be found!

Many people claim that gold cannot be found with a metal detector. These people believe, erroneously, that since you cannot attract gold with a magnet, a metal detector cannot detect gold! A magnet will not attract gold simply because gold is non-ferrous. Magnets attract only ferrous (iron) objects. When a magnetic field penetrates iron, the molecular structure becomes polarized in such a way that the iron is attracted to the magnet. This polarization does not occur in gold, nor do metal detectors work on the attraction principle. Some people do not believe that gold can be found because they have attempted to detect gold dust and failed. Extremely fine gold cannot be detected because it presents insufficient surface areas for electrical (eddy) currents to flow.

This chapter discusses electronic prospecting primarily through the use of MANUAL-ADJUST VLF type metal detectors. BFOs can also be used in many forms of electronic prospecting but in

Figure 25-1: The author points to solid silver. He found this chunk of ore that weighs nearly fifty pounds, at a mining district near Cobalt, Ontario, Canada. Everything that glitters may not be gold—it can be silver! Electronic prospectors have found vast quantities of silver ore in Canada. This piece was worth about $5,000.00 when found.

most situations the VLF is superior. If you are interested in prospecting, I recommend you obtain a copy of the Ram book, ELECTRONIC PROSPECTING, a complete guide to electronic prospecting using all types of detectors. Also, you should view Garrett Electronics' video presentation, "WEEKEND PROS-PECTING." It will guide you in the various forms of electronic prospecting. (Look for movie listings at the end of this book.)

NUGGET HUNTING

There are many electronic prospecting methods you can use to find gold. First, let's study nugget hunting, which is a popular and easy form of prospecting. There are vast areas in the world where nuggets can be found with a detector and there are numerous ways of finding potential hot spots, including word of mouth, study of governmental records and early-day histories of mining camps, as well as other sources. You need to learn where nuggets have been found previously. For instance, in Northern California there are numerous areas where early-day miners located gold nuggets by sight. The nuggets simply lay on the ground! When you find areas such as this, go to work with your detector! Incidentally, many of those early-day nuggets, especially the larger ones, are on display in some Northern California and Oregon banks.

In Australia, Peter Bridge of P.O. Box 317, Victoria Park

6100, Western Australia, Australia did a study of governmental records dating back to about 1850. These published reports gave the size, depth, and location of all reported gold nuggets found. In analyzing these records, he came to the astonishing realization that a large percentage of the nuggets were at such shallow depths they could have been found easily with a detector. If, he reasoned, miners found tremendous quantities of gold simply by visual search, just imagine the multiplied quantities of gold that must be within range of a good detector! The research information, coupled with Peter's determination to select the right detectors to find this gold led to the modern-day gold rush that began in Australia in the late 1970s. (Figures 25-2, 25-3, 25-4 and 25-5.)

No one can tell you where all the world's gold-bearing regions are located. Even if they knew, they wouldn't tell you; they'd go find all the gold for themselves. To be successful, research is necessary. This same reasoning, of course, holds true in any form of detecting. Whether it be cache hunting or looking for coins, you must do your research to find the best places to go searching. (Figures 25-6, 25-7, 25-8 and 25-9.)

To locate nuggets, scan in the VLF all-metal mode. Use NO target elimination or discrimination. Adjust the detector to eliminate the effects of ground minerals with the searchcoil held from one to two inches above the ground. Scan the searchcoil over the ground maintaining constant height. Until you have become extremely familiar with your detector, you should dig all targets and make no attempt to target eliminate. Granted, you will dig a quantity of iron, nails, and other junk but that is part of treasure hunting. To be successful in nugget hunting, you will have to dig some junk.

Gold nuggets found in water will be rounded (Figures 25-10 and 25-11). However, occasionally flattened nuggets are found. Rounded nuggets are more difficult to detect. The more surface area of the metal that is facing toward the bottom of the searchcoil, the stronger will be the signal. The rounded surface of most nuggets reduces the amount of flat surface that is "looking" at the detector searchcoil and reduce the chances of detection.

Gold nuggets ranging from pinhead size to nuggets weighing nearly one thousand ounces, have been found with metal detectors. There are various techniques to learn in order to become efficient in gold nugget hunting, but these can be acquired through study and field work.

Incidentally, the largest reported gold nugget found in the United States weighed 161 pounds. The largest reported gold nugget found in the world, was found in Australia—it weighed 248 pounds.

Figure 25-2: This is one of most beautiful nuggets found in Australia. It was found near Kalgoorlie in the Western Australia mining district. Photo by Bob Grant.

Figure 25-3: Happy electronic prospectors display numerous found gold nuggets. All of these gold nuggets were found with metal detectors in Australia.

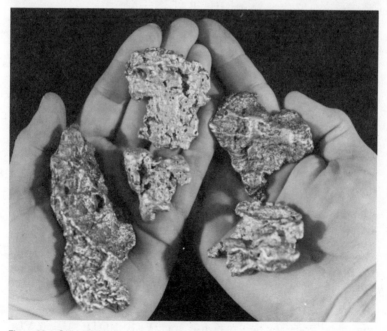

Figure 25-4: Solid gold! Here are a few more gold nuggets found in Australia.

Figure 25-5: This monstrous gold nugget was found in Australia by a diligent, hardworking electronic prospector. It is worth as much as $50,000.00.

HIGH GRADING

One of the easiest and most lucrative form of electronic prospecting is high grading. High grading is the searching of mine dumps, tailings, and dredge piles for gold nuggets and positive-reading ore samples.

When early-day miners tunneled through the earth, following ore veins, they discarded or dumped the worthless material outside the mine (Figure 25-12). Often, gold and other precious metals were accidentally dumped (Figures 25-13, 25-14 and see also 25-1). You can search the tailings and, if you hit it lucky, you will come home with some gold. You can scan an ore dump for conductive ore in the same way that you would scan the ground for nuggets.

Often, miners dropped good ore in mine tunnels or on the ground outside, and occasionally ore chutes (Figure 25-15) will be found where miners left ore that contains conductive metal. Individual ore sampling is the best way to check for good specimens in situations like these. CAUTION: Avoid unsafe mine tunnels, rotted floors in old buildings, etc. Stay out of places that are posted or unsafe in any way. Cave-ins and poisonous gases have injured and killed the unwary.

To ore sample, you can, of course, use your trusty BFO, set in the metal zone, or you may use your VLF. NOTE: Use a VLF

Figure 25-6: Treasure hunter and electronic prospector, Bill Bosh, happily displays this monstrous gold nugget he found in Western Australia's outback region. Bill has learned the value of persistence and hard work. "It pays," he says!

Figure 25-7: For some reason American electronic prospectors are tight lipped. However, if you ever meet Jack Ward, he'll gladly show you numerous photographs of United States gold he has found. Here are a few of the beautiful nuggets he has to his credit.

Figure 25-8: This monstrous gold nugget laced with quartz and iron, was found in Australia's famed Western Australia outback region. As can be seen, it didn't look like much in this state, but if you will take a look at Figures 25-9 and 25-28, you'll see that when a professional chemist like Virgil Hutton removes the quartz and iron, it became a truly beautiful and valuable chunk of ore.

Figure 25-9: Here are several beautiful golden chunks of ore found in Australia. The large nugget is the same as shown in Figure 25-8, except it has been chemically treated by a professional chemist. The smaller nugget the man is holding was also treated to remove quartz and iron.

Figure 25-10: When you find a nugget like this one, if your dog doesn't seem too happy about it, don't worry, it is still gold! Wally, a full blood Nez Perce Indian and friend of the author, proudly displays this beautiful nugget find. Thank you Wally, for sharing with MODERN METAL DETECTOR readers another success story.

Figure 25-11: If you come to believe (from all the photographs) that all gold comes in fist-size chunks, here is some smaller, New Mexico "yellow." This dredge recovery material (black magnetic sand and gold) resulted from a good day's work. Photo courtesy Jack Ward.

Figure 25-12: Charles Garrett and George Mroczkowski examine a nice ore specimen they found at this mine tailing near Cobalt, Ontario, Canada. Even from this distance, the vein of silver in the specimen can be seen. Obviously, those early day miners did not check every rock that came out of their mines. Photo by Roy Lagal.

Figure 25-13: The author digs and digs through this concrete like matrix to expose one portion of the nearly fifty-pound silver chunk of ore (Figure 25-1) that he found near Cobalt, Ontario, Canada. In the immediate vicinity, several other large chunks were also found. Photo by Jack Hube.

Figure 25-14: Professional electronic prospector, Jim Paul and the author examine a chunk of ore that Jim just found. It is a very unusual piece in that it contains a unique, silver vein, structure.

403

Figure 25-15: When searching prospecting areas, don't overlook the lucrative field of high grading. A factory calibrated detector can quickly tell you if an ore specimen contains a predominance of conductive metal. Oftentimes, miners left vast quantities of ore, some of which contains worthwhile gold and/or silver. The author filled his pouch with several dozen valuable ore specimens that were left in this ore shute perhaps fifty or sixty years ago. Obviously, he was the first person to electronically examine this ore shute in all those years. He is using the Pocket Scanner, Model 11770. Photo by Roy Lagal.

detector only if it is factory calibrated for ore sampling. Never use the VLF mode unless you know precisely the point where the true equivalent metal/mineral null is located.

HOW TO SAMPLE ORE

Turn on the detector, set it to the calibrated point and adjust the audio for a faint threshold sound. Bring ore samples one at a time in toward the bottom and center of the searchcoil (Figure 25-15). Keep all samples that give a positive reading, for later evaluation. If the signal decreases or makes no sound, discard the sample. The metal detector signal depends upon the predominant amount of iron or conductive precious metal in the sample. If the specimen has more conductive metal than non-conductive iron, you will get a positive sound.

DREDGE PILES

In many areas along waterways, dredging was done on a large scale. These waterways were literally turned upside down and the material was fed through classifiers (sorters) and then into gold recovery equipment. If there happened to be nuggets too large to pass through classifiers, or if nuggets became mixed in with lumps of clay, they were simply dumped out (unknowingly) with all the other debris. Many prospectors, picnickers, and others have found large gold nuggets simply lying on top of the rock piles you see so often along waterways, mainly rivers, in gold bearing country (Figure 25-16). The best way to scan for gold is to scan the rock piles as though you were looking for nuggets. Incidentally, the ninety one ounce gold nugget I spoke of in the first paragraph of this chapter, was found in a dredge pile!

BLACK SAND LOCATING

When searching for black sand, in hopes that gold will also be found, a quality BFO or VLF is recommended. It's best to use the largest possible searchcoil.

Hold the BFO searchcoil several inches above the ground and tune to a fast motorboating sound in the MINERAL mode. Following this, walk slowly forward with the searchcoil held in front of you—do not scan side-to-side. Use headphones. When the tone increases, however slightly, keep walking until the tone returns to your present threshold level. These two distinct tone change indications mark the limits of the black sand deposit.

To use a VLF, select the all-metal, manually adjustable, VLF mode. Adjust the Ground Elimination control until ground minerals are eliminated from detection. Black sand concentrations, more "dense" than the ground matrix to which you adjusted the Ground Elimination control, will respond with a negative audio (Figure

Figure 25-16: The author documents a find made during the filming of the video presentation WEEDEND PROSPECTING which was filmed in the Great Northwest. Roy Lagal and Virgil Hutton examine a gold nugget that was missed by the early-day dredge operators. When you view the video presentation, you'll get the full story on this one. Photo by Tommie T. Long.

25-17). Follow the same scanning procedure as described in the previous paragraph.

These methods are not infallible, of course, as iron ore deposits and veins can also be located. Since black sand concentrations can, as a rule of thumb, be found only to a depth equal to the diameter of the searchcoil you are using, whenever you think you have found a black sand concentration it is only necessary to dig down to a depth slightly deeper than the searchcoil diameter. If your signal occurs over a large area, and you don't find black sand at the shallow depth, the detector may have detected a deeper ore deposit or metal target.

SEARCHING FOR VEINS

Since the days of the Spaniards, thousands of precious metal ore veins have been brought to within detection range of modern-day metal detectors. Countless miles of tunnels have narrowly missed rich ore that is hidden from eyesight by only inches, or even fractions of an inch of tunnel walls. The electronic prospector, through patient searching, can find these mines and tunnels. A thorough metal detector scan will result in these overlooked veins being discovered.

A BFO, or preferably a VLF, should be used in these searches. Searching techniques are the same as used when nugget hunting.

Figure 25-17: Monty Moncrief (center) and other electronic prospectors use several techniques for recovering silver from Mexico's Batopilas River. Electronic scanning detected the presence of silver placer as well as black magnetic sand concentrations. Then, the men put the dredges to work. See Figure 20-7.

Carefully, and thoroughly, scan the floor, walls, and ceiling. Don't miss an inch. Investigate all positive audio indications.

In Mexico, I located two silver veins and one pocket, in one Spanish mine (Figures 25-18 and 25-19). The pocket and one vein was small, but the second vein turned out to be large. At eye level, my detector gave an obvious audio indication. My friend, Javier Castellanos, owner of the mine lease, placed a stick of dynamite at the location, and lit the fuse. We heard a deafening sound as we waited at the mine entrance. A short while later, after the dust had settled, we returned to the location. A large chunk of rock had been blown out of the wall. We saw a one-half-inch wide native silver vein shining in the dim light of our carbide lamps. A beautiful sight it was!

As the miners hacked away the wall, following the vein as it snaked downward, the vein grew larger. When, finally, the miners reached floor level, the vein of silver was one foot wide. (See Figure 25-19.)

SEARCHING FOR FLOAT

Float is ore that has broken away from the mother lode and worked its way down the mountainside, coming to rest, perhaps slightly buried, beneath the soil and rock of the mountain. Float can be found on mountain slopes and on flat ground. Perhaps, ground that is now flat, was once a mountain that slowly eroded

Figure 25-18: Monty Moncrief, and David Medrano, a Mexican mine owner, Don Garrett, Roy Lagal (examining vein,) and Charles Garrett view an extremely rich, one-foot wide silver vein that was located in an old Spanish dig in Mexico's Canyon de Cobre region. This region is famed for the silver it yields to prospectors. Photograph by George Mroczkowski.

Figure 25-19: A Mexican miner (left), Curley Jones (center), and Javier Castellanos examine ore that was removed from a silver vein the author located electronically. Javier, a friend of the author's, is a successful prospector who maintains numerous mine leases in the Canyon de Cobre region in Mexico's State of Chihuahua.

over eons of time. There is much disagreement as to how the vast quantities of gold came to be in the flat ground in Australia's gold regions. Some believe the country was once very mountainous.

Searching for float is the same as nugget hunting and vein searching. Preferably, use a VLF with large searchcoils. You should seriously consider (as discussed in Chapter 20) using the Depth Multiplier attachment in regions, such as Canada's Cobalt mining district, where monstrous silver chunks have been found (Figure 25-20). Patience is required in this form of searching, but the rewards often make it all worthwhile.

Figure 25-20: Here is more silver from Canada. Well-known successful, electronic prospector Sandy Cline happily displays a one-hundred-forty-pound piece of silver float that contains approximately one thousand ounces of silver. Sandy has worked various of Canada's silver mining districts for years. His success stories have been written about many times in treasure hunting magazines. Thank you, Sandy, for sharing this great find with MODERN METAL DETECTOR readers.

SEARCHING FOR PLACER

Placer (pronounced plaster with the "t" removed) gold is gold that has become trapped, or has accumulated in cracks, fissures (Figure 25-21) and low spots in stream beds. Placer also accumulates downstream behind boulders (Figure 25-22) and other obstructions. Placer can accumulate in various places in rivers and streams where the water action changes its characteristics.

Gold placer, in the form of nuggets, flakes, dust, etc., becomes concentrated because it is heavier than sand and rock. The gold becomes permanently trapped because there is nothing heavier that can come along and force the gold out.

Placer, in sufficient quantity, can be located with a BFO or VLF metal detector. Various sizes of submersible searchcoils are

Figure 25-21: Gold can become trapped in places like this cracked rock. Tommie T. Long inserts a three-quarter-inch probe to determine if conductive elements are present.

Figure 25-22: Placer can accumulate in confined areas where standard sized searchcoils cannot reach. The author probes beneath the boulder to determine if placer gold is present. Photo by Virgil Hutton.

necessary, depending upon the places to be searched. Quantities of black magnetic sand is most often found present with gold. Since black sand can actually aid you in your search for gold placer, a VLF is the recommended detector.

If you will study Roy Lagal's books, GOLD PANNING IS EASY and WEEKEND PROSPECTING, you will learn how, and where, to locate placer gold (Figure 25-23). With your metal detector, equipped with the correct searchcoils, you stand a good chance of finding gold. Small diameter probes are good for locating placer in cracks and beneath boulders. Three-inch to eight-inch diameter searchcoils (Figure 25-24) are good sizes to use in confined places. Tune the detector the same as when nugget hunting or vein searching. You may do more probing and "sticking," of the searchcoil, than scanning, so it is necessary that the VLF be accurately adjusted to eliminate the effects of ground minerals. Research is necessary to locate the correct places. Then, patience is required in order to achieve maximum success (Figure 25-25).

SEARCHING ANCIENT STREAM BEDS

Placer can be located in present-day river and stream beds, or dry, ancient stream beds. In the gold country, often near rivers and streams, you can find these ancient stream beds by being on the

Figure 25-23: Putting his Gravity Trap gold pans to work, Roy Lagal has panned one shovel full of bedrock concentrates at this site near Cobalt, Ontario, Canada. Note the quantity of silver and other elements that were in that one shovel full of concentrates he removed from bedrock.

411

Figure 25-24: Nugget hunting around boulders often require the use of small three-to-four-inch diameter searchcoils. Larger coils cannot reach into the many tight areas where gold can hide. Virgil Hutton digs where his metal detector said dig. He uses a Gravity Trap gold pan as a quick means of locating the target.

Figure 25-25: A beautiful lady, Virginia Quirk Hovland, refills the gas tank on her portable dredge. Virginia spent many years of her life in a teaching career, but upon retirement, is now busier than ever. When she and husband, Bob, are not using metal detectors, they are searching streams and dry desert areas for gold.

lookout for deposits of sand and rounded, smooth rock. The rocks became rounded eons ago by the action of water, sand and other rock. Perhaps, earth upheavals caused the stream beds to be thrust upward above water level. Placer deposits that were formed when water was flowing, can still be found in the same place where they were formed (Figure 25-26). Scan these ancient river beds using the same techniques as described above in wet searching. Some good finds have been made in these ancient river beds. Learn to identify these sand and rock deposits, it might pay off!

YOU NEED PATIENCE

It is quite possible that many people claim no one can find gold with a detector because they are not sufficiently patient to stay with gold hunting long enough to be successful. To be a successful electronic prospector, you must have patience to spare. You must be willing to search all day, for days at a time, perhaps in the same location. Do not expect to run into a gold prospecting area, turn on your detector, scan for a few minutes, and start finding nuggets. It just doesn't happen! It takes time, it takes study of the area, it takes a lot of searching, and it takes, oftentimes, a lot of digging in order to be successful. Your success will be in direct proportion to your efforts.

Figure 25-26: Tommie T. Long and Virgil Hutton watch as Roy Lagal removes a shovel full of sand and rock from an ancient river bed. Roy's detector gave a positive reading which prompted him to dig at that spot. Often, gold nuggets and placer are found in dry river beds like this one.

413

Figure 25-27: Even though Bob Lilly (Mr. "Cowboy") retired from the NFL Dallas Cowboys football team, he has not retired from hard work. One of his pursuits is electronic prospecting. He and the author discuss various aspect of gold and silver recovery with metal detectors. Photo by Melvin Climer.

Figure 25-28: Charles Garrett, Virgil Hutton, Roy Lagal and George Mroczkowski attend one of George Massie's Gold Prospector's Association of America (GPAA) gold shows. Of course, at these gatherings, conversations always turn to discussions about gold. The men examine the two gold nuggets shown in Figures 25-8 and 25-9. Photo by Woody Caldwell.

Figure 25-29: At one of George Massie's (right) Gold Prospector's Association of America (GPAA) shows, which was held in Reno, Nevada, several prospectors including the author, Roy Lagal and George Mroczkowski discuss gold recovery techniques. Visitors to these shows can see first-hand what prospectors are recovering. Also, on display are the latest gold-recovery equipment and products. George Massie, Woody Caldwell and other GPAA instructors teach gold recovery seminars to GPAA members. Photo by Monty Moncrief.

Figure 25-30: This is a group of students who attended one of Roy Roush's Los Angeles City College Treasure Hunting and Prospecting seminars. Roy demonstrates the correct techniques of panning and sluicing for gold.

415

Figure 25-32: When you discover a majestic place like this, you never want to leave. At this location, in central Washington, the author, Roy Lagal, and Frank Duval spent several days searching for gold. It is one of the most beautiful, peaceful places on earth.

The main thing to do now is to get out your detector, head for the gold fields and practice. Plan to spend many hours and many days scanning your detector and, hopefully, digging gold targets.

You may decide to travel to different areas and search for different elements. The more you search, the more you study, the more you learn the capabilities of your detector and what it is telling you—the more successful you will be!

CHAPTER 25 QUESTIONS

1. Found treasure is truly _____ _____ .
2. Many people claim that _____ cannot be found with a metal detector because they say that a magnet will not attract it.
3. Extremely fine gold cannot be detected if it presents insufficient surface _____ for electrical eddy currents.
4. In most situations, the Manual-Adjust VLF is the superior electronic prospecting detector.
      True _____   False _____
5. Some of the best locations to be successful in nugget hunting, are areas where the old-timers found nuggets by eyesight, or at very shallow depths.
      True _____   False _____

6. When searching for nuggets, it is best to scan in the VLF all-_____ mode.

7. Gold nuggets ranging from pinhead size to any size can be found with a quality Manual-Adjust VLF metal detector.
    True _____   False _____

8. Perhaps the easiest and most lucrative form of electronic prospecting is _____ _____ .

9. Name two reasons why you should be extremely careful when electronic prospecting around old mines and buildings. (Each correct answer is worth 3 points)

10. When ore sampling (high grading), the metal detector signal depends upon the predominent amount of _____ mineral or _____ metal in the sample. (Each correct answer is worth 3 points)

11. Any specimen that has more _____ metal than non-conductive iron will give you a positive metal detector sound.

12. The best way to scan dredge piles for gold nuggets is to scan the pile using the same technique as you would use searching for gold nuggets buried in the ground.
    True _____   False _____

13. There have been many gold nuggets found in dredge piles by prospectors, picnickers, and electronic prospectors, including one gold nugget that weighed _____ ounces.

14. When using a BFO to search for black sand concentrations, you tune the BFO to a fast motorboating sound in the _____ mode.

15. When using a VLF to find black sand concentrations, use the all-metal, manually adjustable, VLF mode.
    True _____   False _____

16. The approximate maximum depth to which black sand concentration can be located is: (A) a depth equal to the thickness of the black sand concentration; (B) a depth equal to the diameter of the searchcoil you are using; (C) maximum depth capability of the metal detector you are using; (D) depends upon how well you have learned to use your metal detector.

17. When you are searching for gold nuggets in a black sand concentration, and you adjust the ground elimination control to eliminate detection of the black sand, all "hot rocks" are definitely eliminated from detection.
    True _____   False _____

Questions 2 and 12 are worth 5 points each when answered correctly. Each of the other questions answered correctly is worth 6 points. Perfect score is 100. Answers given in Appendix 2.

417

CHAPTER 26

Metal Detectors in Archaeology and Historical Field Research

MODERN METAL DETECTORS addresses the metal detector needs of many professions. The book would not be complete without presenting the relationship of metal detectors to modern archaeology and historical field research. Only a few years ago, a student of archaeology would not have heard of the metal detector and its connection with archaeology. Today, many colleges are not only presenting the metal detector as a valuable tool but are using them at their archaeological sites.

The role of the metal detector in archaeology is analogous to the role that it plays in law enforcement. In proceeding with the search or "dig," the collection of evidence, or artifacts, with screening/digging tools and metal detectors, is similar.

Of course, the two professions do not utilize all the same equipment. Law enforcement crime scene managers use finger-printing equipment which archaeologists do not use. Archaeologists use vertical aerial surveying to obtain a plain "view" of the ground. They use electrical resistance surveying, which makes use of variations in the humidity of the soil, to obtain a "map" of underground ditches, pits, walls and other structures. Vertical aerial surveying and electrical resistance surveying equipment and metal detectors are all valuable tools. The metal detector can be the eyes that "see" into the ground to locate metal objects that are of interest to archaeologists.

CASE HISTORIES

Recently, a remarkable metal detector "find" was related to an employee at the Garrett factory. Egyptian archaeologists believed that a second burial vault was located beneath an existing vault discovered thirty years earlier. Rather than destroy the floor of the existing vault on the basis of this theory alone, a metal detector was brought into the vault. Metal detector signals indicated that there was metal beneath the floor. A portion of the stone floor was removed, below which was discovered the second vault containing priceless artifacts.

At Custer's battlefield in Montana, archaeologists, historians, and war buffs undertook a new type of research and documentation to further their knowledge about the events that took place on that fateful day of June 25, 1876. Modern-day archaeologists believed the ground would yield clues to solve many mysteries about the battle. Metal detectors were deployed on a foot-by-foot survey of the historic site.

Hundreds of shells from the troopers' Springfield carbines and the Indians' Henry .44 caliber rifles were located, numbered, bagged and plotted on maps. The shells established previously unknown skirmish lines and indicated that by the end of the battle, Indians were using Army ammunition taken from dead soldiers. Because of the success of the metal detector surveys, the work will continue.

In downtown San Antonio, Texas, archaeologists excavated an eleven acre site uncovering artifacts from the 1836 battle at the Alamo between the Mexican Army and the Texas Mission defenders. Since much of the area around the Alamo had never been seriously examined, as complete a survey as possible was undertaken. Metal detectors were among the tools used by the archaeologists. Coins, musket balls, buttons, weapon fragments and many other metal historical relics were located.

Mel Fisher, Robert Marx and Bert Weber, men well-known for their discovery of sunken Spanish galleons, use underwater metal detectors in their quest for treasure and priceless artifacts these ships carried to their watery graves. Marx, perhaps the world's most knowledgeable and experienced underwater archaeologist, has used metal detection equipment all over the world at countless underwater historical sites. His discoveries could fill dozens of museums.

Doctor Richard Fales has done archaeological work both in the United States and the Holy Land. He deploys metal detectors in his work and has located many valuable metal artifacts (Figures 26-1 and 26-2). The work that he has planned will consume much of his time.

In Israel, where thousands of sites have been worked and where probably ten times as many await the hands of the archaeologists metal detectors are being used on an increasing scale (Figures 26-3 and 26-4.) Metal detectors are being used not only at digs but at sites where ground level surveys are being made which will aid the archaeologists and historians in their future planning and historical surveys. For instance, metal weapons and armor found at a site might be conclusive evidence the location is the battlesite archaeologists want to excavate.

Kent Ubil, an amateur archaeologist, made a name for himself when his curiosity got the best of him. For many years he and his wife, Becky, walked over and explored what apparently was an old, North Texas, ranch or farm house site. They had seen old construction bricks and relics lying about that indicated the area had once been a place of residence and work for some unknown

419

Figure 26-1: This Babylonian arrowhead dating to the siege of Jerusalem (Circa 587 B.C.) was found with a Pocket Scanner, Model #11770, in the Kidron Valley between the Mount of Olives and the Eastern Gate, the ground over which Jesus walked many times. The coin is a denarius (K.J.V. "penny"). The denarius is mentioned in Matthew 22:19; Matthew: 20:2; Luke 10:35; and John 12:5. The denarius coin of Tiberius was tribute required of every Israelite at the time of Jesus. Photo Courtesy of Dr. Richard Fales.

Figure 26-2: These buttons were located on a battlefield in the eastern United States by Dr. Richard Fales. Photo courtesy Bob Grant.

420

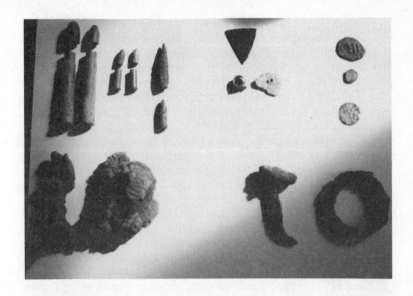

Figure 26-3 and Figure 26-4: Our thanks to Bob Livingston, of Jerusalem, Israel for sending these photographs of his valuable finds. In the top photograph, are bullets and casings, Byzantine coins, various pieces of shrapnel and a Roman nail and ring made of iron. In the lower photograph, are some coins he found that date to the Roman and Byzantine periods. Mr. Livingston is working closely with Israeli archaeologists at several locations near Jerusalem. He has reported pheneomenonal results.

persons. Kent decided to do a little exploring, not only by digging an exploratory trench or two, but by using a metal detector to see what he could find. The results of his work are related in issue number eight of the SEARCHER publication. See PUBLICATIONS following the Appendixes.

He found, with his metal detector, horse shoes, cartridges, weapons, axe heads, stove and other appliance pieces, weapon fragments, kitchen utensils, thimbles, square nails, harness buckles, hinges, single tree parts, wagon parts, scissors, garment buckles and numerous other items in use during the 1880s and 1890s. During the course of his work, he proved the value of the metal detector at historical site investigations. Of course, he spent many hard hours excavating various parts of the area, cleaning and preserving finds, drawing maps and sketches (Figure 26-5) and recording every detail of his discoveries. The metal detector was, simply, an important tool that he used, quite successfully, in his work. Kent's research site was assigned Texas State Site Number 41PP307.

Several years ago I made a metal detector survey of an Indian site. The ground was covered with arrowhead flint chips. Many holes had been pounded into the flat rocks. Corn had been ground, time after time, slowly but surely making the holes deeper. I was

Figure 26-5: Kent Ubil researched and excavated a North Texas farm site. He dug several exploratory trenches and spent considerable time using his metal detector. He found horseshoes, cartridges, weapons, axeheads, stove and other appliance pieces, weapon fragments, kitchen utensils, thimbles, square nails, harness buckles, hinges, single tree parts, wagon parts, scissors, garment buckles, and numerous other items in use during the 1880s and 1890s. During the course of his work, he proved the value of the metal detector at historical site investigations. He proved the metal detector is an important archaeological and historical research tool.

curious about the age of the site. I scanned the area for three hours. Not one piece of metal did I find. Obviously, the site was very old.

In West Texas there are many adobe ruins. The settlers who lived in the area were constantly fighting the Indians. One day I scanned the inside walls of what was apparently the main building or the home where the settlers lived. I found only one metal object in the walls—a pre-civil War era lead projectile. The projectile was in the wall immediately across the room from the door. Assuming that the bullet was fired from a gun outside the building, I stood near the wall and sighted through the door. Approximately thirty-five yards away was the corner of a crumbled wall that was probably a storage or work area. It seemed logical to me, that sometime prior to, or during the Civil War era, someone, probably an Indian, fired his gun while standing within the protection of the out building. That particular bullet traveled through a window in the door—or through an open door—and struck the wall on the opposite side of the room. This was a very small bit of discovered historical evidence, no doubt, but, nevertheless, a moment of history brought into the future.

I received the following letter, the contents of which are self explanatory, from Jim Paquette of Negaunee, Michigan.

Mr. Charles Garrett
Garrett Metal Detectors
2814 National Drive
Garland, Texas 75041

Dear Mr. Garrett,
I am writing this letter to inform you of an exciting and important discovery I made this past summer.

While involved in an archaeological survey in search of possible habitation sites of the ancient "Old Copper" culture Indians, I hit a "needle in a haystack" and discovered an extremely rare habitation/quarry/workshop area. The site, which shows evidence of extreme antiquity, has thus far produced an archaeological sampling of copper, quartzite, and flint artifacts. Although I am keeping the location of this site under wraps pending further extensive excavations, I have contacted some university archaeologists here in Michigan of this discovery, and needless to say, it has caused quite a stir. Currently, I am awaiting word from the State Archaeologist, John Halsey, on the identification of some of the artifacts.

The reason I am writing to you about this discovery is that the site was uncovered through the use of my Garrett Electronics ADS VLF Deepseeker. The site is located in a wooded area which made it extremely difficult, if not impossible, to locate

423

any signs of prehistoric habitation areas using traditional surface inspection survey methods. However, with the detector, I was able to "see" through the forest floor cover, and, consequently, I discovered this most important site.

My initial discovery was a buried cache of copper artifacts which has been buried eons ago by ancient Archaic Indians. This initial find lead to further discoveries of more copper artifacts including projectile points, awls, and numerous worked pieces. Sample excavations of the area produced an assemblage of quartzite artifacts which may prove to be among the oldest ever uncovered in this region of the Great Lakes area. The finding of these quartzite weapons and tools lead to the additional discovery of nearby surface deposits of high-grade quartzite from which the material for the manufacture of the artifacts was quarried.

Preliminary indications are that this site may be one of the most important archaeological discoveries ever made in the state of Michigan. You can be proud, Mr. Garrett, that this discovery was made with one of your detectors. I will keep you posted on further developments.

Incidentally, you may have read some of my articles on treasure and relic hunting. They have appeared in TREASURE, LOST TREASURE, and WESTERN & EASTERN TREASURES magazines under my real name, as well as my pen name, Nick Roberts. (See "Furnace Town Treasures Found," by Nick Roberts, TREASURE MAGAZINE, May, 1984, for example.)

Sincerely yours,

Jim Paquette

Thank you, Mr. Paquette, for sharing this remarkable find with MODERN METAL DETECTORS readers. Certainly, your work and discovery is an inspiration for all of us to work with archaeological groups in their quest to learn more of our great history. We look forward to reading more about your future work.

METAL DETECTOR APPLICATIONS

Archaeological and historical researchers can justify the metal detector as an important tool because of the many ways metal detectors can aid them in their work. An initial survey of a given land or underwater site can help locate all metal items down several feet deep. This pinpointing of metal objects can help the archaeologist in determining the scope, layout and occupancy characteristics of the site.

The metal detector can help locate and trace buildings and structural foundations by locating window and door hinges and other metal construction items. As mud walls "melt" into the ground, metal items also fall to the ground, thus, marking the location of building features for the archaeologist.

A site can be scanned for metal artifacts of all types or just non-ferrous, high conductivity, metal items such as items made of copper, brass, aluminum, silver and gold. Since these non-ferrous metals do not corrode, they may bear a visible manufacturer's name, date or other valuable research information.

A complete detector scan of an area, with flags placed at each target location, helps in determining the areas most likely to be productive.

Quick dating of a site can be made from coins (Figure 26-6) found with metal detectors. I found numerous coins, Circa 400 BC, at a site in southern Europe. Metal detectors can be the "last" tool used by archaeologists at dig sites. When "ground zero" has been reached, the metal detector will sniff out buried caches, relics and other metal objects that were hidden in the ground by the occupants.

Metal detectors can help determine when true "ground zero" has been reached. A scan can be made of the ground and from a study of metal objects found, it can be determined if the original ground level has been reached.

A quick metal detector survey of a "suspect" area can "prove" the site is the one historical field researchers wish to investigate, and the same investigation can prove the site is NOT the one to investigate.

In all communities, past and present, the patterns of refuse disposal can be determined. In prior years, town occupants tended to discard their refuse near the back door, the front door or in any near by depression, preferably in natural erosion areas. The great attraction for archaeologists to these areas is that these sites are the deliberate depository for relics and artifacts of the day (Figures 26-7, 26-8 and 26-9.) Dating can be very precise as these depositories often filled quickly.

The metal detector is the perfect tool to use in locating these time capsules. Often, metal of all kinds wound up in these dumps. Because of the vast quantity of metal, the dumps can be located to great depths. The two-box, Depth Multiplier attachment is the perfect accessory to use in locating these sites. About all that is necessary, is for the archaeologist to walk, at a moderate speed, over the ground in a grid fashion. The metal detector will search deeply and will perfectly outline the shape of the depository.

As important as refuse depositories are, their importance can be overshadowed by the results that can come from excavation of

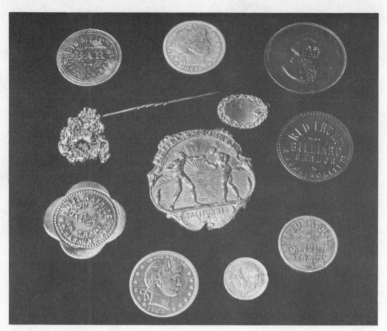

Figure 26-6: Searching ghost towns and historical sites with detectors can yield amazing results, as shown in this photograph. Roy Gene Rolls and Ray D. Rolls spend much of their time searching sites in America's northwest. The coins, tokens, the gold nugget stickpin and other items tell a lot about the history of several sites where they have successfully used their detectors. Photo courtesy Ray D. Rolls.

Figure 26-7: Gary Fuller of Forest Ranch, California shares with MODERN METAL DETEC-TOR readers, several of the unique and valuable finds he made at ghost town sites. Relics such as this tell a great deal about the life and times of the occupants of long-deserted ghost towns.

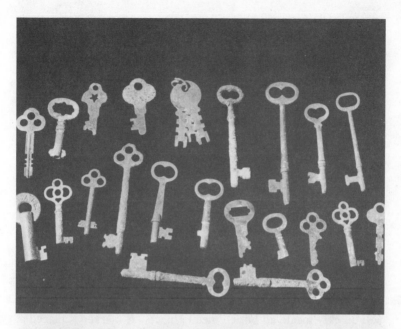

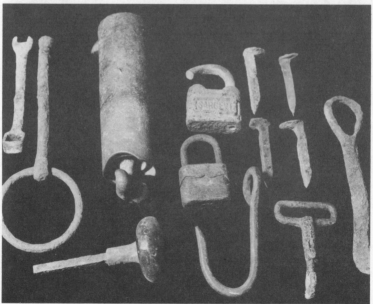

Figure 26-8 and 26-9: Again, thanks to Ray D. Rolls for these two photographs which show many unusual finds that he and his brother, Roy, have made at northern California ghost towns. These photographs show a very small portion of the many types of keys and locks, and other relics they have accumulated over the years.

427

ancient outhouses or privies. Many times, outhouses prove to be storehouses of many artifacts. The majority of the artifacts will be non-metallic, but often, considerable metal trash is mixed in with everything else. Since a metal detector "sees" all-metal items within the detector's detection pattern, a few small items can look like one large target to the metal detector. Consequently, outhouse refuse pits can be detected quite deeply. The same scanning techniques used when locating refuse dumps should be used when scanning for outhouse pits.

RESCUE ARCHAEOLOGY

Rescue archaeology, sometimes called "Salvage Archaeology," is a technique archaeologists use during emergency situations when a site is soon to be covered by the rising waters of a new lake or by the construction of buildings, highways and railroads. This technique is also used at canal excavation sites.

In situations like these, archaeologists realize that only a small fraction of the historical relics can be saved, but, even a small part is better than nothing. Thus, compromises are made to recover, as quickly as possible, relics from the site. The metal detector is just the tool to help the archaeologist in his plight. The metal detector will quickly locate all buried metal objects. A marker is placed at each location and a team of people can come behind the detector operators to recover the detected items. One metal detector can keep numerous "recovery" teams busy.

Using Rescue Archaeology, much knowledge of the history of a site can be obtained that, otherwise, would be forever lost. A community can be rewarded with the knowledge of a portion of the history of their ancestors. Educational museums can be established for the townspeople.

METAL DETECTOR RECOMMENDATIONS

The most versatile and deep seeking of them all, the VLF MANUAL-ADJUST VLF with a full range of accessories, is the recommended metal detection equipment for the archaeologist. The Ground Elimination all-metal mode is the primary mode and the most useful for the archaeologist. Often, every single metallic item, regardless of its size and metallic content, is to be recovered— and sometimes to great depths.

Trash Elimination is sometimes specified because only the more important non-ferrous metals are to be located and recovered.

Various size searchcoils are often required. The three-inch to four-inch diameter sizes are important because of their selective nature in high trash areas, especially when only non-ferrous metals are wanted. The general purpose size, the seven-inch to eight-inch diameter searchcoils, will be used most often. Larger diameter searchcoils are often needed when more deeply buried objects are searched for such as money caches below ground level.

The two-box Depth Multiplier is an important accessory because sites are often covered with many feet of soil, and archaeologists need all the detection depth they can get to recover large objects.

Underwater searchcoils are needed if the work involves underwater scanning. As an example, at Civil War battlefield sites, relics are often found in water. In Louisiana cannon balls have been found in wet creek beds. A large quantity of twenty pound Parrott shells were found where soldiers had either dumped them in a creek or a supply wagon had fallen in the water, dumping its ammunition cargo.

Normal scanning procedures, the same as used in coin, cache and relic hunting, will give the greatest efficiency. Plastic, non-metal marker flags are recommended so that they will not interfere with nearby metal detector operation or give false signals that would confuse the recovery team's detection (pinpointing) efforts.

Recovery teams can come immediately behind the deep seeking metal detectors, or they can come later as time permits the retrieval of objects. Recovery teams will be the most efficient if they have their own metal detectors. It is of the utmost importance that objects not be damaged in the recovery process. Consequently, the person digging must occasionally use a detector in the process of precisely relocating, pinpointing and recovering targets. A Pocket Scanner type metal detector (Figure 25-15) is recommended because of its portable, easy to maneuver size. These instruments do an excellent job of pinpointing objects. While the main, deeper seeking instruments are used when scanning the ground on the initial search, the recovery teams can be digging targets more quickly and carefully with the small hand-held detectors providing the signals needed for careful retrieval.

429

CHAPTER 26 QUESTIONS

1. As with many other professional groups, metal detectors are valuable _____ of the archaeologist and historical field researcher.

2. The role of metal detectors in archaeology is analogous to the role that metal detectors play in _____ _____ .

3. Metal detectors are of no value in scanning tombs.
   True _____   False _____

4. Since only cartridge shells and other artifacts were located at the Custer battlefield site, and no treasure was found, metal detectors are no value whatsoever in research such as this.
   True _____   False _____

5. A metal detector can "prove," without much digging, that a particular site is the one researchers wish to investigate further. A metal detector can also "prove" a particular site is _____ the one to investigate.

6. The finding of metal objects can define the perimeters of a ground site, the same as found metal objects can define the perimeters of _____ .

7. If, at an excavated site, a cache of coins is found below ground level, that find serves to prove that the present ground level is not "ground zero."
   True _____   False _____

8. The recommended type metal detector for the archaeologist is the deep seeking, versatile, MANUAL-ADJUST _____ .

9. In shallow, heavy metal trash areas, when only non-ferrous metal objects are to be searched for, large searchcoils are the preferred size to use.
   True _____   False _____

10. To speed up the recovery of detected targets, and to lessen the likelihood of target damage by the recovery team, a Pocket _____ type metal detector should be used.

Each of the 10 questions answered correctly is worth 10 points. Perfect score is 100. Answers given in Appendix 2.

CHAPTER 27

The Metal Detector's Place In The World Of The Handicapped

Of all the many ways the metal detector owner can be of service to his or her community, working with the handicapped is the most rewarding. Since President John F. Kennedy's Mentally Retarded Awareness Program of the early 1960s, the public has striven to recognize and improve the world of the handicapped. Metal detector users in every community can do their part.

One of the desires of blind citizens is to participate in outdoor activities and sports. Metal detecting is an excellent outdoor hobby. Roy Sexton of Grand Island, New York, is a leader in the move- ment to introduce the blind to the world of coin and treasure hunting. For many years, Roy, his wife Pat, and their son Peter, were active treasure hunters. They travelled widely enjoying their hobby. They rarely missed a treasure hunt and have travelled as far south as Texas to attend competition treasure hunts and other metal detecting activities.

Recently, Roy lost most of his sight. In this strange, new world, Roy diligently fought to maintain a normal life. Of the many activities he pursues, metal detecting continues to occupy much of his time. He finds great enjoyment and satisfaction in being able to continue to find coins and treasure with his metal detector. During his training at a blind school, Roy made friends with many people. Because of the happiness he experienced when detecting, he suggested to his school instructors that his fellow classmates might also enjoy detecting.

His instructors agreed, and Ms. Judith Engberg of the Blind Association of western New York set up a program. Several stu- dents enrolled in a vocational exploration program employing metal detectors. Roy Sexton volunteered to take the students out to local school yards where they explored with detectors for two hours each day, once a week for four consecutive weeks. Roy instructed the students in the proper use of the metal detectors. This school is believed to be the first formal metal detector school for the blind (Figure 27-1).

In a letter Roy wrote to me, he said he realized great satisfac- tion in helping these students do something new. The course proved that with perseverance, metal detecting could be a hobby for everyone. Roy related that the students enjoyed their new

431

Figure 27-1: Instructor, Roy Sexton (right) and his students of the Blind Association of Western New York, prepare to scan this yard as part of their vocational exploration program employing metal detectors. As part of the program, the students worked with detectors two hours a day for several days. Roy instructed the students in the proper use of metal detectors. This school is believed to be the first formal metal detector school for the blind. Photo courtesy Roy Sexton.

hobby very much (Figure 27-2). They were thrilled at being able to find a penny or even a bottlecap! He believes that metal detecting classes will continue to be taught at the school.

MENTAL RETARDATION

Mental retardation can be severe or minor. Almost regardless of the degree of impairment, metal detecting programs can be developed that will provide much enjoyment for the mentally handicapped and help them to in still greater confidence in themselves and their abilities.

In a Utah school for the retarded, teachers developed a special metal detector Easter program. The teachers acquired a quantity of chocolate Easter eggs that were wrapped in conductive foil. Several Pocket Scanners were obtained for the students to use in this historical Easter egg hunt. A group of students, who were selected to be the first to use the detectors, were taught how to use the instruments. The other students then hid Easter eggs in their hats and pockets of their clothing.

The searchers then began scanning for the chocolate eggs. The searchers were permitted to keep all the eggs they found. Then, the searchers exchanged places with the "hiders." The teachers could hardly believe the excitement that this most unusual hunt generated among the children. It was certainly one of the most enjoyable things the children had ever done.

432

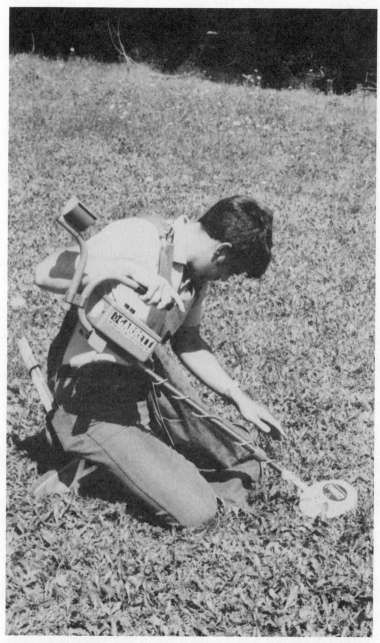

Figure 27-2: Roy Sexton related the students of the Blind Association of Western New York thoroughly enjoy their new hobby of metal detecting. They are thrilled at being able to find a penny or even a bottlecap! Photo courtesy Roy Sexton.

Various other metal detecting programs have made history at schools for the mentally retarded. Treasure "maps" were placed in metal containers. The containers were buried or hidden at various locations. Working in pairs, or small groups, the kids began their search with metal detectors. The teachers put the kids on the right trail and helped them find the first treasure map. When the kids dug up the container and found a map inside, they were very excited. This first map gave instructions on how to find a second map. It was then up to the kids to search, on their own, for the second container. Slowly, but surely, the kids found all the maps and eventually found the treasure which was theirs to keep. Who can doubt that these kids enjoyed this treasure hunt as much as chocolate pie, a ride on a school bus, or a trip to a movie!

At all schools for the mentally retarded, as many activities and facilities as possible are provided for the kids. Canned soft drinks and candy vending machines are provided in canteens and cafeterias. The kids think it is a grand thing to have their own money and be able to go to the vending machines to get their own candy and drinks. Providing metal detecting coin hunts is a perfect way to give these kids a real fun day by letting them "earn" their own canteen money. Within a designated area, coins are buried at shallow depths (about one inch). The kids are given preliminary instructions on the use of metal detectors and retrieving coins with spoons or other non-dangerous digging tools. Then, in pairs, the kids are turned loose in the planted area.

If you think these kids are not capable of enjoying or understanding what they are doing, you must reshape your thinking. The mentally retarded of all degrees are just like you and me; we are all like kids when it comes to finding buried treasure. Summer heat or winter cold doesn't slow these kids down. And, the finding and recovery of treasure is only half the fun; the trip to the canteen rounds out a perfect day for them!

THE DISABLED AND THE HANDICAPPED

The disabled, including those on crutches and confined to wheelchairs, enjoy using metal detectors as well. They gain further confidence when they are successful in finding treasure with their metal detectors. The elderly, who are handicapped in that they cannot pursue more active hobbies, are finding that metal detectors give them just the right amount of exercise they need. They can work at their own speed. Many have reported that coin hunting is a sport that they wish they had learned about at a much earlier age. Metal detecting is a very healthy and body improving activity! My father, who is in his 80s, still enjoys finding treasure!

Over the years, I have seen many disabled people using metal detectors. I often stand in amazement when I see these people go about their metal detecting activities in spite of their handicaps. One young lady especially stands out in my mind (Figure 27-3). She enjoys her hobby of coin hunting even though she has to use crutches to get around. She and her husband came by the factory and explained their dilemma. She wondered if we could attach a searchcoil to one of her crutches. If we could, she would not have to hold both the detector and her crutch in her hand.

We installed a searchcoil mounting bracket on the lower end of one crutch. We positioned the searchcoil so that as she swung the crutch, the searchcoil moved over the ground. We installed a detector hipmount kit so that she could carry the control housing on her belt.

Sometime later, she and her husband came back to the factory and related how the searchcoil and housing arrangement allowed her to spend lots of enjoyable time pursuing one of her favorite hobbies. Needless to say, everyone at the factory experienced great satisfaction knowing that we had been able, in this small way, to help her.

HANDICAPPED AWARENESS PROGRAMS

The Boy Scouts have always been active in handicapped awareness programs. At meetings, outings, and even International Jamborees, they hold handicapped awareness programs. They blindfold themselves and, for a certain period of time, perform all activities that blind persons perform.

The Scouts sit in wheelchairs and play basketball and other games in order to get the true "feel" of the handicapped.

One group of Utah scout leaders suggested the scouts go on a metal detector treasure hunt. The scouts thought that would be easy until their leaders placed blindfolds over their eyes. Then, the situation changed! But, that is what handicapped awareness programs are all about, to give a first-hand idea of what it is like to be handicapped.

In writing this chapter, my goal is to bring to YOUR AWARENESS what YOU can accomplish by developing and sponsoring metal detecting and other programs for the handicapped and disabled in your community. These kids and adults have feelings and desires just like you and I. Their problem is that they must depend upon others to help them do the things they want to do...the things that you and I take for granted. Why don't you devote some of your free time to help the less fortunate people enjoy life a little more? Is there any greater Found Treasure?

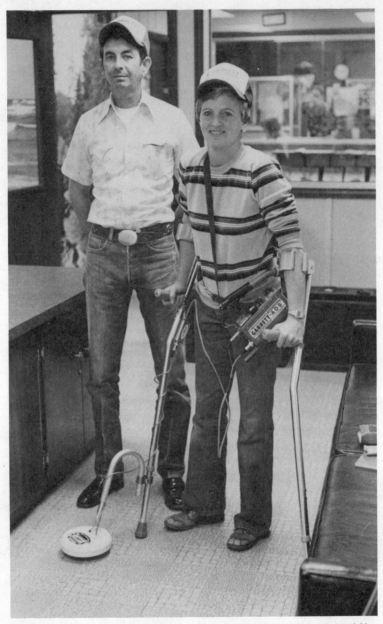

Figure 27-3: This young lady is now well equipped to continue her coin hunting activities. Employees at Garrett Electronics installed a metal detector searchcoil on one of her crutches. She carries the detector control housing on a sling-mount. Later, she and her husband came back to the factory and related how the searchcoil and housing arrangement allowed her to spend lots of enjoyable time pursuing one of her favorite hobbies.

CHAPTER 27 QUESTIONS

1. Of all the many ways the metal detector owner can be of service to his or her community, working in the field of the handicapped is the most _____ .

2. _____ was the instructor of what was probably the first formal metal detector school for the blind.

3. Even though the mentally retarded may not be able to understand how metal detectors work, they can still enjoy using metal detectors to find treasure.

     True _____   False _____

4. Aside from the fun that everyone, regardless of age, can have when treasure hunting, the metal detecting hobby is a very _____ activity.

5. The activity is called _____ _____ when Scouts blindfold themselves and ride around in wheelchairs, while they play at sports and go about everyday activities.

6. How many handicapped and disabled groups in your community can you think of who might enjoy and benefit from the activity of metal detecting?

7. Name at least three forms of "treasure hunting" with metal detectors that mentally retarded children and adults would enjoy.

Each of the 5 questions answered correctly is worth 20 points. Perfect score is 100. No credit is given for questions 6 and 7 as these are designed for group discussion. Answers given in Appendix 2.

CHAPTER 28

The Metal Detector Dealer

The majority of detectors are sold through dealers, most of whom are honest and knowledgeable and will correctly guide you in the selection of a detector. Hopefully, after reading this chapter you will be able to find a good dealer and will stick with him. The rewards will be yours.

All dealers must make a profit in order to stay in business. There are dealers who do not place sole priority on making money, but also upon serving the customer. These dealers know that customers are their reason for existence. They know that a satisfied, well-trained customer will be the main reason they will still be in business tomorrow. The greatest number of sales result from customer referrals and word of mouth. It's just human nature to want to deal with a store or company that treated you or someone you know quite well, and gave them good service.

It gives a person a good feeling to know that he has been truthfully advised about a product. It is equally disheartening to learn that, after you have just spent several hundred dollars, you didn't get the best detector possible, or you find it about one-half as capable of performing as you were told it was. Select your dealer wisely and reap the rewards.

You will probably benefit from buying from a factory trained metal detector dealer. You may *not* get what you want if you buy from a mass merchandising outlet. I'm not saying these people aren't honest, what I am saying is that the salesmen may not be sufficiently knowledgeable about detectors. They may barely know one end of the detector from another. Certainly there are good metal detectors being sold in merchandising stores, but if you want to learn about a product go to a professional for advice. You may save a lot of money purchasing a detector through a bargain outlet but the amount you save may soon be lost when you begin to use an inadequate detector and/or you didn't get adequate training.

If you have a local dealer, he's the man you should start with. If there is more than one detector dealer in your area, visit them all. Contact detector manufacturers and ask them to recommend one or more dealers in your area.

As a rule, when you find a good dealer, in all probability he will fit a certain "mold" and will have many credits to his name. Select a dealer who is factory or seminar trained and who has one or more graduation certificates posted on his wall. It's true that no one can learn all there is to know about metal detectors by simply attending seminars. However, it is a good indication that the dealer who goes to the time and expense of attending factory seminars has his customers at heart. Generally, the trained dealer is more closely attuned to the factory and will be more knowledgeable about the latest detectors, accessories and detector application techniques. Detectors are improving at a dramatic rate and only the conscientious dealer, who makes an effort through study, can keep up with the advances.

Many small dealers cannot afford to travel great distances to attend factory seminars (Figures 28-1, 28-2, 28-3 and 28-4). These same dealers, however, can be as well-trained as the factory-trained dealer. Those who spend lots of time in the field searching and have learned their equipment have the knowledge to teach you. So, try to select, first and foremost, the dealer who is field knowledgeable and can (and will) teach you the basic ''how-to-use'' knowledge about the detector you are purchasing. The dealer who gets into the field and uses his equipment is the man who knows more about that equipment and how to use it. Of course, there are many aspects of treasure hunting such as coin hunting, prospecting and, relic hunting. If a dealer specializes in water searching, he may not have a lot of experience in land coin hunting but at least he has some field experience and can guide you much better than one who has no field training.

Figure 28-1: Dealers from around the United States regularly attend Garrett Electronics' dealer seminars. Continuing classes are held throughout the seminar. The dealers learn about new equipment and the latest metal detector operational techniques. They look forward to these regular seminars as it gives them an opportunity, not only to learn about the latest metal detectors, but also to meet with their friends and fellow dealers.

439

Figure 28-2: As a regular part of Garrett's dealer training seminars, the dealers enjoy their own treasure hunt. Coins, and prize tokens are buried in this field near the company building. When the gun sounds it's a mad scramble as the dealers furiously scan to recover the buried objects. It's a fun time, but yet gives the dealers one more opportunity to learn to increase their expertise in using their equipment.

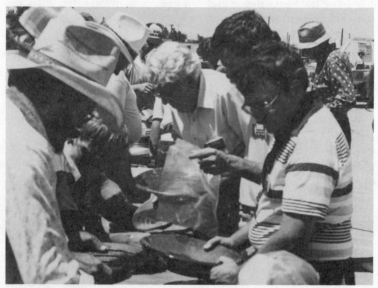

Figure 28-3: At Garrett seminars classes, subjects other than metal detecting are taught. Here you see the dealers thoroughly enjoying training in the use of the Garrett "Gravity Trap" gold panning equipment. There is real gold in that trough and the dealers are enjoying every minute of it. Many Garrett dealers who live in precious metal districts have become successful prospectors in their own right.

Figure 28-4: It's not all work at Garrett dealer seminars. Here, the dealers line up for chow. Throughout the seminar period, meals are served and various other group activities are held for the benefit of the dealers and their families.

Perhaps the greatest problem concerning the detector user is lack of adequate initial training. If a dealer takes the time to train you in the use of your equipment, he's concerned about you and wants you to be successful. Time is money for you and the dealer. If he takes his time to train you, in all likelihood he will be a full, or near full, retail priced dealer. In order to stay in business a dealer must make money. He cannot show a profit if he discounts his equipment and then spends hours training his customers. Some dealers offer detector training schools, often free, while other dealers charge up to fifty dollars or more for training seminars. If a dealer charges for a training seminar ask him for the names of half a dozen people who have taken the seminar; call them and get their opinion. Find out how long the seminar lasts, how many total hours of instruction there are and the percentage of hands-on training that you will get. Seminars should provide up to fifty percent hands-on training.

A good dealer is one who won't destructively criticize another brand or another man's product. He may be very quick to point out the good features of the product that he recommends and he may be very quick to tell you he believes his brand is the best for you and give you reasons why.

Keep in mind that there is no "one best" detector. There are a lot of "best" detectors and not just the one that happens to be hanging in a dealer's showroom. The one you want is the one best suited for your needs.

The dealer who downgrades another brand, or another man's detector, may be the dealer you should avoid. It's all a dealer can do to learn everything possible about one or two brands of detectors. No dealer has time to evaluate every brand. To adequately and completely analyze a given detector under all environmental conditions, and under all situations, requires countless hours of testing. Few have that kind of time. Even if a fault were found with a detector, it could be quite simply the fault of that one particular instrument and it could be that the manufacturer has learned of that fault and has taken steps to correct it in future production. If that particular detector is faulted and destructive criticism gets out, it could seriously and unjustly damage the reputation of that manufacturer and/or that particular product. This is one reason why the various treasure hunting magazines should never negatively and critically analyze the brands of detectors which they field test. In their product reviews, they point out the detector's good features and highlights, they leave the final judgment up to the person thinking of buying the product. For them to negatively criticize the product would be wrong and certainly an unjust thing to do. When a dealer begins to destructively criticize another man's product, perhaps you should walk out the door and leave him talking.

A good brand, high quality product sells itself. Word of mouth is a key thing for which to look.

The dealer who says that the brand he is pushing is the best and all others are no good, may be the man who either owns part of the manufacturing company or is a distributor and gets a kickback on each detector sold in his area, perhaps he makes more money when he sells the particular brand of detector that he is promoting. There is nothing wrong with making money but when it comes to untruths, YOU LOSE!

AUTHORIZED DEALERS

An authorized dealer is an individual or retail outlet authorized by a manufacturer to sell that manufacturer's metal detectors (Figure 28-5).

Check your local dealer's bulletin board for his Authorized Dealer certificate. Each manufacturer should supply their dealers with just such a certificate. A dealer may be an authorized dealer for several brands of detectors but may bootleg one or more brands into the store. Authorized dealers may be better trained than unauthorized ones. You have the full protection of the manufacturer if a product needs repair or if you need a particular service, when you deal with an authorized dealer. The authorized dealer

Figure 28-5: When the World's Fair was held in Spokane, Washington, Garrett dealers, Harry and Lucile Bowen leased this sign on a major thoroughfare. It proved to be a perfect way to introduce metal detecting to the World's Fair visitors.

may sell fresher stock. A manufacturer's warranties may not cover their products purchased from unauthorized dealers.

Most manufacturers feel that the dealer is the strongest link between them and the customer. Some manufacturers place customers on their mailing lists. This regular contact keeps customers alert as to what is going on in the field, including new products and accessories, and it provides new operating tips and procedures that could be of benefit to that manufacturer's product users.

BASIC GUIDELINES

Be open with the dealer you visit. Explain as best you can what you intend to do with the detector.

Tell the dealer how much you prefer to spend.

Don't pretend to know more about detectors than you really do.

Don't be afraid to ask questions. Definitely expect good answers.

When you ask a question, listen intently to the answer; if you don't understand it, say so.

Ask the dealer what detector or detectors he uses.

Ask why.

Ask what are the limitations of the detector recommended.

Ask about warranties and guarantees.

And, ask about training and service after the purchase.

443

AFTER YOUR PURCHASE

After you purchase your detector, make it a habit of staying in contact with your dealer. Stop by occasionally and talk with him. Let him know what you are doing, if you are having problems, etc. Keep in mind that a satisfied customer is the best advertising a dealer can have (Figure 28-6).

Figure 28-6: In Australia's famed Western Australia gold regions, the author could not resist the temptation to sign up this kangaroo dealer. Obviously, the kangaroo is enjoying himself. Dealers know that a satisfied customer is the best advertising a dealer can have.

CHAPTER 28 QUESTIONS

1. The greatest majority of metal detectors are sold through retail
_____ .

2. Most dealers know that satisfied, well-trained, customers will be the main reason why tomorrow the dealer will still be in _____ .

3. The greatest number of metal detector sales result from customer referrals and word of mouth.
True _____   False _____

4. A factory or seminar-trained dealer is one who (select the answers that apply): (A) may be better qualified to recommend the best detector for you; (B) may be better trained to instruct you in the proper use of your metal detector; (C) may be more concerned about the success of his customers than a dealer who has not attended seminars; (D) may be more up-to-date on the latest equipment and metal detecting techniques. (Each correct answer is worth 3 points)

5. Perhaps the greatest problem concerning the detector user is the lack of adequate initial training.
True _____   False _____

6. If a dealer takes the time to train you in the use of your equipment, then he is concerned about you and wants you to be _____ .

7. The ideal metal detector training seminar provides approximately fifty percent hands-on training and fifty percent classroom instruction.
True _____   False _____

8. Since it is easy to evaluate all brands of detectors, you can believe the dealer who tells you that all other brands of detectors are no good except the brand he is selling.
True _____   False _____

9. A good brand, high quality product sells _____ .

10. An authorized metal detector dealer is: (A) one who is licensed to sell metal detectors; (B) one who is taking courses in metal detector use; (C) one who sells several different brands of detectors; (D) one who is authorized by the manufacturer to sell that manufacturer's metal detectors.

11. Most manufacturers feel that the dealer is the strongest link between them and the _____ .

12. Keep in mind that a _____ customer is the best advertising a dealer can have.

Question 4 is worth 12 points when answered correctly. Each of the other questions answered correctly is worth 8 points. Perfect score is 100. Answers given in Appendix 2.

Maintenance and Field Repair

Sooner or later a detector being used in the field may fail to perform as it should. If that ever happens, don't despair; the chances are about fifty/fifty the problem can be discovered and remedied in the field.

As simple and plain as it might be, the most likely problem you'll encounter is dead batteries. For unexplained reasons, treasure hunting trips are called off, people go into the state of near shock, and detectors are shipped back to the factory and to service centers for repair, when all they need is fresh batteries.

One lady at a treasure hunt in Oklahoma City brought her detector to me and said, "My detector won't work and now my whole trip is ruined." I discovered that the batteries in her detector were the same ones that were installed by the factory when the detector was built four years earlier! New batteries "corrected" her problem!

So, if your detector fails, CHECK YOUR BATTERIES! Always carry along a fresh set on every hunt. Place these into your detector and see if the problem is corrected. Some batteries will, on rare occasions, show a good state of charge yet not be capable of current delivery. A high internal battery impedance can develop that prevents the battery from delivering power.

Some battery check circuits check all batteries. Some only check the batteries that power the detection circuits. If your detector has no means of checking the "audio" battery, simply continue using the detector until the audio drops to an unacceptable level and then change the batteries.

Make sure you insert new batteries correctly and they test satisfactorily. Give your detector an extremely thorough visual inspection. Check battery terminals for tightness. Carefully examine the detector by looking through any doors and portals, and observe every component for damage. Look for pinched wires that may have occurred when you last changed batteries. When panels are replaced, detector wires can be pinched, setting up a potential problem that can result in failure in the field. If your detector is factory sealed, don't open it unless you accept the risk of having your warranty voided.

BATTERY CHARACTERISTICS
There are four types of batteries you can use in your metal

detector. These are carbon zinc, heavy duty, alkaline, and nickel cadmium (ni-cad).

CARBON ZINC: They cost the least and deliver current the shortest length of time. They operate the most efficiently at temperatures from thirty-two to above one hundred degrees Fahrenheit. They are more prone to leak corrosive acid than alkaline and nicads. Their performance during their active life is satisfactory.

HEAVY DUTY (zinc chloride): This type is generally more expensive than carbon zinc but will give additional life. They are more prone to leak corrosive acid than alkaline and nicads. Their performance during their active life is satisfactory.

ALKALINE (alkaline manganese): They cost more than carbon zinc and heavy duty types and give considerably more current for a much longer period of time. They last longer in storage and are less susceptible to leakage. Their performance is better in extreme temperatures. Their use is probably cheaper in the long run than carbon zinc and heavy duty types. Their performance during their active life is satisfactory.

NI-CAD RECHARGEABLES (nickel cadmium): They can be recharged and used over and over hundreds of times. Manufacturers claim they can be recharged one thousand times. They are more expensive than the above three types. Longer life and best performance can be obtained if they are used often and recharged immediately at room temperature. They will take a ''set'' if repeatedly used the same length of time. For example, if repeatedly used one hour per day, and then recharged, the nicads will take a ''set'' and one hour is the maximum length they will deliver current. It's good to often let the batteries run down completely before recharge. At least once every three months completely discharge and recharge to restore full charge. This cycle will extend ni-cad life. Ni-cads will power a given circuit only forty to fifty percent as long as carbon zinc. For example, if carbon zinc batteries power your detector twenty hours, ni-cads will power it for eight to ten hours. Since ni-cad operating voltage is less than carbon zinc, ni-cads will read lower on detector battery check meters and lights. Their performance during their active life is satisfactory.

SPEAKER CONTAMINATION

Oftentimes contamination such as dirt, black magnetic sand, small metal shavings and other things can fall down into the searchcoil cover and speaker. This can cause erratic sounds that are very annoying and give the appearance of a faulty detector. It is easy to clean out a searchcoil cover but if magnetic particles are sticking to the speaker cone, turn the detector upside down so that the particles can fall out of the detector. Turn on the detector and adjust it to make a sound. Sometimes, the vibrating effect of the speaker tone can loosen particles that have become magnetically attached to the speaker cone. A small magnet may pull the particles out.

CABLE CONNECTOR INSPECTION

If you carry along a set of small tools, you can do a little further investigation if you hear erratic sounds when you lightly twist the searchcoil cable where it goes into the cable connector. Remove the connector cable clamp screws. With the cable clamp removed, visually inspect the wiring. Rotate the wire *slightly,* if necessary, to test for broken connections. These broken connections can be repaired on the spot if you have a small soldering iron. Of course, in making corrections of this type you should have some knowledge of electronics and soldering. Then, as soon as possible have a reputable repair technician examine the repair job.

TESTING SEARCHCOILS AND CABLE

Erratic operations and no audio can be the fault of the searchcoil and/or cable.

Pick up the detector, turn it on, grasp the searchcoil and gently twist it back and forth. Gently pull on the cable where it goes into the searchcoil; sometimes wiring breaks loose at this point. Should this occur, you may find that you can press the searchcoil cable down, or tape the cable, in a certain way that will cause the detector to operate, with care you can continue scanning. Of course, you would need to eventually make permanent repairs, but this, on occasion, has allowed treasure hunters to continue their work and not have to call off an entire trip. You could also try another searchcoil. If the detector now works, you will know you have a faulty searchcoil.

INTERMITTENT SOUNDS

If this occurs, check the battery connections. In fact, it's a good idea to occasionally check these connections to make sure they are tight. With an eraser or some similar tool, carefully push the female connector clips toward center so that when the male mates up there is a tight connection. Don't short out the battery. Make sure that none of your batteries are corroded. Sometimes, batteries will leak a small amount of battery acid, creating a small amount of errosion on the contacts. Visual examination will reveal corrosion.

NON-DETECTION

If a coin, lying on top of the ground, produces no detection, make sure you have your detector correctly adjusted in the ground elimination mode. If you are using a TR discrimination mode, make sure you press the retune button or tune the detector searchcoil at the correct operating height. If you retune the detector while the searchcoil is held in the air and then lower it toward the ground, heavy ground minerals can detune the detector so seriously that coins on top of the ground will not be detected. Also make sure that you have not turned your trash elimination control too high.

AUDIO THRESHOLD DRIFT

If your detector audio threshold won't remain where you set it and slowly drifts up or down, check your batteries. Some detectors require warmup time, make sure you have allowed at least five to ten minutes adequate warmup time.

Removing your detector from an air conditioned car and then operating it in direct sun can cause components to heat up, necessitating a few minutes warmup time.

DETECTOR STOPS WORKING AFTER YOU
HAVE SUBMERGED THE SEARCHCOIL

If a manufacturer states that searchcoils are submersible, it's all right to submerge them right up to the cable connector. Searchcoils have been known to leak, however. Sometimes the cable covering has been punctured either by careless handling or by thorns when the detector was brushed up against bushes, a barbed wire fence or other sharp object. Underwater detector searchcoil cables have been punctured by sharp coral. Water can seep into punctures and down through the cable into the searchcoil. Also, searchcoil leakage has been known to happen when a detector, after having been stored in a hot trunk, was removed and the searchcoil suddenly plunged into cold water. The hot, expanded air inside the searchcoil cooled, causing a vacuum to form inside pulling water in through a punctured cable or at the point where the cable connector goes into the searchcoil plastic. Should you suspect your detector failed due to water seeping into the searchcoil, let it dry out for several days in a warm place. Do not place it in a hot oven as it may permanently damage the searchcoil. If you can locate the place where the water seeped into the coil, use a silicone material which can be purchased in tubes at most hardware stores. Apply this generously to the location where you suspect the leak occurred and let it dry thoroughly before using.

After water searching, do not elevate the searchcoil above the level of the control housing. Any water that is trapped in the stem may flow back into the housing. It may be necessary to remove the lower stem to remove accumulated water. Searchcoil covers are highly recommended, as they provide excellent protection for your searchcoil.

450

INTERMITTENT AUDIO, UNSTEADY THRESHOLD SOUNDS

This, in all probability, is caused by operating the detector near high voltage power lines, televisions, TV transmission lines, airports or another metal detector. Citizen band radios, operating close by, have been known to cause this problem. The solution is to get away from these electromagnetic interferrence sources. Co-axial searchcoils eliminate a great amount of electromagnetic interference.

If your detector appears to fail, unplug your headphones! A broken headphone wire will cause erratic operation or the detector may quit working completely. If this happens, you can continue your search using the speaker or a spare set of headphones.

SHORT BATTERY LIFE

If this occurs and you use ni-cad rechargeable batteries, read the battery section in this chapter. If it occurs with regular batteries, place a guaranteed fresh set into the detector and keep careful track of the amount of hours the new batteries give you. You may find the batteries were actually not fresh to begin with. Use headphones instead of the speaker. Your detection efficiency will improve and you'll extend battery life as headphones use less power than a speaker.

NO DETECTION DEPTH

If your detector correctly tunes, you can achieve threshold sound and your batteries are good and strong, in all probability the problem lies with you and not the detector. Of course, searchcoils can go bad and if you have an extra searchcoil along, place it on your detector and check for depth. If the detector is still giving poor depth detection, re-read the instructions and carefully follow the manufacturer's operating procedures. If you constructed a test plot as described (Chapter 23) then you can regularly check your detector's performance.

CHECK-POINT TEST

Many of the previous problems and a few more, have been compiled into a check-point test. Should your detector fail to operate correctly in the field, you should follow the check-points listed below.

1. NO OPERATION
   Battery checks zero:
   Check battery holder and battery cable connector.
2. NO OPERATION
   Battery checks normal, power on:
   Check for disconnected connectors.
3. OPERATION NORMAL
   Battery checks zero:

Check for cold solder joints at battery check switch and other wiring points.

4. SOUND NORMAL

No meter operation nor battery check:
Check for disconnected wire to meter.
Check for defective meter.
Check for cold solder joints at battery check switch.

5. NO SOUND

Meter operation normal:
Check for disconnected speaker connector.
Check for loose wires at speaker.
Check for a damaged headphone jack or plug.
Jack springs can "spring" open.

6. CONSTANT SOUND

Substitute a good coil.
Check pushbutton or Master Control switch and associated cables.
Clean connector pins. (Use pencil eraser.)

7. METER OPERATION LOW OR COMPLETE FAILURE

Check for a pinched wire.

8. WILL NOT TUNE

Substitute a good coil.
Check pushbutton or retune switch and associated cables.
Clean connector pins. (Use pencil eraser)

9. INTERMITTENT OPERATION

Check for loose terminals on battery holder or batteries.
Check tarnish on coil connector pins.

10. BATTERY HOLDER DIFFICULT TO INSTALL

Look for restricting wiring.
Use flat file (six inch or eight inch) on battery holder or tray to smooth out nicks in runners, etc.
Check for bent or misaligned battery tray and mating connector pins.

11. MODES REVERSED

Control switch connected backwards.
Wires reversed in control switch cable connector.

12. ERRATIC OPERATION

Substitute a good coil.
Check for excessive stem movement.
Clean coil cable connector pins.
Check for loose connector and housing screws.

ADDITIONAL TIPS

Your detector is a sensitive electronic instrument and, although it is built to be rugged, care in transporting and handling will extend its life.

Do not store in sunlight or subject detector to high temperatures such as storing in an automobile trunk.

Keep detector clean. Wipe housing and wash coil after use if necessary. Protect from dust and sand as much as possible. Disassemble stem and clean after use in sandy areas, especially after working in or near salt water.

For storage periods longer than one month, remove batteries from detector and/or battery tray.

Never use spray cleaners or lubricants on the P.C. board or controls. Such materials leave harmful residues. Never use any petroleum product on or in your detector.

And, again, don't forget to check the headphones. Headphones have been known to fail, especially the connecting wires where they are soldered to the earphone plug. With the detector turned on and operating, wiggle the headphone wires. Pull on them slightly where they go into the headphone pieces and where the wires go into the plug. Detectors have been returned to repair stations when the only problem was the headphones.

If all of the above procedures fail and you cannot get your detector working, factory or service center repairs are necessary. If you are on an extended trip, you can perhaps find a local dealer who can examine your detector. Many dealers are highly qualified and are factory trained and can make minor repairs. Some may charge a small service fee. Don't overlook this possibility as one way of getting back into the field rather than going home.

If the detector must be shipped to a service center, be sure to pack the detector very carefully and use a lot of packing material. It is not necessary, in most cases, to return stems, headphones, etc. Please do not pack digging tools, etc., which would add weight and increase the cost of postage. Be sure to enclose a letter with your name and address and a *brief,* yet complete, description of the problem, how often the problem occurs and any special conditions under which the problem occurs.

Let's hope your detector never fails in the field but don't baby it to protect it. USE IT! Quality detectors are built to stand up in the field even during many years of hard use.

CHAPTER 29 QUESTIONS

1. Should your metal detector fail to operate in the field, your chances are about _____ that the problem can be discovered and remedied on the spot.

2. The most likely metal detector problem you will encounter is dead batteries. (Answer based upon author's experiences and knowledge of other metal detector user experiences)

    True _____ False _____

3. The first thing to do when your detector fails to operate, is to

_____ _____ _____ .

4. Name the four common types of batteries you can use in your metal detector. (Each correct answer is worth 2 1/2 points)

5. If carbon zinc batteries power your detector for twenty hours, rechargeable ni-cads will power it for eight to ten hours per charge.

    True _____ False _____

6. One good way to "test" a faulty searchcoil is to try another _____ .

7. Which type searchcoils eliminate a great amount of electromagnetic interference: (A) co-planar; (B) BFO; (C) co-axial; (D) concentric

8. When you use headphones instead of the speaker, your detection efficiency will _____ and you'll extend _____ life. (Each correct answer is worth 5 points)

9. Your detector can be damaged if you store it in the sunlight or in an enclosed high temperature area such as an automobile trunk.

    True _____ False _____

10. For storage periods longer than one _____ , remove the batteries from your detector and/or battery tray.

11. It's a good idea to use spray cleaners and lubricants on your PC board and controls if you want to improve performance of your detector.

    True _____ False _____

12. When you pack your instrument to return it to a factory or service center, do not pack digging _____ and other personal items.

Questions 4 and 8 are worth a total of 10 points each when all parts are answered correctly. Each of the other 10 questions answered correctly is worth 8 points. Perfect score is 100. Answers given in Appendix 2.

CHAPTER 30

A Study of Product Warranties

A study of manufacturer's warranty is a very important step in your selection of a metal detector. While it is true that the Federal Trade Commission regulates certain aspects of warranties, there are others that they do not regulate, for instance a lifetime guarantee. Does a lifetime guarantee really buy you anything? Obviously, no one can guarantee a product as complicated as a metal detector, for a lifetime, unless there are certain provisions that protect the manufacturer. For a manufacturer to give an unconditional lifetime warranty, even to the original purchaser, without requiring a certain monetary return from that customer should repairs be needed, could prove disastrous for that manufacturer. When you study warranties, read the fine print!

Does the warranty protect you, the initial purchaser, and then is voided should you sell the product? If a warranty is not transferable during its stated protection period, the value of your detector may be reduced should you try to sell it; the new owner would have no recourse to protect himself should the detector malfunction. Who pays shipping on detectors sent in for repairs? Does the manufacturer pay the return shipping to you or do you pay it? Some warranties require that each time you ship an instrument in for repair, you must pay freight both ways and also send in a surcharge. When a detector under warranty is sent in for repairs, are there any base charges, or does the manufacturer pay for everything including parts and labor, within the warranty period? Does the customer have to pay perhaps fifteen, twenty, or fifty dollars each time the detector under warranty is repaired? The charges could add up.

Some warranties specify that repairs will be made for a period of time after which you will be charged for certain repairs and components. For instance, a five year warranty might protect you for ninety days against most failures, but then, following this first period, charges will be made for labor with maybe a surcharge added to the bill.

Some warranties state that if the detector malfunctions, you must take it to the dealer from whom you purchased it. This dealer then wraps the detector, packs it and returns it to the factory. You must pay that dealer a fixed amount, perhaps five or ten dollars, to cover shipping postage. Also, you must include five or ten dollars with the detector, which pays for return postage. That puts the responsibility on the dealer to pack, ship, keep records, and submit statements to the manufacturer for a refund of his expenses.

Some manufacturers, and rightly so, charge a fixed fee if a detector needing only fresh batteries is sent in for repairs. Check those batteries before you send your detector in for repairs!

Does the warranty say anything about guarantees on replaced parts? Some companies give reduced time warranties on replaced components. In other words, let's say a searchcoil malfunctions and you have eighteen months left on the original detector warranty. The searchcoil will be replaced under the warranty, but the new warranty sent to you with the replacement searchcoil states that the searchcoil is only guaranteed for ninety days. Thus, you have a metal detector control housing with an eighteen month warranty and a new searchcoil with only a ninety day warranty.

You will find dealers who make a concerted effort to repair their customer's detectors in their shops. If a detector malfunctions, the dealer encourages the customer to return it to him. He then makes every possible attempt to repair that detector himself. Sometimes a dealer can spot the problem himself, correct it and/or call the factory for quick shipment of a new replacement part.

Man-made products are prone to failure, and when they do, the necessary steps to have them repaired must be taken. There is no manufacturer who wants his products to fail, but when they do, he understands the problems and inconveniences created for the customer. Be assured that the manufacturer wants that detector repaired and back into the hands of his customer as soon as possible!

A copy of each manufacturer's warranty that covers the products a dealer is selling, should be prominently displayed in the dealer's store. Also, a customer can acquire a manufacturer's warranty by writing to the manufacturer.

CHAPTER 30 QUESTIONS

1. A study of the manufacturer's _____ is a very important step in your selection of a metal detector.

2. When you read a manufacturer's warranty, you should determine the length of time that parts and labor are guaranteed, and you should determine if there are any miscellaneous charges, including shipping, when you send in your detector for repairs.
   True _____   False _____

3. You should always check your _____ , because some manufacturers charge a fee if detectors needing only fresh batteries are sent in for repairs.

4. Before sending in your detector to the manufacturer or a repair station, it is a good idea to first check with the dealer from whom you purchased your detector. The dealer may be able to correct the problem.
   True _____   False _____

5. A copy of each manufacturer's warranty that covers the products the dealer is selling should be prominently displayed in that dealer's store.
   True _____   False _____

Each correct answer is worth 20 points. Perfect score is 100. Answers given in Appendix 2.

CHAPTER 31

Organizational Structure:
What It Takes To Build Quality

The metal detector manufacturing process is far more complicated than the average person understands. Within the confines of
a metal detector manufacturing plant, many people perform many
functions.

There are dozens of departments, including engineering design,
testing, planning, purchasing, procurement, quality control,
manufacturing, product testing and evaluation, packing, shipping,
receiving, dealer/distributor coordination, customer service,
accounting, bookkeeping, public relations, advertising, sales, sec-
retarial pools, marketing and maintenance. All of these are necessary to keep a large metal detector manufacturing company running smoothly, producing quality detectors and extending the best
possible service to its customers. The best way to give you an idea
of the size, scope, and complexities of a manufacturing company
is to include in this chapter a diagram of a company's organizational structure. The accompanying Garrett Electronics organization chart (Figure 31-1) includes the various departments and how
they are interrelated.

Each department and/or function is represented. The interconnecting lines represent the association the departments have with
each other. It would be impossible to show all of the interconnecting lines because each department is more or less dependent upon
every other department.

Each department is equally important and necessary for the
smooth functioning of the entire company. You can compare an
organization to an automobile; it contains various components and
parts, all put together in a precise way, each depending upon the
other. You cannot say the wheels are more important than the
motor; if you remove either, the automobile will no longer operate
as it should. All employees within an organization must be trained
to do specific jobs within performance guidelines. Even as a chain
is as strong as its weakest link, the quality, dependability and other
characteristics of a metal detector are basically determined by the
weakest manufacturing link.

The accompanying Garrett Electronics organization chart is
self-explanatory. As the company expands and grows, more departments and more personnel will be required to maintain that growth.

GARRETT ELECTRONICS' ORGANIZATIONAL CHART

31-1

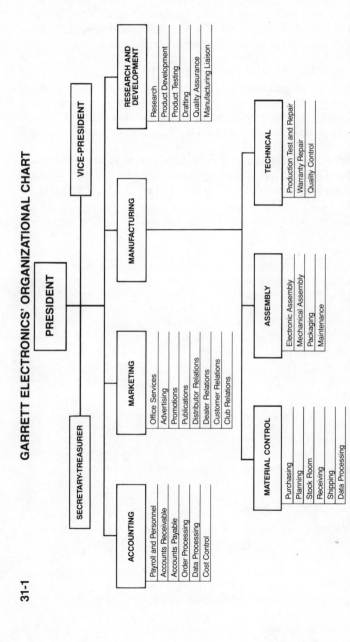

Figure 31-1: This Garrett Electronic's organizational chart shows the various company departments and how they are interrelated. The interconnecting lines represent the association the departments have with each other. Of course, it would be impossible to show all the interconnecting lines because each department is more or less dependent upon every other department. Each department is equally important and necessary for the smooth functioning of the entire company.

Keep in mind that in order for this company to operate smoothly to produce quality, dependable instruments and to service its many thousands of customers, dealers, and distributors, all personnel must work and pull together for a common cause. Main goals at Garrett Electronics are to produce the best possible equipment at the lowest possible price and to give the best possible service. It is not easy. It takes a lot of perserverance and teamwork; if one person fails, the entire company suffers. If all employees do their job correctly and pull together, the products that are built will be of good quality, customers will be happy, sales will continue, and more quality products will be built that make more customers happy and so on in an unending cycle. That's what manufacturing a quality product is all about!

MODERN METAL DETECTORS was written to show you what the world of metal detecting and...*following the Treasure Trail*...are all about! GOOD HUNTING...I'LL SEE YOU IN THE FIELD!

Figure 31-A: Charles Garrett displays one of every major instrument and accessory that the company manufactures. Garrett Electronics manufactures the widest equipment range of any metal detection company in the world. The company manufactures complete lines of equipment for the hobbyist, professionals, law enforcement and security groups and industrial and utility companies. The company was chosen to supply metal detection security equipment to the 1984 Los Angeles Summer Games and the 1984 Republican National Convention. Garrett Electronics is proud of its equipment, its achievements, its people and its dealers and distributors worldwide.

461

Figure 31-B: Here are some of the employees who built the security equipment for the '84 Olympics and the Republican National Convention. They have just loaded the truck with nearly one-thousand metal detectors which were then trucked to Los Angeles to be deployed at the various Olympic sites. When a company has a proud team like this one, you can expect quality products and service.

Figure 31-C: Quality control is the by-word at Garrett Electronics. Inspection after inspection is given to all components, assemblies and products produced by the company. Here this quality control inspector is carefully inspecting a metal detector printed circuit board assembly.

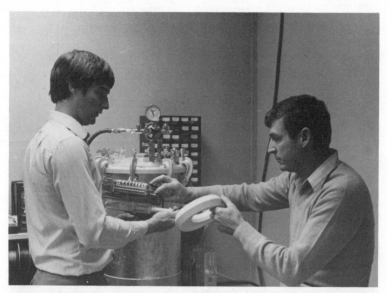

Figure 31-D: Testing is a very important part of product development. Bob Podhrasky and Monty Moncrief spend long hours testing the company's underwater metal detection equipment. Monty (of NASA, Houston, Texas) is part of the team that developed the precision Sea Hunter line of instrumentation.

Figure 31-E: Long before the first prototype of a new product is built, many hours of planning, and design work are spent to insure that down to the last component and assembly, quality is assured.

Figure 31-F: In the manufacturing of quality metal detection equipment you cannot eliminate the personal touch. Trained, quality-minded workers assemble the products and put each and every instrument through rigorous testing to insure that all specifications are met or exceeded.

Figure 31-G: No detail is too small to receive close scrutiny when quality instrumentation is to be guaranteed. Design, testing, improvement redesign, and retesting is an ongoing regular function of the product development at Garrett Electronics.

Figure 31-H: Exacting standards can be met only when each and every worker is trained in their work. No detail or product test can be overlooked in the construction of quality products that continues to perform in the field long after lesser products have been discarded.

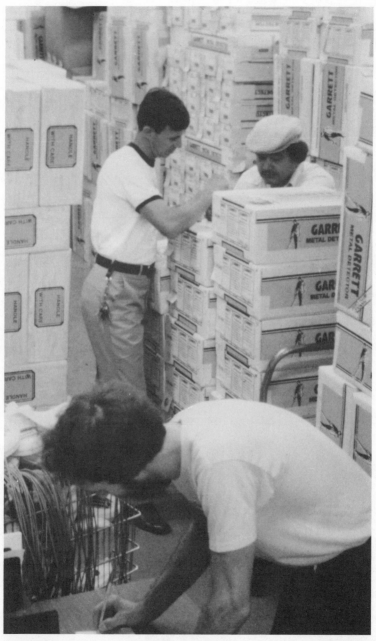

Figure 31-I: The stockroom and shipping departments of Garrett Electronics are always busy. The dedicated performance of a company's employees assures customers of quality products and service.

Glossary

(See also Chapters 7 and 8 for additional metal detector terminology)

ABS PLASTIC — A form of plastic that is preferred in the manufacture of detector searchcoils, etc. It is extremely rugged and durable.

AIR TEST — A method to determine the detection distance and sensitivity of a metal detector. The test is performed in air. Depending upon the type detector and soil conditions, actual depth performance can be more or less than air tests.

AMPERE — A unit of electrical current or rate of flow of electrons in a conductor.

AMPLIFIER — An electrical circuit which draws its power from a source other than the input signal and which produces an output voltage/current that is an enlarged reproduction of the essential features of the input signal.

ANTENNA — The component of a transmitter or receiver that actually radiates or receives the electromagnetic energy. (see Searchcoil)

AUDIO ADJUST — The control used to adjust the metal detector to the desired audio "threshold" or "silent" audio level settings. Also designated as TUNING.

AUTOMATIC (AUDIO) TUNING — A circuit incorporated in some detectors which keeps the AUDIO level at a predetermined level by automatically compensating for detector drift and changing environmental conditions that affect detector AUDIO tuning. Do not confuse with AUTOMATIC VLF GROUND ELIMINATING (CANCELING).

AUTOMATIC VLF GROUND ELIMINATION (CANCELING) — A type metal detector circuit that requires no manual adjustments to achieve iron earth mineral elimination (canceling). Circuits continually analyze the soil beneath the searchcoil and automatically adjust the detector circuitry to "ignore" the minerals. Do not confuse Automatic VLF Ground Elimination with Automatic (Audio) Tuning, as they have two entirely different characteristics.

BACK-READING — A false signal caused when the detector is used in the Trash Elimination (discrimination) mode or when junk metal comes to within one inch of the searchcoil's bottom.

BEAT — The periodic variations that result when energy waves of two different frequencies are superimposed upon each other.

BEAT FREQUENCY — Also called heterodyne, it is one of the two different resultant frequencies produced when energy waves of two frequencies are superimposed upon each other. One of the two resultant frequencies is the sum of the two original frequencies, the other resultant frequency is the difference between the original frequencies. For example: mixing together 100,000 Hz and 100,060 Hz produces a beat or heterodyne frequency of 200,060 Hz (sum frequency) and 60 Hz (different frequency). See also Chapter 12.

BLACK SAND — See Magnetic Black Sand.

BODY MOUNT — A detector configuration in which the control housing is strapped to the body.

CALIBRATION — This generally refers to the "zero" rejection calibration setting of the Ground or Target Eliminator control. Some manufacturers factory calibrate their prospecting detectors so that persons using the detectors for ore sampling (a form of electronic prospecting—also called High Grading) can readily and accurately "set" the controls when it is desired to check ore samples for conductive metal content. Certain models are permanently calibrated and require no adjustment.

CHIMNEY — In prospecting, a column of ore created when the earth's internal heat and pressure forced molten ore up through cracks and fissures in the earth's surface. The ore cooled, solidified and became exposed when the surrounding, softer earth materials eroded.

CIRCUIT — An electrical or electronic network providing one or more closed electrical paths. More specifically, it is a grouping of components and wiring in devices designed to perform some particular function or group of functions. Examples of circuits are, the transmitter circuit, receiver circuit, antenna circuit, and audio amplifier circuit.

CIRCUIT BOARD — The thin sheet of material upon which components are mounted and, generally, the wiring and components themselves. If the circuit board is completely self-contained, with wires to and from it only for power (input and output), it is usually referred to as a module. Circuit boards may be hand wired or have the interconnectors printed electrochemically upon them. They are abbreviated "PC."

CLASSIFICATION, AUDIO — An audio method (or methods) of classifying detected targets into conductivity classes or categories.

CLASSIFICATION, VISUAL — A visual (metered or light) method (or methods) of classifying detected targets into conductivity classes or categories. See also COIN ALERT.

CO-AXIAL SEARCHCOIL — A type of searchcoil in which antenna windings are positioned around the same axis and stacked atop one another.

COIL — See Searchcoil.

470

COIN ALERT (TONE) — An audio method of producing a special tone whenever coins (or silver or high conductivity gold items) are detected. All other detected targets produce normal accept/reject audio sounds.

COMPONENT, CIRCUIT — An essential part of a circuit, i.e., resistor, capacitor, coil, tube, transistor, etc. Or, complete, functional units of a system; i.e., transmitter component, receiver component, searchcoil component, etc.

CONCENTRIC SEARCHCOIL — A type of searchcoil in which antenna windings are positioned around the same axis and in the same plane.

CONDUCTANCE — The ability of an element, component or device to permit the passage of an electrical current, i.e., eddy currents. It is the reciprocal function of resistance.

CONDUCTOR — A wire, bus bar or metal mass (coin, bullet, etc.) capable of conducting electric current.

CONTROL HOUSING — The box or container in which is placed all or most of the electronics assemblies, batteries, etc., of a metal detector.

CO-PLANAR SEARCHCOIL — A type of searchcoil in which the internal coil windings are positioned in the same plane.

CRYSTAL-CONTROLLED OSCILLATOR — An oscillator which employs a crystal to determine its output frequency.

CYCLE — One complete alternation or cycle of an AC voltage source.

DEPTH DETECTION — A term often used to describe the ability of a detector to detect metal objects to certain or given depths.

DEPTH PENETRATION — Applied specifically to electronic metal detectors, the term means the distance into a given medium that the instrument is capable of satisfactorily illuminating, or how deep into a matrix the unit will sense targets and produce a detection signal.

DETECTION PATTERN — SEE SEARCHCOIL DETECTION PATTERN.

DETUNING — A term used to describe when an instrument is "down tuned" in order to more precisely pinpoint, etc. Audio threshold is achieved while the instrument is detecting the target. Ground minerals can also "detune" an instrument, but, generally, in an adverse or undesirable manner.

DISCRIMINATOR — An expression used to describe the capability of a detector to more or less identify ranges of detected targets. See Elimination.

DRIFT — An expression used to describe the ability of an instru-

471

ment to remain tuned at a preset tuning point. Causes of DRIFT: temperature, battery condition, faulty components, poor design, etc. See Stability.

DUAL COIL — A searchcoil head with more than one antenna winding arrangement operating at the same time or independently as selected by the operator.

EDDY CURRENTS — Also called Foucault currents, they are induced in a conductive mass by the variations of electromagnetic energy radiated from the detector, and tend to flow in the surface layers of the target mass. Flow is directly proportional to frequency, the density of the electromagnetic field and the conductivity of metal. Eddy currents flowing in a target produce the same effect as that of a shorted-turn secondary and reflect a resistive load back into the antenna circuit of beat frequency detectors, which lowers the effective inductance of the antenna and raises transmitter frequency. Eddy current generation is also a main electrical phenomenon that produces metal detection signals in TR, VLF and Pulse Induction metal detectors.

ELECTROMAGNETIC FIELD — An invisible field which surrounds the transmitter winding. Generated by the alternating radio frequency current which circulates in the transmitter antenna windings.

ELECTROMAGNETIC INDUCTION — The voltage induced in a coil (or object, as a conductive target) due to changes in electromagnetic lines of force which pass through the coil or object.

ELECTRONIC CIRCUIT — A circuit wherein current flows through wires, resistances, inductances, capacitances, transistors and other components.

ELECTRONIC PINPOINTING — A detector mode to cause a "sharpening" of detector signals when objects are detected. An electronic aid to target pinpointing.

ELIMINATION — There are two forms: Ground Eliminating (also called Ground Canceling) and Target (Trash) Eliminating (also called Discriminating). Detector circuits eliminate the earth's IRON MINERALS from detection. Other circuits eliminate SELECTED UNDESIRABLE METAL OBJECTS from detection. "Elimination" accurately describes these functions.

FALSE DETECTION — Responses to objects or anomalies other than sought targets.

FARADAY-SHIELD — The metal foil wrapping, metal tube, metallic paint, or other metallic cover surrounding the searchcoil antenna wires (or other components) of a metal detector. Its purpose is to provide electrostatic shielding and reduce ground and wet grass capacitance effects and "false" detection signals.

472

FERRITE CORE SEARCHCOIL — A type of searchcoil using a ferrite core upon which are wound the antenna windings.

FERROUS — Pertains to iron and iron compounds.

FERROUS-NON — Pertains to non-iron metals and compounds, i.e., brass, silver, lead, aluminum, etc.

FLOAT — In prospecting, describes ore which has broken away from the Mother Lode and has "floated" or moved away from point of break.

FREQUENCY — As applied to alternating current or voltage. The term means the number of periodic recurrences of a complete alternation or cycle Zero, plus-maximum, zero, negative-maximum, zero, current or voltage levels that occur within one second.

FREQUENCY DESIGNATIONS -

Very Low	VLF	3-30	kHz. (cycles or Hertz)
Low	LF	30-300	kHz.
Medium	MF	300-3000	kHz.
High	HF	3-30	mHz.
Very High	VHF	30-300	mHz.
Ultra High	UHF	300-3000	mHz.
Super High	SHF	3000-30,000	mHz.

GAIN — An increase in voltage, current or power with respect to a previous quantity or a standard reference. Gain occurs in vacuum tubes, transistors, transformers, etc., as gain per component, gain per stage and gain per assembly. Such gain can be measured in terms of voltage, current, power or decibels.

GEIGER COUNTER — Also called Geiger Mueller or G-M counter. It is a device that detects atomic radiation by pulse discharge produced in a gas-filled metal tube when nuclear particles in the atmosphere enter the tube window and temporarily ionize the gas. Readout is by meter or audible sound.

GROUND ELIMINATION (ALSO CANCELING) — The ability of a metal detector to eliminate (ignore—cancel) the detection effect of iron minerals.

HEADPHONES — A device that converts electrical energy waves into audible waves of identical form. For metal detector users working in noisy or windy locations. They will do everything loudspeakers will do, and most of the time they do it better. In addition, they are less susceptible to damage by rain, and require much less power than a speaker.

HERTZ (Hz) — A unit of frequency equal to one cycle per second.

HOT ROCK — A mineralized rock that produces a positive signal in a metal detector.

INDUCED CURRENT — The current that flows in a conductor or

conductive mass when a varying electromagnetic field is present. Except for eddy currents, induced or secondary currents flow only when there is a complete circuit or closed loop. Eddy currents are, in themselves, closed loops.

INJECTION MOLDED — Plastic components such as searchcoil covers, are constructed by injecting ''liquid'' plastic into a mold cavity. The plastic hardens and is ejected from the mold.

MAGNETIC BLACK SAND — Magnetite, a magnetic oxide of iron and, in a lesser degree, hematite. Also contains titanium and other rare-earth minerals but serve mainly as an indicator of the possible presence of placer gold.

MAGNETOMETER — Not a metal detector even though the term is often used interchangeably, especially when walk-through (doorway) type metal detectors are discussed. An instrument for measuring magnetic intensity, especially the earth's magnetic field. Treasure hunters, searching for a buried iron safe, will use a magnetometer to locate increased earth's magnetic field density caused by the safe. Prospectors use to detect magnetic anomalies and gradients, etc.

MATRIX — The entire area below a searchcoil and being illuminated by the transmitted electromagnetic field. A matrix may wholly, partially or intermittently contain conductive and/or nonconductive and/or ferrous and/or non ferrous materials. The matrix may contain moisture, salts, sulfides, metallic ores, etc. The detection pattern is only a portion of the matrix.

MEDIUM — See Matrix.

METAL DETECTOR — An electronic instrument or device capable of sensing the presence of conductive objects lying within the earth, or otherwise out of sight, and of providing the operator with an audible or visual indication of that presence.

METAL/MINERAL — Meaning primarily that a given metal detector has metal/mineral detection characteristics and/or the ability to distinguish between the two.

MODE — A manner of operating, generally controllable at the operator's option, i.e., search modes, metal or mineral modes, VLF all metal mode, trash elimination, etc.

NARROW SCAN — A scan width less than full searchcoil diameter. In earlier days, TR detector searchcoils scanned an effective area equivalent to about thirty to forty-percent of the diameter of the searchcoil being used.

NULL — A tuning or audio adjustment condition that results in ''quiet'' or zero audio operation.

OSCILLATOR — The variation of an observable or otherwise detectable quantity of motion about a mean value.

OVERSHOOT — A metal detector "false" signal characteristic. When the searchcoil is passed over a junk metal target, the detector audio will be pulled down into the null (quiet) zone. The automatic tuning circuitry senses the change and immediately starts to push the audio back up to where it can be heard. As soon as the searchcoil passes the target, the junk metal releases its negative effect on the detector and the sound is momentarily pushed up to an audible overshoot level before it returns to normal threshold sound. This generally occurs in TR discriminating/automatic mode detectors.

PENETRATION — The ability of a detector to penetrate earth material, air, wood, rock, and water to locate metal targets. Penetration is a function of detector design and type—detector, material being penetrated, etc.

PERFORMANCE — The ability of a detector to perform the functions which the manufacturer claims his detectors will perform.

PERMEABILITY — The measure of how a material performs as a path for magnetic lines of force as measured against the permeability standard, air. Air is rated as 1 on the permeability scale, diamagnetic materials less than 1, paramagnetic materials slightly more than 1 and ferromagnetic materials much more than 1.

PHASE — The angular (mathematical or time concept) relationship that exists between current and voltage in all AC circuits... regardless of type. When both voltage and current cycles rise and fall in exact unison, voltage and current are said to be in phase. When the rise of current flow lags behind the rise of voltage, the circuit is said to be inductive. Conversely, when the rise of current leads the rise of voltage, the circuit is said to be capacitive.

PHASE ANGLE — The number of angular (mathematical concept) degrees that AC current and voltage peaks are out of phase—or out of step with each other.

PINPOINTING — The art of determining exactly where a detected target is located.

PLACER — This is pronounced plas-er. It sounds like plaster with the "t" removed. In prospecting, an accumulation of gold, black magnetic sand and other elements of specific gravity higher than sand, rock, etc., found in same area. Generally occurring in low spots, in streams downside of boulders and other obstructions, etc.

POCKET — In prospecting, an accumulation of ore created over a period of time, found in a concentrated spot, area, etc.

POTTING — A method of encapsulating component parts or component assemblies within a housing or container by using wax, resin or other solid material having high insulation and waterproofing qualities. Potting provides additional mechanical stability to delicate parts and wiring, slows down the effects of fluctuating ambient temperatures and provides water and dust proofing.

PUSHBUTTON — A retuning and mode change feature incorporated in certain metal detectors.

"Q" — A symbol for quality factor. In an inductor, it is the ratio of its reactance to its coil resistance at a given frequency. In a capacitor, it is the ratio of its susceptance to its shunt conductance at a given frequency.

RECEIVER — That portion of the instrument circuitry of a metal detector which receives the information created by the presence of targets, acts upon that information and processes it according to design intentions, and then activates the readout system in proportion to the nature of the received information.

RECEIVER GAIN — The amplification of input signals to whatever extent required.

RESPONSE TIME — This indicates in a general sense, the presence (or absence) of time delay in the audio section of a detector that describes the interval between target-sensing and audio and/or meter indication.

RETUNING — The retuning (restoring) of a detector's audio sound (threshold) to a predetermined level. This is accomplished by pushing a button, flipping a switch, adjusting a knob, etc.

REVERSE DISCRIMINATION — A technique whereby targets can be classified as "good" or "bad", "hot" rocks indentified, etc. Performed only in TR discriminate manual mode.

ROTO MOLD — A method to fabricate plastic parts such as detector control housings, dredge floats, etc., which are molded by spinning "liquid" plastic in a hollow mold. The plastic cools and takes the shape of the walls of the mold.

SCANNING — The actual scanning or movement of the detector searchcoil over the ground or other objects being searched.

SCRUBBING — A method used to achieve maximum depth detection in the TR DISCRIMINATE MODE. Also, it minimizes earth mineralization disturbance.

SEARCHCOIL — The component of the detector which houses the transmitter and receiver antennas. The searchcoil is attached to the control housing by way of an adjustable connecting stem. The searchcoil is scanned over the ground or other surface.

SEARCHCOIL DETECTION PATTERN — That portion of the electromagnetic field where metal detection takes place. It is located out from and along the axis of the searchcoil generally starting at full searchcoil width and tapering to a point at some distance from the searchcoil. Its actual width and depth depends upon the size and nature of any given target.

SENSITIVITY — The ability to sense conductivity changes in the detection pattern. Sensitivity is one of the most important operational characteristics of an electronic metal detector. The smaller the changes in conductivity that will produce a meaningful readout, the more sensitive the instrument. The greater a detector's sensitivity, the smaller the target that the detector will detect.

SIGNAL — That received, electromagnetically created, intelligence that produces target responses.

SILENT AUDIO — The tuning of the audio in the "silent" (just below threshold) zone. There is no audio sound heard except when a target is detected.

SPLASHPROOF — See WATERPROOF also. Minor wetting of searchcoil (dew on grass, etc) will not affect detector operation.

STABILITY — The ability of metal detector circuits to remain tuned to the predetermined operating point (threshold).

SUBMERSIBLE — This generally refers to the ability of a searchcoil to be submerged a certain distance under water and still continue operating perfectly.

SUPER-SNIPING — A trademarked detecting method, using a small diameter (three-inch-to-four-inch diameter) searchcoil, that enhances individual target detection. Near by target influence is minimized. Especially of value in trashy areas.

SURFACE AREA — That surface area of a target lying horizontal with the plane of the detector searchcoil. In other words, the amount of surface area that is "looking" at the underside of the searchcoil. This is the area through which the electromagnetic field lines pass and on which eddy currents are generated.

SWEEPING — See Scanning.

TARGET — A sought-for object distinct and apart from matrix conductivity anomalies. A coin is a target but a wad of discarded chewing gum wrapper is not. Junk iron is not normally a target but for bottle hounds who use detectors to locate old trash pits, it is. A target is any sought object lying within a matrix that may or may not contain other but unsought conductive objects and which, by virtue of its material makeup, is capable of being located with an electronic metal detector. Also used to describe all detectable metal or mineral targets.

TH-ing — An abbreviation for Treasure Hunting.

THRESHOLD — Refers to the low level audio sound achieved when a metal detector is tuned.

TR — The abbreviation for TRANSMITTER-RECEIVER, which is a type of metal detector circuit.

477

TR MODE — The term which identifies the TR operational setting on a TR and VLF/TR metal detector.

TUNING — The manual adjustment that an operator makes to bring the detector audio sound to an audible, silent, or other preferred audio level threshold.

UNIVERSAL CAPABILITIES — A statement or claim that a given metal detector is capable of performing most metal detecting tasks, such as: coin, cache and relic hunting; ghost towning; nugget hunting; vein locating, etc.

VACUUM FORMED — Plastic components, such as a searchcoil housing, that is formed from sheet plastic. The plastic is heated and by vacuum is pulled down over a forming mold.

VACUUM TUBE — Glass contained sets of electronic elements which are within a vacuum that are used to control voltages in electronic circuits. A vacuum tube can correctly be considered to be an electronic gate that controls the flow of electrons which flow from a heated cathode (electron-rich emitter) and migrate through the vacuum to the positive charged, electron deficient plate. The inclusion of elements, usually wires, called grids permit very small control or input voltages to control very large plate or output voltages.

VERSATILITY — A measure of many applications to which a metal detector can be applied. In other words, how many ways can a particular metal detector be used? See, also, UNIVERSAL CAPABILITIES.

VISUAL INDICATOR — Generally means meter indication. It is possible to design a system using only visual indicators, (light, for example.)

VLF — Initials that stand for Very Low Frequency, which is a segment of the RF spectrum that includes frequencies from 3 kHz to 30 kHz. It is also a detector type.

VLF MODE — The term which identifies the VLF operational setting on a VLF and VLF/TR metal detector.

VOLUME CONTROL — A control, generally resistance, used to limit voltage and/or current in an audio amplifier and, thereby, control volume of sound or "loudness" of maximum sound when a target is detected. It is not to be confused with tuning or audio adjustment controls.

WATERPROOF — Generally refers to searchcoil waterproofing that allows a searchcoil to be operated in rain or in heavy dew. Waterproof does not necessarily mean submersible.

WIDE SCAN — Generally implies that the scanning width (detection pattern) of a detector, as the searchcoil passes over the ground, is equal to the full width (or wider) of the diameter of the searchcoil being used.

ZERO-BEAT — The condition whereby two frequencies superimposed upon each other are exactly the same and, therefore, produce no beat note. See Null.

Appendix 2: ANSWERS TO CHAPTER QUESTIONS

Students can determine, to a certain extent, their comprehension of each MODERN METAL DETECTOR chapter by taking the quiz given at the end of each chapter (except Chapter 31). With the exception of Chapter 18 (Law Enforcement and Security Metal Detector Short Course), the material in each chapter contains the answers to all the questions for the respective chapters. Thus, each chapter and its quiz is a complete course of study.

A perfect score of 100 is achieved for each chapter when a student correctly answers all questions asked at the end of each chapter. The value of each question is given immediately following the last question. Note, that some questions require more than one correct answer. In those cases, the value of each individual answer is given, in parenthesis, immediately following the question, unless otherwise indicated.

CHAPTER 1

1. electronic, metal; 2. minerals; 3. study, field application; 4. control housing, antenna; 5. metal

CHAPTER 2

1. Chinese Emperor, life; 2. 1881; 3. mine detectors; 4. dig detected targets; 5. treasure hunting, electronic prospecting, law enforcement, security, archaeology, medicine, lumbering, food processing, traffic control

CHAPTER 3

1. radio; 2. antenna; 3. False (doughnut); 4. detection pattern; 5. eddy current generation, electromagnetic field distortion

CHAPTER 4

1. Beat Frequency Oscillator; Transmitter/Receiver; Very Low Frequency; Pulse Induction; 2. VLF; 3. deeper; 4. task; 5. coin, cache, relic, electronic prospecting; 6. iron, salt; 7. True; 8. locating, tracing; 9. security; 10. metal detectors

CHAPTER 5

1. imagination; 2. B; 3. True; 4. everywhere; 5. guns, knives

CHAPTER 6

1. C; 2. VLF and Pulse Induction; 3. VLF and Pulse Induction; 4. audio and visual; 5. C

CHAPTER 7

1. False; 2. False (eddy currents); 3. Because these two phenomena allow metal detection to take place; 4. False (search matrix); 5. illuminated; 6. conductive, conductive; 7. electromagnetic field; 8. mineralization, salt; 9. capability, performance; 10. distortion; 11. metal; 12. density; area; 13. False; 14. False; 15. False; 16. False; 17. False; 18. C; 19. faith; 20. discoveries

CHAPTER 8

1. False (use a hipmount or armrest); 2. False; 3. False; 4. False; 5. decreases, increases; 6. False; 7. True; 8. True; 9. False; 10. True

CHAPTER 9

1. False; 2. False (recharge immediately); 3. D; 4. False; 5. C; 6. False; 7. frequency change, volume change; 8. True; 9. False; 10. False (submersible)

CHAPTER 10

1. False (iron minerals only); 2. True; 3. False (low conductive matrix); 4. True; 5. False; 6. True; 7. False; 8. B; 9. True; 10. Because they both have approximately the same conductivity and mass structure.; 11. fair, good; 12. True; 13. True; 14. D; 15. C; 16. Super Sniping; 17. True; 18. speaker, headphones; 19. True; 20. detection depth, sensitivity; 21. False; 22. True; 23. True; 24. True; 25. False

CHAPTER 11

1. eight; 2. C; 3. D; 4. electrostatic or Faraday; 5. vegetation; 6. co-planar and cencentric; 7. C & D; 8. How wide a range of target sizes a given searchcoil can detect to a practical depth; 9. Super Sniping; 10. ten; 11. When you are finding targets in the fringe area of detection; 12. hipmount or armrest; 13. D; 14. ground.

CHAPTER 12

1. B; 2. frequency; 3. True; 4. Because of its ability to locate magnetic black sand and accurately identify the relative metal/mineral content of ore samples; 5. Does not have as great a depth capability as other instruments and cannot be adjusted to ignore iron earth minerals; 6. fringe; 7. three; 8. Because ore samples can have a thin conductive vein that can be detected better when the face of the vein is facing the metal detector searchcoil; 9. predominent; 10. To the approximate depth equal to the diameter of the searchcoil being used; 11. False; 12. True

CHAPTER 13

1. True; 2. Eddy current generation and induction unbalance; 3. Because the two windings are electrically balanced; 4. C; 5. coin; 6. decrease detection depth, operate in the silent audio zone, scrub the searchcoil; 7. False

CHAPTER 14

1. D; 2. Very Low Frequency; 3. False; 4. eliminate; 5. iron; 6. trash (reject, undesirable, etc.); 7. time, 8. False; 9. True; 10. deep seeking; 11. C; 12. manually; 13. True; 14. fringe; 15. versatile; 16. searchcoils; 17. eight; 18. pinpointing; 19. twelve; 20. detected; 21. large; 22. iron; 23. prospecting; 24. See Chapter 14, THE LITTLE IRON KETTLE.

CHAPTER 15

1. drift; 2. minerals; 3. False; 4. coin; 5. False; 6. True; 7. fringe; 8. Automatic VLF Ground Elimination; 9. True; 10. pinpointing, tuning.

CHAPTER 16

1. True; 2. True; 3. True; 4. False; 5. C; 6. A; 7. True; 8. False; 9. True; 10. A,C.

CHAPTER 17

1. 5; 2. Pulse Induction; 3. black sand; 4. simultaneously; 5. fresh; 6. threshold; 7. A,C,D; 8. detection; 9. size; 10. A,B,D; 11. A,B; 12. C; 13. True; 14. Target elimination, trash elimination, interchangeable searchcoils, selectable depth, rechargeable batteries, land/sea conversion stems.

CHAPTER 18

1. True; 2. C; 3. True; 4. True; 5. D; 6. A; 7. A; 8. D; 9. C; 10. True; 11. C; 12. True; 13. C; 14. B; 15. A; 16. D; 17. True; 18. Pulse Induction; 19. C; 20. C; 21. C; 22. False; 23. True; 24. False; 25. True; 26. D (actually, all are true); 27. A; 28. D; 29. B; 30. C; 31. C; 32. True.

CHAPTER 19

1. locator, tracer; 2. locating; 3. True; 4. True; 5. searchcoils; 6. conductive, inductive; 7. conductive, inductive; 8. A,B,D; 9. ground, pipe, null; 10. True; 11. True; 12. False; 13. True.

CHAPTER 20

1. True; 2. law enforcement, security; 3. False (considerably more); 4. beach; 5. electronic; 6. million; 7. $10,000.00; 8. Yes; 9. False; 10. True.

CHAPTER 21

1. hipmount, armrest; 2. A,B,C,D; 3. True; 4. C; 5. False (3 months)

CHAPTER 22

1. ability, versatility, capability, quality; 2. False; 3. yourself; 4. False; 5. False; 6. False; 7. False (small coin); 8. C; 9. True; 10. No, a better choice would have been a MANUAL-ADJUST VLF ground eliminating type with a much larger searchcoil and/or a Depth Multiplier type accessory; 11. ignores (rejects); 12. False; 13. ground; 14. False; 15. high; 16. False; 17. False (trash elimination control); 18. True; 19. True; 20. A.B.C.D; 21. False (larger searchcoil); 22. conductive; 23. True.

CHAPTER 23

1. True; 2. True; 3. instructions (training); 4. persistence; 5. instruction manual; 6. zero; 7. progressing, learned; 8. True; 9. True; 10. False; 11. dig up next; 12. skipping, overlapping; 13. False; 14. True.

CHAPTER 24

1. anything; 2. healthful; 3. research; 4. Not!; 5. hard work; 6. False; 7. patience; 8. patience; 9. five; 10. backyard; 11. find; 12. length; 13. can; 14. False (when you sell it).

CHAPTER 25

1. sudden wealth; 2. gold; 3. area; 4. True; 5. True; 6. metal; 7. True; 8. high grading; 9. cave-ins, poisonous gases; 10. iron, conductive; 11. conductive; 12. True; 13. ninety one; 14. mineral; 15. True; 16. B; 17. False.

CHAPTER 26

1. tools; 2. law enforcement; 3. False; 4. False; 5. not; 6. buildings (structures); 7. False (lost items: True); 8. VLF; 9. False (three-inch to eight-inch diameter sizes); 10. Scanner

CHAPTER 27

1. rewarding; 2. Roy Sexton; 3. True; 4. healthful; 5. handicapped awareness

CHAPTER 28

1. dealers; 2. business; 3. True; 4. A,B,C,D; 5. True; 6. successful;
7. True; 8. False; 9. itself; 10. D; 11. customer; 12. satisfied.

CHAPTER 29

1. 50-50; 2. True; 3. check your batteries; 4. carbon zinc, heavy
duty, alkaline, nickel cadmium (ni-cad); 5. True; 6. searchcoil; 7.
C; 8. improve, battery; 9. True; 10. month; 11. False; 12. tools.

CHAPTER 30

1. warranty; 2. True; 3. batteries; 4. True; 5. True.

Appendix 3: Metal Detector Dealer

For more information about treasure hunting

and related equipment call toll free—

1-800-527-4011 or 1-800-442-4889 (in Texas)

or write Search International ,

2814 National Dr., Garland, Texas 75041-2397 USA.

NOTES

NOTES

NOTES

Appendix 4: Bibliography

Bridge, Peter J.: *Article: Australia's Electronic Gold Rush - How It All Started,* The Searcher Periodical #5, 1983.

Garrett, Charles L.: *Successful Coin Hunting.* Revised Edition. Dallas, TX: Ram Publishing Company, 1978. ISBN 0-915920-44-1.

_____ and Roy Lagal: *Electronic Prospecting.* Dallas, TX: Ram Publishing Company 1979. ISBN 0-915920-38-7.

Kerchner, Russel M. and George F. Corcoran: New York: *Alternating - Current Circuits.* John Wiley and Sons, Inc., 1956.

Lagal, Roy: *Detector Owner's Field Manual.* Revised Edition. Dallas, TX: Ram Publishing Company, 1978. ISBN 0-915920-43-3.

_____ and Charles Garrett: *The Complete VLF/TR Metal Detector Handbook.* Dallas, TX: Ram Publishing Company, 1979. ISBN 0-915920-32-8.

LeGaye, E.S.(Rocky): *Electronic Metal Detector Handbook.* Houston, TX: Western Heritage Press, 1969. L/C #72-100686. (Out of Print)

Middlemiss, Ross R.: *College Algebra.* McGraw-Hill, Inc., 1952.

Moore, Kenneth C.: *Airport, Aircraft & Airline Security.* Butterworth Publishers, Inc., 1976. L/C #76-45104. ISBN 0-913708-26-7.

Sams, Howard W. & Company, Inc.: Indianapolis/Kansas City/New York: *Reference Data for Radio Engineers.* 1970.

Sears, Francis Wester and Mark W. Zemansky: *University Physics.* Reading, MA: Addison - Wesley Publishing Company Inc., 1957.

Sinkankas, John: *Gem Stones of America.* New York: Van Nostrand Reinhold Company. 1975. L/C #75-20851. ISBN 0-442-27623-0.

von Mueller, Karl: *Treasure Hunter's Manual #7.* Dallas, TX: Ram Publishing Company. 1972. ISBN 0-915920-09-3.

_____ : *Master Hunter Manual.* Dallas, TX: Ram Publishing Company. 1973. ISBN 0-915920-12-3. (Out of Print)

von Tersch, L.W. and A. W. Swago: New York: *Recurrent Electrical Transients.* Prentice-Hall, Inc., 1955.

Appendix 5: Metal Detector Course Outline

The following suggested course outline is a highly condensed program designed to cover only the fundamentals of metal detectors, the various types, and how they work. Course length is nine hours (includes a one hour lunch break). If classes are kept small (about ten students maximum,) then, the allocated one hour, forty-five minutes buddy-system field training, should be sufficient. Extra field training is encouraged. Larger classes will require more outside field time.

The instructor should be thoroughly versed and knowledgeable of the various subjects, so that correct time allocations for each subject can be carefully maintained. The final, written quiz, needs to adequately cover the material studied. A twenty-five question, twenty-minute quiz with ten minutes for the instructor to ask students for correct answers, is suggested. The instructor should select appropriate questions from questions given following the covered chapters.

If time permits, various film are available from the Garrett Film, Video, and Slide Library. These film are instructional and will improve the quality of any course.

Metal detector courses of one day's length, can cover only the essentials of metal detectors. Actually, two day courses with suggested instruction times doubled are recommended.

Semester-length Community College courses, based upon the entire contents of Modern Metal Detectors, are recommended.

I. Introduction To Course . . . . 5 min.
II. What Is A Metal Detector? . . . . 10 min. (Chapter 1)
III. Historical Overview of
    Metal Detectors . . . . 25 min. (Chapter 2)
IV. How Metal Detectors Work . . . . 25 min. (Chapter 3)
(Ten Minute Break) . . . . (End of first hour)
V. Characteristics of Metal Detection and
    The Search Matrix . . . . 35 min. (Chapter 7)
      A. Detectable Metals and Minerals
      B. Eddy Currents and Secondary Electromagnetic
         Field Generation
      C. Electromagnetic Field Distortion
      D. Search Matrix
      E. Surface Area Detection
      F. Fringe Area Detection

LETTERS, CERTIFICATES AND AWARDS RECEIVED BY GARRETT ELECTRONICS AND THE AUTHOR

To Charles Garrett
With my personal best wishes and appreciation to you for
a job well done in supplying metal detection equipment
and security training at the 1984 Republican National
Convention held in Dallas, Texas.

Ronald Reagan

J. Walter Coughlin & Associates
6907 Kings Hollow Drive · Dallas, Texas 75248 · (214) 744-7082

September 4, 1984

Mr. Charles Garrett
President
Garrett Electronics, Inc.
2814 National Drive
Garland, Texas 75041

Dear Charles,

Thank you for making the 1984 Republican National Convention such a great success.

You and your professional staff, as well as your excellent equipment, are what allowed all of the security aspects of the convention to work perfectly.

All of us involved in security with the Republican National Committee owe you and your company a great deal of gratitude.

Thank you.

Sincerely,

J. Walter Coughlin
Director of Security
Republican National Convention

JWC:tg

Security Consultants

497

Charles L. Garrett

IN RECOGNITION AND
APPRECIATION FOR
YOUR CONTRIBUTION TO
THE SUCCESS OF THE
GAMES OF THE XXIII OLYMPIAD
LOS ANGELES, 1984

LOS ANGELES
OLYMPIC
ORGANIZING
COMMITTEE

© 1980 L.A. Olympic Committee TM

PAUL ZIFFREN, CHAIRMAN

PETER V. UEBERROTH, PRESIDENT

HARRY L. USHER, EXECUTIVE VICE PRESIDENT
AND GENERAL MANAGER

Garrett Metal Detectors

IN RECOGNITION AND
APPRECIATION FOR
YOUR CONTRIBUTION TO
THE SUCCESS OF THE
GAMES OF THE XXIII OLYMPIAD
LOS ANGELES, 1984

LOS ANGELES
OLYMPIC
ORGANIZING
COMMITTEE

© 1980 L.A. Olympic Committee ™

PAUL ZIFFREN, CHAIRMAN

PETER V. UEBERROTH, PRESIDENT

HARRY L. USHER, EXECUTIVE VICE PRESIDENT
AND GENERAL MANAGER

LAW ENFORCEMENT OFFICERS TRAINING SCHOOL

CERTIFICATE OF ATTENDANCE

THIS IS TO CERTIFY THAT

CHARLES GARRETT

ATTENDED A SPECIALIZED SCHOOL IN

GENERAL LAW ENFORCEMENT

HELD AT

EL PASO, TEXAS

FROM JUNE 22, 1983 TO JUNE 23, 1983

UNDER SPONSORSHIP OF

EL PASO POLICE ACADEMY

IN COOPERATION WITH THE FEDERAL BUREAU OF INVESTIGATION

TRAINING DIRECTOR

HONORARY FOUNDER

Garrett Electronics Inc.

Recognized for a generous contribution to aid
in the perpetuation and enhancement of Utah's
wildlife resource.

This certificate is given with grateful
appreciation this 18th day of August , 1982.

RESEARCH AND DEVELOPMENT FUND
of the
UTAH DIVISION OF WILDLIFE RESOURCES

In Special Recognition and Appreciation

of

Garrett Electronics

for

their continued support of the nation's sheriffs
and the advancement of law enforcement capabilities and services
through participation as an exhibitor

at

The National Sheriffs' Association

Annual Informative Conference

1984

PRESENTED TO

Charles Garrett

OF

GARRETT ELECTRONICS

For His Assistance In Supplying
Electronic Metal Detective Equipment
Which Was Used In The
U.S.A.F. F-16 Fighter Aircraft Recovery Project
At The Great Salt Lake, Utah
May 17 - June 18, 1982

PRESENTED BY
CROSS INTERNATIONAL
SEARCH & RECOVERY, INC.
OREM, UTAH

to Charles Garrett
from Plebe Cino
by Alberto Fremura

RECOMMENDED SUPPLEMENTARY BOOKS

The books described below are among the most popular books in print related to treasure hunting. If you desire to increase your skills in various aspects of treasure hunting, consider adding these volumes to your library.

MODERN METAL DETECTORS. Charles Garrett. Ram Publishing Company. NEW! This advanced handbook explains simply yet fully how to succeeed with your metal detector. Written for home, field, and classroom study, MMD provides the expertise you need for success in any metal detecting situation, hobby or professional. Easily understood chapters on specifications, components, capabilities, selecting and operating a detector, choosing searchcoils and accessories, and more — increase your understanding of the fascinating, rewarding fields of metal detector use. 544 pages. 56 Illustrations, 150 photos.

DETECTOR OWNER'S FIELD MANUAL. Roy Lagal. Ram Publishing Company. Nowhere else will you find the detector operating instructions that Mr. Lagal has put into this book. He shows in detail how to treasure hunt, cache hunt, prospect, search for nuggets, black sand deposits ... in short, how to use your detector exactly as it should be used. Covers completely BFO-TR-VLF/TR types, P.I.'s, P.R.G.'s, P.I.P.'s, etc. Explains precious metals, minerals, ground conditions, and gives proof that treasure exists because it has been found and that more exists that you can find! Fully illustrated. 236 pages.

ELECTRONIC PROSPECTING. Charles Garrett, Bob Grant, Roy Lagal. Ram Publishing Company. A tremendous upswing in electronic prospecting for gold and other precious metals has recently occurred. High gold prices and unlimited capabilities of VLF/TR metal detectors have led to many fantastic discoveries. Gold is there to be found. If you have the desire to search for it and want to be successful, then this book will show you how to select (and use) from the many brands of VLF/TR's those that are correctly calibrated to produce accurate metal vs. mineral identification which is so vitally necessary in prospecting. Illustrated. 96 pages.

GOLD PANNING IS EASY. Roy Lagal. Ram Publishing Company. Roy Lagal proves it! He doesn't introduce a new method; he removes confusion surrounding old established methods. A refreshing NEW LOOK guaranteed to produce results with the "Gravity Trap" or any other pan. Special metal detector instructions that show you how to nugget shoot, find gold and silver veins, and check ore samples for precious metal. This HOW, WHERE and WHEN gold panning book is a must for everyone, beginner or professional! Fully illustrated. 112 pages.

THE COMPLETE VLF-TR METAL DETECTOR HANDBOOK (All About Ground Canceling Metal Detectors). Roy Lagal, Charles Garrett. Ram Publishing Company. The unparalleled capabilities of VLF/TR Ground Canceling metal detectors have made them the number one choice of treasure hunters and prospectors. From History, Theory, and Development to Coin, Cache, and Relic Hunting, as well as Prospecting, the authors have explained in detail the capabilities of VLF/TR detectors and how they are used. Learn the new ground canceling detectors for the greatest possible success. Illustrated. 200 pages.

ROBERT MARX: QUEST FOR TREASURE. R. F. Marx. Ram Publishing Company. The true story of the discovery and salvage of the Spanish treasure galleon, *Nuestra Señora de la Maravilla*, lost at sea, January 1656. She went to the bottom bearing millions in gold, silver and precious gems. Be there with the divers as they find coins and priceless artifacts over three centuries old. Join Marx's exciting adventure of underwater treasures found. The story of the *flotas*, dangers of life at sea, incredible finds ... all are there. Over 50 photos. 286 pages

TREASURE HUNTER'S MANUAL #6. Karl von Mueller. Ram Publishing Company. The original material in this book was written for the professional treasure hunter. Hundreds of copies were paid for in advance by professionals who knew the value of Karl's writing and wanted no delays in receiving their copies. The THM #6 completely describes full-time treasure hunting and explains the mysteries surrounding this intriguing and rewarding field of endeavor. You'll read this fascinating book several times. Each time you will discover you have gained greater in-depth knowledge. Thousands of ideas, tips, and other valuable information. Illustrated. 318 pages.

TREASURE HUNTER'S MANUAL #7. Karl von Mueller. Ram Publishing Company. The classic! The most complete, up-to-date guide to America's fastest growing activity, written by the old master of treasure hunting. This is *the* book that fully describes professional methods of RESEARCH, RECOVERY, and TREASURE DISPOSITION. Includes a full range of treasure hunting methods from research techniques to detector operation, from legality to gold dredging. Don't worry that this material overlaps THM #6 ... both of Karl's MANUALS are 100% different from each other but yet are crammed with information you should know about treasure hunting. Illustrated. 334 pages.

SUCCESSFUL COIN HUNTING. Charles Garrett. Ram Publishing Company. The best and most complete guide to successful coin hunting, this book explains fully the how's, where's, and when's of searching for coins and related objects. It also includes a complete explanation of how to select and use the various types of coin hunting metal detectors. Based on more than twenty years of actual in-the-field experience by the author, this volume contains a great amount of practical coin hunting information that will not be found elsewhere. Profusely illustrated with over 100 photographs. 248 pages.

TREASURE HUNTING PAYS OFF! Charles Garrett. Ram Publishing Company. This book will give you an excellent introduction to all facets of treasure hunting. It tells you how to begin and be successful in general treasure hunting; coin hunting; relic, cache, and bottle seeking; and prospecting. It describes the various kinds of metal/mineral detectors and tells you how to go about selecting the correct type for all kinds of searching. This is an excellent guidebook for the beginner, but yet contains tips and ideas for the experienced TH'er. Illustrated. 92 pages.

PROFESSIONAL TREASURE HUNTER. George Mroczkowski. Ram Publishing Company. Research is 90 percent of the success of any treasure hunting endeavor. You will become a better treasure hunter by learning how, through proper treasure hunting techniques and methods, George was able to find treasure sites, obtain permission to search (even from the U. S. Government), select and use the proper equipment, and then recover treasure in many instances. If treasure was not found, valuable clues and historical artifacts were located that made it worthwhile or kept the search alive. Profusely illustrated. 154 pages.

BOOK ORDER BLANK

See your detector dealer or bookstore or send check or money order directly to Ram for prompt, postage paid shipping. If not completely satisfied return book(s) within 10 days for a full refund.

____MODERN METAL DETECTORS $9.95
____DETECTOR OWNER'S MANUAL $8.95
____ELECTRONIC PROSPECTING $4.95
____GOLD PANNING IS EASY $6.95
____COMPLETE VLF-TR METAL
DETECTOR HANDBOOK (THE) (ALL
ABOUT GROUND CANCELING
METAL DETECTORS) $8.95

____ROBERT MARX. QUEST FOR
TREASURE $11.95
____TREASURE HUNTER'S MANUAL #6 $9.95
____TREASURE HUNTER'S MANUAL #7 $9.95
____SUCCESSFUL COIN HUNTING $8.95
____TREASURE HUNTING PAYS OFF. $4.95
____PROFESSIONAL TREASURE
HUNTER $7.95

Please add 50¢ for each book ordered (to a maximum of $2) for handling charges.

Total for Items	$ _____
Texas Residents Add 7 1/4% State Tax	_____
Handling Charge	_____
Total of Above	$ _____

ENCLOSED IS MY CHECK OR MONEY ORDER $ _____
I prefer to purchase through my MasterCard (   ) or Visa (   ) account. (Check one.)

MasterCard

VISA

_____
Card Number

_____
Bank Identifier Number

_____
Expiration Date

_____
Signature (Order must be signed.)

NAME _____

ADDRESS _____

CITY _____

STATE _____ ZIP _____
PLACE MY NAME ON YOUR MAILING LIST ☐

RAM
BOOKS

Ram Publishing Company
P.O. Drawer 38649, Dallas, Texas 75238
MMD-3
214-278-8439
DEALER INQUIRIES WELCOME

507

BOOK ORDER BLANK

See your detector dealer or bookstore or send check or money order directly to Ram for prompt, postage paid shipping. If not completely satisfied return book(s) within 10 days for a full refund.

_____MODERN METAL DETECTORS $9.95
_____DETECTOR OWNER'S MANUAL $8.95
_____ELECTRONIC PROSPECTING $4.95
_____GOLD PANNING IS EASY $6.95
_____COMPLETE VLF-TR METAL
DETECTOR HANDBOOK (THE) (ALL
ABOUT GROUND CANCELING
METAL DETECTORS) $8.95

_____ROBERT MARX. QUEST FOR
TREASURE $11.95
_____TREASURE HUNTER'S MANUAL #6 $9.95
_____TREASURE HUNTER'S MANUAL #7 $9.95
_____SUCCESSFUL COIN HUNTING $8.95
_____TREASURE HUNTING PAYS OFF. $4.95
_____PROFESSIONAL TREASURE
HUNTER $7.95

Please add 50¢ for each book ordered (to a maximum of $2) for handling charges.

Total for Items	$ _____
Texas Residents Add 7 1/4% State Tax	_____
Handling Charge	_____
Total of Above	$ _____

ENCLOSED IS MY CHECK OR MONEY ORDER $ _____
I prefer to purchase through my MasterCard ( ) or Visa ( ) account. (Check one.)

MasterCard

VISA

_____
Card Number

_____
Bank Identifier Number

_____
Expiration Date

_____
Signature (Order must be signed.)

NAME _____

ADDRESS _____

CITY _____

STATE _____ ZIP _____

PLACE MY NAME ON YOUR MAILING LIST ☐

Ram Publishing Company
P.O. Drawer 38649, Dallas, Texas 75238
MMD-3
214-278-8439
DEALER INQUIRIES WELCOME

509

THE GARRETT FILM, VIDEO AND SLIDE LIBRARY

Outdoor Family Entertainment and Instructional Programs. All available in 16mm, VHS and BETA Video Cassette except as noted. See note at end of listings for ordering information.

"The Silent Past"   Running time 26:23 min.

An old prospector, killed by hostile Indians after he discovers a silver mine, is transformed into a ghost whose destiny is to roam the Big Bend area of West Texas until one of his descendants comes to the area. His great-great-grandson and parents travel to the area and discover many artifacts buried during the passage of time.

"Gold and Treasure Adventures"   Running time 34:26 min.

Charles Garrett, president of Garrett Metal Detectors, takes us on a visit to a competition treasure hunt in the California desert, and on a treasure hunting trip to Europe. While in the desert, Charles and a field team hunt an old mining area where many good recoveries are made. Actor John Quade is featured and narrates part of the film.

"The Treasures of Mexico"   Running time 19:30 min.

Host Charles Garrett invites us along with the Garrett field team on an outing to the fabulous Canyon de Cobre, near Batopilas, Mexico. The team searches a beautiful old city, silver-laden rivers, and finally, an old mine. As you will see when you take this trip, electronic prospecting in these areas is very productive.

"Treasure of the Indian Ocean"   Running time 26:30 min.

Robert Marx, internationally known American underwater archaeologist and treasure salvor, leads a team of professionals on a search for the 18th century wreck site of the French merchant ship, the *St. Geran,* wrecked in 1744 off Mauritius, which is an island about 500 miles east of Madagascar. This color and sound film has great historical interest which shows many different methods of recovery, as well as touching on research and archaeological procedures.

510

GARRETT'S CONSUMER (HOBBYIST) VIDEO LIBRARY

Outdoor family entertainment and instructional programs. Available in Video Cassette only. See note at end of listing for ordering information.

"Weekend Prospecting"
(VHS and BETA only)   Running time 54:00 min.

This video production was filmed while Roy Lagal, Tommie T. Long, Virgil Hutton and Charles Garrett were on a gold hunting expedition in the Northwest country of the United States. It accurately depicts "weekend prospecting," gold locating, and recovery techniques that all family members can put to productive use during vacations and weekend trips to the gold country. All forms of electronic prospecting with metal detectors, and both wet and dry gold panning and recovery techniques are fully illustrated. Very informative, instructional and interesting with outstanding scenery. Roy Lagal's book, WEEKEND PROSPECTING, produced by Ram Books, is a "companion piece" as the book covers in greater detail everything presented in this video production.

GARRETT'S SLIDE LIBRARY

The following instructional and interesting slide presentations are available:

"Advanced Coin Recovery"   Running time 35:00 min.

This program consists of sixty 35mm slides shipped in a standard Kodak carousel tray, accompanied by a standard audio cassette. The slides depict methods of probing and recovering coins without causing sod damage. Charles Garrett demonstrates various probing tools.

"Gold Panning Is Easy"   Running time 30:00 min.

This program consists of fifty 35mm slides shipped in a standard Kodak carousel tray, accompanied by a standard audio cassette. The program illustrates methods of using the GRAVITY TRAP and other pans in both wet and dry panning for gold and other materials of high specific gravity. You'll learn where and how to locate gold. Roy Lagal demonstrates these gold recovery methods. See Idaho's beautiful gold country!

511

GARRETT'S LAW ENFORCEMENT AND
SECURITY VIDEO LIBRARY

Garrett has VHS and BETA video presentations that explain and demonstrate the various types of metal detectors used in law enforcement and security applications. These tapes are available for law enforcement and security use only. Not available for general public viewing. See end of these listings for additional ordering instructions.

"The New Role Of The Metal Detector
In Law Enforcement And Security"   Running time 30:00 min.

A comprehensive overview of the new and innovative ways law enforcement and security officers are effectively using metal detectors to meet the challenge and problems created by modern-day criminals and terrorists.

"Metal Detection In Modern Security"   Running time 30:00 min.

This video presentation is entitled, "The Advanced Role of Metal Detection in Olympic Security." It draws an informative parallel between Prison and Olympic Security. The video is narrated by Captain Bruce Daniels of the Utah State Prison. The presentation will be of value to any security officer, in any security setting.

ORDERING INFORMATION

To order these Garrett productions, contact Customer Service, Garrett Metal Detectors, 2814 National Drive, Garland, TX 75041. Call (214) 278-6151. Make your request for the production(s) you need and give date(s) when the production(s) will be shown. You are required to pay for shipping and insurance, both ways.

PUBLICATIONS

THE SEARCHER: This periodical is published and distributed by Search International, an association of metal detector enthusiasts. As a member, you are entitled to receive, free, each issue of THE SEARCHER, other publications and news bulletins as may be produced, and a 10% discount on all Ram books purchased through Search International. Each issue of THE SEARCHER is filled with treasure stories, treasure hunting and metal detecting "how to" information, and articles about found treasure by SEARCHER readers. Send name and address and $3.00 for one year's membership to SEARCH INTERNATIONAL, 2814 National Dr., Garland, TX 75041-2397. One year free membership with purchase of any Garrett metal detector from any Authorized Garrett dealer.

SPECIALIZED BOOKS

The Law Enforcement and Security Division of Garrett Metal Detectors has developed and is prepared to teach and assist law enforcement and security agencies in authorized seminars or police schools in the following areas:

A). Metal detection in Modern Security:
Separate Programs:

1. Prison security
2. Courtroom security
3. Federal, state and local legislative security
4. Olympic and special events security
5. Industrial security
6. Executive and corporate security
7. Postal or mail security
8. Military security

B). New Role of Metal Detection in Law Enforcement

1. Crime scene management (general)
2. Arson matters
3. Fish and wildlife violations
4. Bombing matters ·
5. Electronics of underwater recoveries
6. Civil defense

Avalanche, flood, earthquake, hurricane, tornado, fire, mudslide, bombing, airplane, accidents, and explosion

The above security and law enforcement areas are one and two hour programs which are incorporated into our half day, full day, and two day metal detection security and police schools.

Index

When you are studying a particular subject, refer to Chapters 7, and 8, and the Glossary for additional metal detector terminology. Illustrations and Tables are not included in the Index, but are listed under Figure numbers in the front portion of MODERN METAL DETECTORS. Not every term and subject is included in this Index. The author compiled this Index and selected the terms he believed would be referred to most often.

NOTES

NOTES

NOTES